Warwick & Warwick

AUCTIONEERS AND VALUERS
www.warwickandwarwick.com

SELLING YOUR COINS AND BANKNOTES?

Warwick and Warwick have an expanding requirement for coin and banknote collections, British and worldwide and for coins and notes of individual value. Our customer base is increasing dramatically and we need an ever larger supply of quality material to keep pace with demand. The market has never been stronger and if you are considering the sale of your collection, now is the time to act.

FREE VALUATIONS
We will provide a free, professional and without obligation valuation of your collection. Either we will make you a fair, binding private treaty offer, or we will recommend inclusion of your property in our next public auction.

FREE TRANSPORTATION
We can arrange insured transportation of your collection to our Warwick offices completely free of charge. If you decline our offer, we ask you to cover the return carriage costs only.

FREE VISITS
Visits by our valuers are possible anywhere in the country or abroad, usually within 48 hours, in order to value larger collections. Please telephone for details.

VALUATION DAYS
We are staging a series of valuation days and will be visiting the following towns within the next few weeks:
Please visit our website or telephone for further details.

EXCELLENT PRICES
Because of the strength of our customer base we are in a position to offer prices that we feel sure will exceed your expectations.

ACT NOW
Telephone or email Richard Beale today with details of your property.

Warwick & Warwick Ltd.
Chalon House, Scar Bank, Millers Road, Warwick CV34 5DB England
Tel: (01926) 499031 • Fax: (01926) 491906
Email: richard.beale@warwickandwarwick.com
www.warwickandwarwick.com

6

THE

COIN
YEARBOOK
2008

Edited by
James Mackay, MA, DLitt
John W. Mussell, FRGS
and the Editorial Team of COIN NEWS

ISBN–10 1 870 192 82 6
ISBN–13 978–1 870 192 82 8

Published by
TOKEN PUBLISHING LIMITED
Orchard House, Duchy Road, Heathpark, Honiton, EX14 1YD
Telephone: 01404 46972   Fax: 01404 44788
e-mail: info@tokenpublishing.com. Website: http://www.tokenpublishing.com

Printed in Great Britain by Haynes Publishing, Sparkford, Yeovil

8

Contents

Foreword

TRADITIONALLY we have looked at the numismatic climate in the context of the global economy. Ironically this is being written on the eve of the G8 Summit meeting in Germany where the global climate—or more precisely, its rapid change—is being assessed in economic terms. Oxfam has come up with a "tax bill" which, it insists, the rich nations who do most of the pollution must pay in order to compensate for the damage they are doing to the globe in general and the Third World in particular.

Coping with the ravages of global warming will cost an estimated $50 billion (£25.2 billion) a year and Oxfam insists that the rich countries must assume responsibility. The United States accounts for 44 per cent of carbon emissions, Japan 13 per cent and Germany 7 per cent while the UK, France, Italy and Canada each contribute about 5 per cent, and Australia, Spain and Korea are in the 3 per cent bracket. However, India, Mexico, Brazil, South Africa and China are not far behind, and already it is being predicted that by the end of the decade China will have overtaken the rest of the world. After all, this is a country which is building a new coal-fired power station every four days.

By the time you read these words, however, the G8 Summit will be long gone, the USA will have totally rejected the proposals on cutting carbon emissions and lowering global warming, and it will be "business as usual".

There has been a number of coins in recent years with the theme of "Save Planet Earth" (usually a vehicle for images of exotic, if endangered, species), but environmental and ecological issues have so far had little impact on numismatics. Certainly the fears for the sort of world that our children and grandchildren will inherit have had absolutely no impact on our hobby. Perhaps we feel powerless to do anything individually, other than check the lagging in the loft and invest in low-powered light-bulbs. Instead, we immerse ourselves in a hobby which takes us out of ourselves, absorbs us in the history and culture of past civilisations, or whatever else grabs our attention.

Perhaps there is an escapist element about coin-collecting. It is interesting to note that, in a period of dramatic upheavals on the economic and monetary front, numismatics is continually on the up and up. Last year we noted that the FTSE briefly broke through the 6,000 barrier for the first time in four years. Since then it has remained well above that level and is currently ten per cent higher than the same time last year.

Meanwhile the pound has continued strongly against the US dollar. In July 2006 it stood at $1.85; in June 2007 it was standing at just under $2 and, indeed, briefly crossed that threshold in the late spring, for the first time in almost a quarter of a century. Of course it could be argued that this position reflects the parlous state of the once-mighty dollar rather than the robust health of sterling, but the pound has also tended to increase in value relative to the euro. No wonder that Gordon Brown ended his ten years as Chancellor of the Exchequer in buoyant mood as he embarked on his premiership. Older readers may have a sense of déjà vu, recalling the words of Harold MacMillan half a century ago when he told us that we had never had it so good.

There is something rather worrying about an economy in which the most dramatic growth has been in banking and money-lending, while the manufacturing base continues to decline and more and more of what we used to invent is developed elsewhere and what we made has now shifted to the Third World where labour costs are infinitely lower.

These matters impact in areas which we know and understand, namely in the currencies in everyday use. We may laugh at the antics across the pond where the US Treasury is making its third valiant attempt to get a circulating dollar coin into circulation but is virtually overwhelmed by the vested interests of the cotton states (whence comes the rag paper) and the embattled Bureau of Engraving and Printing in Washington (which has already seen much of its business disappear, since the US Postal Service has abandoned engraved stamps). So long as George Washington continues to grace the dollar bill the new Presidential coins have no chance of getting into circulation. Furthermore, the Treasury is worried about the astronomical quantity of Sacagawea dollars lying in drawers and cookie jars because the American public is too lazy to trade them in, let alone try to spend them.

Why the United States should run counter to the rest of the world in matters of coinage, is a puzzle. How can a country of its size and importance get by with only four circulating coins, of which the largest, the quarter, has a value equivalent to 13p? You need a handful of them to make an out-of-town phone call. No matter, the humble but very useful quarter has become a very popular coin indeed, thanks to the reverse motifs representing all fifty states.

The hobby in general is in very good heart and we venture to suggest that it has never been stronger. Certainly all the world's treasuries, national banks and mints are reporting record profits, with sales of collectors' coins at an all-time high. Of course this may be due to the steadily increasing volume of new issues, not overlooking the fact that coins, unlike stamps, usually change their dates each year, thus encouraging the sale of year sets. Moreover, we observe an increasing trend towards marketing the same product in different forms. Proof coins have now reached the sort of volumes we used to expect from the ordinary versions, but merchandise is the name of the game these days and so the public clamour to buy everything from souvenir folders to wedding and new baby sets. Just where this market will lead is anyone's guess.

There is also a trend towards frequent changes of design. We have had this for many years now, in regard to the pound coin, with the two-pound piece as an increasingly popular vehicle for commemoratives, but many other countries (notably the USA, France, Germany, Russia and Canada) are finding that frequent changes stimulate public interest in coins; if even a small percentage of these people move on to become committed numismatists the hobby is in good heart.

This is borne out by the performance of coins at auction over the past year. Saleroom results are always a guide to the state of the market and in view of the numerous records broken lately this proves the point. With the stock market riding high there is not the flight of money into tangibles that we have seen in periods of economic uncertainty, yet more and more money is coming into the hobby. At grass roots level we have noted a steady increase in attendance at coin fairs in London and the provinces and the growth of the smaller auction houses beyond the capital.

When compiling such a publication as COIN YEARBOOK we are inevitably dependent to a large extent on a number of recognised experts in their respective fields, for advice and assistance as well as a precise assessment of current market values. This edition is no exception and we are indebted to our trade colleagues and a number of specialist collectors for their help and co-operation. In particular we would like to thank Patrick Mackenzie (Decimal), Stephen Mitchell (Hammered), Royston Norbury (Milled), Chris Rudd (Celtic), Nick Swabey (Maundy) and Mike Vosper (Roman). Additionally we are indebted to the many dealers and auction houses for permission to use images from their catalogues.

The year
at a glance!

An at-a-glance resume of the main events and occurrences that affected the coin hobby during the past months, as reported in COIN NEWS . . .

September 2006

Part of author Jeffrey North's £13,000 gift to the British Numismatic Society will be used to establish a North Book Prize that will be awarded every two years to the book that is considered to have made the best contribution to British numismatics.

The Worthing and District Numismatic Society celebrate their 40th anniversary.

eBay is fast becoming a choice venue for the buying and selling of all things numismatic. In July three British postal orders of the 1905 design with a stamp space in the bottom corner and overprints in Canadian dollars achieved a final bid of £7,123 at the on-line auction site.

William Mackay is appointed Publicity Officer for the British Numismatic Society (BNS).

The Royal Canadian Mint is to produce both circulating and non-circulating coins for the winter Olympics and Paralympics of 2010 and Olympic medals for the Vancouver Games.

A live bidding via telephone service as well as in-house bidding is launched by the *Antiques Trade Gazette* allowing world wide access to a Baldwin's Hong Kong sale.

Coin News continues its efforts to bring in young collectors by offering a £150 prize to the junior collector who submits the best essay on which coin they would spend their winnings on and why they would buy it. There are also second and third prizes of £100 and £50.

The Royal Dutch Mint produces three bimetallic coins celebrating the 400th birthday of Holland's most famous artist Rembrandt Harmenszoon van Rijn. They can be seen on-line at www.muntpost.nl/leidenset.

Tokens are gaining in popularity among numismatists and there is much news in all numismatist publications about them. Newest of the genre are the shopping cart tokens.

Once again the debate to keep or get rid of the US penny waxes and wanes but no decision has yet been made.

A coin shop operator is offering an authentication service for banknotes, but he cautions that some of the fakes are worth more than the genuine article.

The inaugural meeting of the Banknote Society of Scotland (BNSS) takes place in Edinburgh.

Formed from the Scottish chapter of IBNS the new Society will focus on the collection of Scottish banknotes

October 2006

Edmund C. Moy is appointed new director of the United States Mint and in an interview made mention that the mint was expecting to be very busy implementing the Presidential $1 Coin Act of 2005 which is to produce more $1 coins, portraying past presidents on the obverse.

Royal Numismatic Society of New Zealand president David Galt is pleased to see the proliferation of on-line sites for numismatic collectors but he also warns new collectors to be wary of buying modern decimal circulated coins that will not hold their value.

Pobjoy Mint is the first ever British mint to be awarded a contract for commemorative coins from the Finance Ministry of the Tajikistan government.

The Intermediate People's Court of Taizhou City, China finds 30 people guilty of producing counterfeit Panda coins. In Zhejiang in 2000 the courts handled 676 cases involving the manufacture of fake coins. A police crackdown saw the number drop by 90 percent in the first half of this year.

John Andrew wins the 2005 *Coin News* Author of the Year award which is decided by the votes of readers.

The Royal Canadian Mint introduces a 14 carat gold coin featuring the Imperial State Crown with enamel highlighting the most valuable of the Crown's Jewels such as the Sapphire of King Edward the Confessor and the Black Prince's Ruby. You can pick one up for the not unreasonable price of £1,520.95.

The death is reported of Michael Marsh. He was well known for his studies *The Half Sovereign* and *The Sovereign*. .

The Royal Canadian Mint unveils a new mint mark which will now appear on all Canadian coinage. The design is a stylized maple leaf emerging from the letter M encased in a circle.

The Reserve Bank of New Zealand announces that the bulk of the 5 cent coins struck in 2004 and the 10, 20, and 50 cents coins for 2005 will be melted down to make way for the demise of the 5 cent coin and new sizes for the rest.

Along with a new director of the US Mint, President Bush has appointed Henry M. Paulson Jr. to be the 74th Secretary of the US Treasury. His is one of two signatures that will be on every US Treasury note issued during his tenure.

November 2006

Coincraft's newspaper style catalogue celebrates its 300th issue. It is now issued every three weeks and has subscribers and collectors worldwide.

Una and the Lion, everyone's favourite British coin, is sold by US auctioneers, Ira & Larry Goldberg for the tidy sum of $41,000.

The Token Corresponding Society joins the IT revolution by launching a website to make the work and goals of the Society known to a wider audience. They can be found at www.tokensociety.org.uk.

The San Francisco Old Mint Commemorative Coin Program gives thanks to the Denver ANA show for the proceeds of their auction which will go towards transforming the old San Francisco Mint into a museum incorporating the American Money and Gold Rush Museum.

The Perth Mint installs a state-of-the-art minting machine. The 360 ton machine utilises the latest computer control systems. The Mint recently won the contract for the 2006 Asian Games commemorative coin programme.

Celtic coin specialist Chris Rudd reports that the prices for top quality Celtic gold coins continues to rise, realising prices that have ranged from £1,050 to £1,500 in recent sales.

Although the US Government is going to keep trying with its new Presidential $1 coins coming out soon it is speculated that the US Mint is sitting on 115 million of the Sacagawea $1 coins and the banks refuse to take them knowing the people will not use them as long as the $1 banknote is in circulation.

A visit by Derek McGroarty to the Singapore Mint reports that it has earned a well deserved high image by publicity, coin conventions and more importantly, quality.

Russia's 5,000 rouble notes were destroyed when the currency was redenominated in 1998 but now Russia is re-issuing new 5,000 rouble notes to meet increasing demand. At current exchange rates this note is the equivalent of just under £100.

Leslie Allen known to many dealers and collectors as a real gentleman and who took a keen interest in commemorative medals has died.

Shopkeepers in New Zealand find themselves wondering where all the change went at Christmas when they ran short of coinage.

In the last weeks of November the slimmed-down, smaller sized 20 cent coins seemed to disappear down a black hole.

December 2006

The world record price for a banknote was set in December when Heritage Auction Galleries brokered a deal involving the sale of the only available red seal $1,000 note, P350, popularly known as the "Grand Watermelon". The price of US$2,255,000 was more than twice the previous record.

At the beginning of the month the Bank of Korea introduces new smaller and lighter copper-plated aluminium 10 won coins. South Korea is the first country to use copper-plated aluminium for coins.

A recent ruling at Croydon Crown Court brings to light the fact that it is illegal to buy and sell coin dies even those no longer in use. 99 percent of dealers and collectors are ignorant of that fact which could lead to trouble with the law as ignorance of the law is no defence the Court pointed out.

The sale at Spink of the Colonial and British Commonwealth coins collected by the late Jerry Remick (1928–2005) fetches a total of £1,277,915. All proceeds go to Jerry's beloved Canadian Geological Foundation.

The Reserve Bank of New Zealand opens its new Museum, the official honours being undertaken by Peter Hillary, son of Sir Edmund Hillary who appears on New Zealand's current $5 note.

The US Mint has put out warnings about the National Organization for the Repeal of the Federal Reserve Act and the Internal Revenue

Code (NORFED) which has been producing Liberty Dollar medallions that have been mistaken for legal US coinage.

A call goes out for volunteers to help in a proposed update of the listing by Boyne Williams of 17th century tokens. David Griffiths plans to produce an update by using collaborators for each county.

Germany celebrates the 800th Anniversary of Dresden by issuing a silver €10 coin featuring a townscape of the modern city.

The UK's first grading and encapsulation (slabbing) service is launched at the end of November by CGS (Coin Grading Service) UK. A website service is available for the service at www.cgs-uk.biz.

Following the trend for mint marks which are all the rage the New Zealand Mint announced its first one. It shows a fern frond the words Silver Fern and New Zealand within a circle.

The Bermuda Monetary Authority gives permission to the Royal Mint to strike 12 triangular-shaped $3 coins, inspired by the Bermuda Triangle, for their silver proof collections.

The Reserve Bank of New Zealand has to release its reserve of 4.75 million of the new 20 cent coins to cover the shortage of coins in circulation. The Bank states that there was an abnormal demand for the coins, but there is no explanation as to what triggered the "abnormal" demand or where the coins disappeared to.

January 2007

The British Association of Numismatic Societies (BANS) holds its AGM in London and elects Phyllis Stoddard as its new secretary taking the reins from Philip Mernick who retired after many years of service. Also elected are Harold Mernick and Peter Preston-Morley to the new posts of Website Manager and Publicity Officer respectively.

The amazing Alderley Collection, one of the most complete collections of English pennies in existence ranging from 1797 to the present, with many extremely rare bronze and copper proofs, goes under the hammer.

The world's largest gold coronation medal, originally produced by Spink for the coronation of George V and Queen Mary in 1911, returns to the auction house. It was last seen at the sale of the Palace Collections of Egypt in 1954.

The 55th Congress of the International Association of Professional Numismatists beaks new ground when it is held in St. Petersburg, Russia .

The University of Oxford's Ashmolean Museum launches the most advanced coin website in the world. Called Roman Provincial Coinage Online, the site comprises one of the largest collections of images and inscriptions from the ancient world. Its web address is: www.rpc.ashmus.ox.ac.uk.

The first official coins of the XXIX Olympiad were unveiled at a joint ceremony conducted by the People's Bank of China and the Beijing Organizing Committee for the games.

New Zealand Post issues a small number of sets containing New Zealand's current banknotes on behalf of the Reserve Bank of New Zealand, much to the relief of collectors who have been stymied at not being able to get the notes since the Reserve Bank stopped selling new notes to the public.

February 2007

On February 14 the Archaeological Museums at Newcastle University announces the rediscovery of the Anthony and Cleopatra silver denarius of 32 BC. Its press release is headlined "Ancient Coin Destroys Myth of Cleopatra's Beauty" with the opening statement that that the pair were not as good looking as Hollywood's beauty standards. Elizabeth Taylor and Richard Burton were probably horribly miscast.

Coins marking the Chinese New Year of the Pig are more elaborate than ever, with bi-metallics, tri-metallics, holographic images, colours and other unusual strikings.

The Michael Broome collection of Islamic coins is deposited at the Fitzwilliam Museum under the Acceptance in Lieu (AIL) scheme which allows taxpayers to transfer important pieces of art and historic objects into public ownership in lieu of inheritance tax.

The UK Numismatic Trust which offers small grants to numismatic conferences and seminars is anxious to hear from organisers.

One of the world's biggest numismatic fairs, the World Money Fair is taking place this month at the Estrel Convention Centre in Berlin. One of the highlights of the fair is the opportunity for engineers, suppliers and production partners to discuss experiences and other technological aspects of minting at the Technical Forum.

The gold double florin of Edward III found by a detectorist last year has been lent to the Fitzwilliam Museum for display in the Medieval and Renaissance Gallery.

Dr Martin Allen has been announced as the first winner of the £500 North Prize for his book *The Durham Mint.*

The passing of two dealers, Ken Bryant and Siegfried, "Fred" Schwer is noted. Also dying this month is Nigel Davies, a collector and researcher noted for his extensive collection of photographs for research.

The US Mint announces the minting of new half ounce gold "companion" coins for the upcoming $1 presidential coins. These non-legal tender coins will have the faces of the presidential First Ladies on the obverse.

The Irish International Dublin Show takes place on February 17–18 at the Royal Society in Dublin. Huge queues of eager collectors purchase the set of coins minted especially for the show.

The United Nations releases a new postage stamp series featuring the flags and coins of member nations.

Greenland announces it plans to issue its own currency next year.

The National Bank of Kazakhstan's name on the new issue of 2,000 tenge and 5,000 tenge notes was misspelled which was discovered only after circulation had begun and the bank opted to allow circulation to continue. Security, it seems took precedence over grammar. The spelling error is on the back of the note.

March 2007

On March 6, Switzerland celebrates the centenary of the Swiss National Bank with a pair of stamps reproducing the obverse and reverse of the current 100 franc note.

Since Link House in June 1964 started publishing the magazine under the title *Coins and Medals,* and several name changes and publishers later, editor John Mussell proudly points out that this month is the 500th issue of *Coin News.*

A £2 coin is struck in silver and gold commemorating the 300th Anniversary of the

Act of Union which brought together Scotland and England under one Parliament. The design incorporates the rose of England, the thistle of Scotland and a portcullis to represent the Parliament. This handsome coin it can be seen at www.royalmint.com.

Slovenia adopts the euro, the first of the ten countries to enter the newly-expanded European Union to do so.

Duncannon Partnership, UK agent for Lighthouse and Hawid, has always been noted for their vast range of numismatic accessories from testing machines to coin albums is now getting on the IT bandwagon with a website that makes pursuing their catalogue and ordering so much easier at www.duncannon. co.uk.

Last year *Coin News* reported a story of the daughter of the late Israel Switt of Philadelphia who found a box of 1933 $20.00 US Gold Eagles in his safety deposit box and took them to the US Mint for identification and evaluation where they were immediately seized by Mint officials on the grounds that they were never legally distributed and therefore it was illegal for anyone to have them. At the time the family threatened to sue and this month the US District Court in Philadelphia will hear what will probably be just the first round of the lawsuit. It would seem fair for the Mint to just buy the coins back but apparently that is not to be.

On March 19 both the Royal Australian Mint and the Perth Mint issue coins to celebrate the 75th anniversary of the Sydney Harbour Bridge.

Dealers and collectors are warned to be on the lookout for cashiers' cheques issued by a California bank on behalf of a fraudulent buyer going by the pseudonyms of Marcus Smith or James Gilmore.

New rules from the USA state that you cannot leave the country with more than $5 in change. The reason for this is the rising price of base metals which makes it profitable for unscrupulous persons to collect US coinage and melt is down for its base metals.

April 2007

Spink is one of the first auction houses to raise the buyer's premium from 15 percent to 20 percent. The expectation is that other salerooms will follow suit shortly.

People in some parts of Germany have turned their backs on the euro and decided to use alternative, unofficial currency. One region, Chiemgau, has produced the "chiemgauer" which is accepted by shops and tradesmen. The Bundesbank, so far, has not opposed the use of the notes.

The US Bureau of Educational and Cultural Affairs (ECA) posts a proposal to renew the import restrictions on cultural property originating in Cyprus.

A new numismatic search engine is launched to search numismatic websites. The site is purely a numismatic one and also boasts a search facility which allows you to type in a description of a poorly preserved coin to find its identity. URL is www.coins2.com.

The Franklin Mint's new Chief Numismatist is none other than Jay Johnson a former director of the US Mint. At his direction the Mint has recommenced minting coins and medals after a 5 year hiatus.

The detectorist's dream of finding a hidden hoard came true for not one but three when, together, they recently uncovered a hoard of ancient British gold staters near Buckingham. The precise number of coins is not yet known but it is believed to be near 40.

The New Zealand Mint signs an agreement which will make it the only authorised designer, producer and distributor of commemoratives for the Pitcairn Islands.

Coin News regular Geoffrey Cope establishes a new website www.petitioncrown.com to display and celebrate coins as works of art.

The final disposal of the famed Jerry Remick collection at Spink's brings a total for the entire collection of almost £2,000,000.

May 2007

The work of one of the great line engravers of the 20th century, John Harrison goes under the hammer at Bloomsbury. The Harrison Archive of Waterlow engravings contains Harrison's work for Waterlow and Sons for whom he worked for most of his life.

Britain's first auction market place dedicated to raising money for charity has been launched at e2bid.com. 100 percent of the fees collected at the auctions will go to charity.

Only 2 weeks into circulation, errors are found in the new $1 US presidential coins. It seems that the mottoes E. PLURIBUS UNUM and IN GOD WE TRUST have been omitted from the coin edges where they were placed to allow the presidential images on the obverse to be maximised. Many thousands of these coins have been circulated and they are only coming from the Philadelphia Mint. One early eBay sale made $612, but as more surface the price seems to have settled down to about $50.

One of Australia's leading numismatic companies, Downie's celebrates its 75th anniversary. The firm was founded by Phil Downie in New Zealand in 1932.

Coin covers have become very collectable and in response to this Buckingham Covers have started making a small number of coin covers to run alongside their traditional first day covers and have created a Coin Cover Club. For more information go to www.buckinghamcovers.com.

David Pottinger, an authority on tokens and author of many informative articles on the subject and regular contibutor to *Coin News*, dies at Reading.

There have been reports in the press recently on the subject of copyright infringement of auction catalogues. Sparking the debate is a lawsuit filed in the US by Heritage Auction Galleries against Superior Galleries. One particular area of infringement the plaintiffs allege concerns a description for a 1798 Flowing Hair half dollar. The outcome of the lawsuit will have implications in the auction world.

The International Bank Note Society chooses the 1,000 franc note issued by Banque Centrale des Comores as this year's Bank Note of the Year. The note carries an impressive array of security measures.

The Bank of England's Museum holds an exhibition which charts the development of the design of a Bank of England note over its 300 year history including the introduction of security features starting with watermarks in 1697.

During the renovation of an old church organ, workers discover a tin containing 240 white five pound notes including a consecutive run of 160 O'Briens and a consecutive run of high grade Catterns. It is estimated they will bring between £20,000 and £40,000 at auction.

June 2007

The winners of the "Junior Collector" Competition. Winners are: 1st place: Jerome

Luchesa Smith, 12, from Somerset, 2nd place: Matthew Woollons, 9, from Yorkshire and 3rd place: Victoria Butterworth, 11, from Kent.

The annual Eurovision Song contest is commemorated with a medallion sold as part of the 2007 FDC coin set of euro coins issued and circulated in Finland.

From an estimate of A$40,000, a Holey dollar test strike on a 1799 halfpenny zooms up in ferocious bidding to a final sale price of A$233,000 at a sale held by Australian auctioneers Noble Numismatics Pty Ltd.

Ex-Rolling Stone guitarist, Bill Wyman becomes an avid detectorist. While still waiting to achieve his first "big" strike he has become a real champion of the hobby.
The sale of the late Don Lee's collection of coins is handled by Chris Rudd and Lockdales. The collection includes such items as Stone Age axe heads, Roman glass, Viking brooches and bronze rings.

A Miami lawyer files a suit on behalf of collectors who feel they have been duped by paying and extra US$30 for coins that the US Mint labelled "first strike" but it seems that there is no real difference in a first strike coin that sets it apart from any other coins in a die run and buyers who paid the premium want their money back.

The Royal Mint marks the bicentenary of the abolition of slave trading in Great Britain with a £2 coin. The reverse carries the text AN ACT FOR THE ABOLITION OF THE SLAVE TRADE and the date 1807, the 0 shown as a broken link in a chain.

The Governor of the Bank of England, Mervyn King, announces an auction of low-numbered £20 Adam Smith banknotes with the proceeds going to The National Literacy Trust's initiative "Reading is Fundamental,

UK" and the Chance to Shine charity which encourages sports participation in schools.

The Reserve Bank of Zimbabwe issues $5,000 and $50,000 banknotes with expiration dates which are not accepted by any foreign exchange, just to meet the domestic needs of the public which has to endure annual inflation rates of 1,700 to 2,000 percent.

The 1913 US Liberty Head nickel set a new record price for a coin when it fetched $5 million in a Southern California private sale.

New Maltese banknotes are to have designs which will reflect all members of the EU.

The ATM at the Tallinn branch of the Estonian Central bank receives complaints from customers that the notes coming from the machine have the appearance of having been chewed. When bank officials opened the ATM they discovered that a mouse had set up housekeeping inside and was chewing up the notes to make nesting material.

July 2007

The summer meeting of the British Numismatic Society and the Royal Numismatic Society presents discussions and speakers dealing with its theme this year "Currencies in Crisis". The meeting deals with the origins and impact of crises that have affected British and world currencies.

A Distinguished History and a Modern New Identity

The Royal Mint lies at the heart of the British coinage. It has been responsible for producing coins of the realm for over a 1,000 years, there being an unbroken link from the scattered workshops of the moneyers of Anglo-Saxon London to the modern coining plant in Llantrisant, South Wales. From the silver pennies of Alfred the Great to the gold nobles of medieval kings, from the most famous of British coins, the gold sovereign to modern day design classics, the Royal Mint's history spans three millennia while at the same time, tracing the social, economic and political history of the nation.

It was, therefore, a carefully considered decision to introduce a new identity in 2007 to encapsulate the Royal Mint's unique qualities of royalty, heritage, craftsmanship and experience.

After extensive research and a great deal of deliberation, approval for the elegant and powerful logo was sought from the College of Arms, the Lord Chancellor and ultimately Her Majesty The Queen. The design is a modern depiction of the crowned Royal Arms surrounded by a repeating pattern, the inspiration for which is to be found in the Tudor rose reverse design of the first gold sovereign struck in 1489. The use of gold and silver colours evokes the premium qualities of a royal institution and alludes to the precious metals used in striking high quality Proof coins.

The Royal Mint continues to embrace its royal heritage while at the same time cultivating creativity and innovation. Today notable events in British and world history, as well as important royal occasions, are marked by the issue of collector coins and medals struck to the Royal Mint's highest standard.

To see the full range of beautifully produced Proof and Brilliant Uncirculated coins and medals visit our secure website at www.royalmint.com

Or contact our Customer Services Team on: **0845 60 88 300**

or write to us quoting ref: CYB08 to:
The Royal Mint
FREEPOST NAT23496,
PO BOX 500,
Llantrisant, Ponytclun CF72 8YT
United Kingdom

In the period under review, roughly from mid-2006 to mid-2007, there was a lack of the really major events that grab the headlines and inspire the world's mints to produce coins in their honour. In a period between the great sporting contests, the Olympic Games and the FIFA World Cup, there were relatively few coins with a sporting theme. On the other hand, royalty, a perennially popular theme, nobly filled the vacuum, and bids fair to do well next

year also. The Royal Mint produced a pair of £5 coins in silver edged in gold to mark the Queen's 80th birthday, showing Her Majesty on the throne (Alderney) or on horseback at the Trooping of the Colour (Jersey), in contrast with the less traditional but still very striking £5 coin from the UK itself where a fanfare of trumpets (above) rather than a portrayal of Her Mjesty was used.

Although the Royal Diamond Wedding of the Queen and Prince Philip was not due to be celebrated till November 2007 the Royal Mint was quick off the mark with its crown-sized £5. The obverse, by Ian Rank-Broadley, is arguably his best work to date, showing conjoined busts of the Queen and the Duke, with their names and titles in Latin round the circumference. Interestingly Philip was styled simply as "Princeps" (prince) rather than Duke of Edinburgh—which might have been quite a lot to cram in but it is intriguing to speculate as to how that would have been rendered in Latin.

The reverse, by Emma Noble, is very much in the Royal Mint tradition which eschews pictorialism. Where we might have expected a reproduction of one of the wedding portraits of 1947, instead there is a highly original depiction of the north rose window at Westminster Abbey. The result is quite stunning and will appeal not only to those collectors who concentrate on Royal themes but also is a splendid addition to any collection with an architectural theme.

The UK is probably the only country in the world (other than the Vatican) which still uses Latin inscriptions. I am not ignoring the standard E PLURIBUS UNUM which is required by federal law to appear on all US coins, but am referring to the use of different inscriptions as and when the occasion demands. The choice of TVEATVR VNITA DEVS is very apt, if ungrammatical. It translates as "May God guard those united" and was used on coins of James I and Queen Victoria (1847) referring to the union of the kingdoms. As the word regna (Latin for kingdoms) was understood, VNITA is neuter, so the correct inscription in this instance should perhaps have read VNITOS as it refers to people rather than things.

Perhaps that Latin motto would have been more appropriate in its neuter version to the £2 coin released in 2007 to celebrate the tercentenary of the Act of Union which made Great Britain a political fact and not just the pipe dream of James I. The portcullis in the form of jigsaw pieces is a very clever device to symbolise the union of the kingdoms, denoted by their heraldic flowers. This was one of those occasions when symbolism was the only option; it would have been well-nigh impossible to convey the notion of the Union by any other means.

The other special issues from the United Kingdom could well have adopted a pictorial treatment but did not, perhaps a taste of things to come with the redesign of the coinage next year? This is particularly true of the Scout emblem (50p, below) and a chain on the £2 celebrating the abolition of the slave trade, the zero in the date 1807 forming the middle link in the chain. Some may feel modern coins overdo the symbolism a tad and yearn for the more "artistic" pictoral designs of the past but clearly a great deal of thought goes into their concept

It is interesting to speculate on the reason why the Royal Mint concentrates so much on symbolism where British coins are concerned, whereas it seems to adopt a pictorial approach in the coins it strikes for other countries. Prime examples are the gorgeous crowns struck for the Channel Islands celebrating Britain's naval heritage. Here we have splendid portraits of Sir Francis Drake and Henry VIII, not to mention the exquisite detail in the ships, notably the *Golden Hind* and the *Mary Rose*—and with the White Ensign in full colour to boot.

This is also evident in the long thematic sets from the same mint this past twelvemonth, ranging from the set of 12 triangular $3 coins

for Bermuda, depicting ships which came to grief in the infamous Bermuda Triangle, or the dozen proof crowns from various African countries forming a thematic journey through the Dark Continent with its rich wildlife picked out in gold on a silver landscape. Contrast the simplicity of Britain's pair of VC 50p coins last year with the magnificent series of 18 crowns for the Channel Islands and sundry colonies and dependencies around the world, portraying individual heroes and the actions in which they won their VCs.

Nostalgia has affected the sister hobby of philately in recent years, leading to the revival of old designs, suitably up-rated to take account of inflation. Now this fashion has spread to numismatics, notably in the USA where the motifs of the much-loved Indian Head (below) and Buffalo nickel (replaced by the Jefferson/Monticello nickel in 1938) have re-appeared on a $50 gold coin.

On the subject of gold, Lithuania has produced a 10 litas, heralded as "the smallest gold coin in the world". With a diameter of 13.92mm it's certainly small but by no means the smallest. Nevertheless it is one of the most interesting coins to appear this year, as both obverse and reverse motifs play on the theme of gold. The obverse shows a diagram of the Golden Mean (Sectio Aurea in Latin) while the reverse depicts the Ausros Vartai, the Dawn Gate leading from the village of Medininkai, south of Vilnius, into the capital. Built in the 16th century, it was one of nine gateways in the city walls but the only one to survive the interminable wars of the Baltic region.

The Isle of Man released the 20th in the long-running series devoted to breeds of cat, this time featuring a Ragdoll and two kittens. It seems hard to realise that this series has been running for two decades. Back in the 1980s when the Pobjoy Mint launched the series eyebrows were raised amongst Mints across the world, but now those same institutions seem just as enthusiastic in exploring the thematic potential of coins. When it comes to imaginative treatment of pictorialism, the Pobjoy Mint does well as can be seen in their series from the Falkland Islands portraying the Greatest Britons, or the £2 coin from South Georgia (below) marking the 25th anniversary of its liberation.

Minimalism in coin design is a rare phenomenon these days, usually associated with Swiss commemoratives whose obverse has a tiny Swiss cross in a field that is empty but for the numerals of value. This style has now spread to the Cook Islands which recently released a coin to mark the 180th anniversary of photography. While the reverse is conventional, reproducing the first photograph taken by Nicephore Niepce, the obverse has a ridiculously tiny effigy of the Queen at the top and an otherwise empty field, with a tiny indentation in the centre, perhaps intended to symbolise the pinhole camera used by Niepce in 1827. Far more satisfactory is the coin issued by Slovakia for the birth bicentenary of Jozef Petzval, another pioneer of photography who is best remembered today as the founder of geometrical optics. His bust appears on the obverse, but the reverse depicts the haven guessing lens used in his experiments.

Farther afield, Australia has been producing some very attractive coins. They would be interesting enough if struck in plain silver, but the Perth Mint in particular is a past-master in the art of the multicoloured coin, and

this year's offerings are well up to the high standard of design and execution which we have come to expect from this mint.

Colour has become quite commonplace these days and the results can be, shall we say "interesting"! You only have to look at the coins which celebrated the Chinese New Year of the Pig (or Boar), particularly those from the Royal Canadian Mint (below, left), the Singapore Mint and Malawi's coins struck by the Swiss Mint, where all the colours of the rainbow are richly piled up, and even holograms are used by the Perth Mint (below, right), to see that the traditional single metal, single colour commemorative is a thing of the past for many.

Not so many years ago, bimetallic coins were hailed as a novelty rather than the necessity they have become as high-value coins replace increasingly worthless paper. But now we have three-metal coins in profusion, while the British Virgin Islands has now launched the world's first "quad-metal" coin, the aptly-named royal. Contrasting metals work best in moderation, particularly when gold is used to highlight part of the design (as in Somalia's "Three Wise Monkeys" coin), but some of the New Year coins were really over the top, creating an effect for effect's sake.

Likewise colour works best when some restraint is evident, and this is a lesson which Perth has learned, as the Discover Australia series exemplifies. In the recent Fire Engines series it is rather overpowering, although the use of a coiled fire hose is a stroke of genius.

Another good example of coloured coins was provided by the quartet from Singapore showing delightful vignettes of the rustic coast of the island republic. There must be few of these rustic havens left as Singapore rivals Hong Kong in the density of its housing; perhaps that's why they appear on coins so that people will have a memento of them before they all disappear.

Holographic coins seem to have gone out of favour, although a very dramatic example is to be found on a $20 coin from Canada showing a brigantine on the trade route to the United States.

On the other hand, gimmicks are well to the fore. The Cape Verde Islands released a pair of silver 50 escudos highlighting the wreck of the Princess Louisa. The arms of the republic were reduced to microscopic proportions on the obverse, in order to accommodate authentic coin fragments from the shipwreck, the reverse motifs depicting the ship before and after it foundered in a great storm.

The Latvian Mint struck a coin for the Pacific archipelago of Palau to illustrate the dramatic origin of these volcanic islands. The reverse not only shows a volcano erupting but incorporates a genuine piece of volcanic rock. It's magnificent, but would not it jam in slot machines (assuming they have such things in Palau)?

The most unusual gimmick to emerge this year, however, hails from the Congo and features the lighthouse at Munda. A fluorescent technique has been applied to the beams of light by day or night, the first example of a coin that looks much better in total darkness.

Monarchs of England

Here we list the Kings and Queens from Anglo-Saxon times to the present, with the dates of their rule. Before Eadgar became the King of all England the country had been divided up into small kingdoms, each with their own ruler.

ANGLO-SAXON KINGS
Eadgar (959–975)
Edward the Martyr (975–978)
Aethelred II (978–1016)
Cnut (1016–1035)
Harold I (1035–1040)
Harthacanut (1035–1042)
Edward the Confessor
  (1042–1066)
Harold II (1066)

NORMAN KINGS
William I (1066–1087)
William II (1087–1100)
Henry I (1100–1135)
Stephen (1135–154)

PLANTAGENETS
Henry II (1154–1189)
Richard I (1189–1199)
John (1199–1216)
Henry III (1216–1272)
Edward I (1272–1307)
Edward II (1307–1327)
Edward III (1327–1377)
Richard II (1377–1399)

HOUSE OF LANCASTER
Henry IV (1399–1413)
Henry V (1413–1422)
Henry VI (1422–1461)

HOUSE OF YORK
Edward IV (1461–1483 and
  again 1471–83)
Richard III (1483–1485)

TUDORS
Henry VII (1485–1509)
Henry VIII (1509–1547)
Edward VI (1547–1553)
Mary (1553–1558)
Philip & Mary (1554–1558)
Elizabeth I (1558–1603)

STUARTS
James I (1603–1625)
Charles I (1625–1649)
The Commonwealth (1653–
  1658)
Charles II (1660–1685)
James II (1685–1688)
William III & Mary (1688–1694)
William III (1694–1702)
Anne (1702–1714)

HOUSE OF HANOVER
George I (1714–1727)
George II (1727–1760)
George III (1760–1820)
George IV(1820–1830)
William IV (1830–1837)
Victoria (1837–1901)

HOUSES OF SAXE-COBURG-GOTHA AND WINDSOR
Edward VII (1901–1910)
George V (1910–1936)
Edward VIII (1936)
George VI (1936–1952)
Elizabeth II (1952–)

Portraits & Miniatures

by David Trower

In 1969 a miniature portrait of an anonymous Tudor lady, painted by Hans Holbein and measuring a mere one and a half inches in diameter, was sold at Sothebys for £21,000. Less than two years later, in June 1971, The National Portrait Gallery paid 38,000 guineas to secure for the nation a tiny circular portrait of Sir Francis Drake by Nicholas Hilliard.

We are talking of prices achieved 35 and more years ago. Just imagine what such portraits might bring if they were to come up for auction today!

One might think that such prices would place the collection of genuine portrait miniatures beyond the reach of the average collector.

Not so.

Just last month I purchased a very fine contemporary miniature portrait of Henry VIII himself. It cost me something under £240. This full face portrait dates from 1544–47 and the bold, arrogant facial expression is reminiscent of the famous Holbein drawing in the National Portrait Gallery.

Henry VIII.

My latest acquisition is in very fine condition. Rather than detracting from its appearance, the passage of time has enhanced it, laying down a patina on the background which points up the features of the heavily jowled face.

My miniature is of course a coin, in this case a groat, approximately one inch in diameter.

What I am advocating in this article —the collecting of coins for their appeal as portrait miniatures—may at first seem unremarkable. After all, surely numismatists have endeavoured to compile collections representative of each and every reign since coins were first collected!

But wait . . .

To the true numismatist a coin is an object with two faces and an edge and he/she is concerned about the condition of all these features. The collector of coins as portrait miniatures is really only interested in the condition of the obverse side, i.e. the side depicting the bust.

A holed or otherwise disfigured coin is considered worthless and is most likely to be discarded or disregarded by a numismatist, unless it is extremely rare. Such professional Disdain can prove a windfall to the coin portrait collector. A hole, depending on its position on the coin, can often be satisfactorily plugged and/or camouflaged with a frame or mount. Edge knocks or scratches on the reverse are like wise of little concern. Consequently, the collector of coin portraits is able to exploit a segment of the market where significant bargains are still to be had.

A numismatist also tends to define the scope of his/her collection in terms of a series or type of coin. The collector of coin portraits is unrestricted by such considerations. Indeed he/she welcomes diversity in all its numismatic possibilities of size, shape, denomination and colour.

It is no mere coincidence that the first realistic portrait on an English coin appeared in the reign of Henry VII. It was about then that the impact of the Renaissance was making itself felt in England. Out of the anonymity of the medieval tradition, where the effigy had sufficed as the regal symbol, the coinage, along with other art forms, merged into the humanist tradition of the Renaissance.

Man had become the measure. His individuality was glorified and expressed in portraiture on coins as well as in painting and sculpture.

Henry VII.

The now famous crowned, profile portrait (above) which does much to humanise and personalise the later coinage of Henry VII was engraved by a German die sinker, Alexander Bruchsal.

It is significant that the artists and craftsmen who gave initial impetus to the development of coin portraiture in this country came in the first place from the continent. Continental origins are something die engravers shared with the earliest painters of portrait miniatures. Initially too, both artists and engravers relied largely on Royal patronage.

It would take much more space than is available here for even a brief survey of the variety of coin portraits available in just the English series alone. They range from the ebullient portrait of Henry VIII and the haughty likeness of Elizabeth I, through the romantically styled busts of the Restoration coinage to the unadorned portraits of the twentieth century.

Elizabeth I

From an artistic point of view there is much to research and discover. Behind the development of coin portraiture lies the human, often tempestuous, story of the artists, the designers and engravers. Paralleling it too, is the story of the advance of technology from the method of hammering, through the advent of the screw press and the reducing machine to the automated processes of coining employed today. Each and all of these technological advances had an influence on the development of design and reproduction

There remains a closely related field for the collector of numismatic portrait miniatures to consider—that of portrait medallions. These portraits are generally larger than those on coins and the engraving in higher relief. Because they are not subjected to the mass circulation which coins undergo, they are more often found in mint or near mint state.

There are some particularly beautiful coronation and other official and unofficial medallions to be had.

A disadvantage with some medallions is that they are not always struck contemporaneously with the reign of the monarch or celebrity they depict. To the purist, collecting such portraits, is like collecting copies of the originals in that they tend to reflect the artistic values existing at the time they were produced. The collector of genuine coin portraits can rest secure in the knowledge that each one reflects the style and fashion of its period quite as much as genuine painted portrait miniatures.

In displaying his/her finds, the coin portrait collector can call on all the numismatic accessories currently available from plastic coin pocket to coin cabinet. However there is no need to be limited by the restrictions inherent in these more conventional means

*Oliver Cromwell, Queen Anne and Philip and Mary —
framed they, and any other monarchs, could be a veritable portrait gallery in miniature.*

of display. Coin portraits can be mounted in a silver or gold frame such as are commonly used with coin brooch and pendant jewellery. Care must be taken not to overpower the portrait with too ornate a mount but very effective results can be achieved with quite a simple frame.

Among advantages over their hand painted counterparts coin portraits enjoy is they suffer no ill effects from exposure to direct light. In fact they appear to greater advantage in these circumstances

Once framed or mounted these monetary miniatures can be displayed as a scatter in a glass topped cabinet that can double as a coffee table, arranged as a group in a velvet centred gilt frame, or in a velvet lined case. Indeed, the variety of display possibilities, are as many and varied as the whim of the individual collector.

The internet

an alternative place to sell, or buy, numismatic items

Collector WILLIAM McCREATH is an avid user of the internet and in this short article introduces us to the vagaries of trading "on-line". It is assumed that readers are UK-based, have some knowledge of eBay and can navigate the site effectively.

It's been three years since my first report on buying and selling on the internet was published in this Year Book and I wish that this update contained better news for prospective ebay buyers, ebay practically being "the internet" as far as collectors are concerned, but the vital message remains the same, "buyer beware". In the internet news groups for coins and papermoney "threads" about internet buying and selling seldom mention anything other than ebay so dominant is their on-line presence for collectors.

Three years ago the number of UK coins and banknotes listed on www.ebay.co.uk and www.ebay.com combined was around 8,000, this figure is now about 23,000, this is an amazing increase that must make ebay of major interest to all collectors of numismatic items, for collectors of UK tokens around 750 are listed. The growth is mainly in run of the mill common items but there are a few gems to be found but some time has to be invested to weed them out, with TV continuing to be dumbed down the collector can find better entertainment on ebay, given the choice my telly would go before I would part with my PC. The beginner looking for a common note or coin will find many to choose from, the rarer items will of course be more difficult to locate but will probably be listed sooner or later, perseverance is the secret as a truly rare item may only appear once, probably when the collector is on holiday and can't check ebay daily, it would be ideal to only holiday where daily internet access is available but this is probably not very practical. Many mobile phone networks now offer full internet access from a mobile phone which allows collectors to access just about every site they could from a PC. This is available in most countries so those bargains that will inevitably appears just as the collector flies off on holiday will not be missed but check the cost of this GPRS connection before using it.

The feedback system on ebay acts as a safeguard of sorts as a comment can be left by both the buyer and the seller at the conclusion of a sale. If the ebay member is happy with a transaction they can leave a positive comment which will increase that member's feedback score by one if they have not given that member a positive feedback before. If they are unhappy with the transaction a negative comment can be left which will reduce the member's score by one if this is the first negative feedback left for that person. If they are somewhere between happy and unhappy they can leave a neutral that will have no effect on the overall feedback score of that person. The figure in brackets after a person's ebay I.D. is their current feedback score and all comments can be read by clicking on that number. When considering placing a bid have a look at the percentage of positive feedback achieved by the seller and if it's not 100 percent read the negative comments and then decide if you are going to bid or not, if it's below 99 percent read the negatives very carefully as it's probably best not to buy from sellers that are below 99 percent unless their feedbacks number in the thousands. If a seller is below 99 percent positive feedbacks and you are considering placing a bid read the negatives left by the seller as this can be most enlightening, if they insult those that have left them a justified negative then I would recommend not buying from such a person. The feedback system is a useful feature but some bad sellers do have 100 percent positive feedback as some unhappy buyers will not give a negative as they fear a retaliatory negative in return but if a seller deserves a negative it should be given to alert other ebay members. If a seller has received any negatives when buying as a result of giving a negative to a bad seller these can be safely ignored. They should be applauded for accepting the risk of receiving a retaliatory negative from a bad seller as a price worth paying to warn others of bad sellers.

Sellers on ebay range from well known dealers, although from their ebay user name this may not be obvious, to hit and run scammers. An auction title can contain a maximum of 55 characters, if you are a seller use as many of the 55 as possible as usefully as possible by including the most important information about the item you have listed, the date, denomination and grade would be a very good start and it's amazing how often this vital information is missing. If you are a buyer avoid like the plague any seller who's item title contains, "must see", "look", "!!!!!!!!!!!!" or any other repeating character, or worst of all "L@@K", very often I see a listing I'm interested in then I don't click on it as I spot the dreaded "L@@K" in the title, if you are a seller using "L@@K" translates to "avoid" in the eyes of many prospective bidders so don't use it. Some ebay users will search a section using

"-l@@k" which removes all offending listings, the "minus" search function can be very useful. If you are a collector of sixpences for example a search of the sixpences category using "-lucky" will eliminate the common tanners offered for sale as a gift for a bride, these being of little interest to a coin collector, on the other hand if you have a lot of spare time the odd 1952 might be listed, who knows.

Now that your listing has a sensible title please don't spoil it by having a silly main description, a description in ALL CAPITALS is as big a turn off as having "L@@K" in the title. It's amazing how many descriptions consist of a few poorly chosen words followed by several pages of terms and conditions that are often in a very large font size in all caps and with many garish text colours for good measure. Black text on a white background is fine, 25 different text colours will impress no one but the seller. If ALL CAPS was easier on the eye than normal capitalisation then all newspapers and books would be printed in ALL CAPS, it's very irritating ISN'T IT. Huge font sizes are unnecessary as those with poor vision can compensate by changing the screen resolution of their monitor. Always mention the size of an object and including a ruler in the auction picture can be of use to viewers, some sellers include a common coin at the edge of the item image to give an idea of scale, a US one cent or a UK 20p are often used. If you must include terms and conditions in your listing something along the lines of "buyer pays, I send the item" will suffice. Ebay is not the best place to sell a truly rare coin or banknote as 99.9 percent of "rare" items listed are anything but and this leads buyers to view the description "rare" with a considerable amount of justified scepticism. In my nine years experience of ebay coins or notes that are genuinely rare are seldom described as such as the sellers are not aware of their rarity, this can give the knowledgeable collector the chance of an occasional bargain but the chances are few and far between. When listing an item a low starting price will often result in a higher final sale price being achieve. I once listed an old medal on ebay.com with a starting price of $9.99 and after seven days it ended with no bids, it was immediately re-listed starting at $0.99 and after another seven day auction it achieved $14.

The increased availability of broadband is no excuse for following the bad example set by some sellers, many of whom are based in China. Adding twinkling stars, exploding rockets, moving waterfalls and fire breathing dragons to a listing should be avoided, as should music. Three years ago I gave the advice that a clear picture of both sides is essential and this still applies but with spread of broadband keeping the image size below 100k is now less important but don't have it enormous.

Once registered with ebay, a free and painless process, it's possible to search the completed auctions and this can be very useful. There's no point in listing an item if in the past 30 days, the maximum for a completed auctions search, all similar items listed have received no bids. A completed auction search can also suggest the best category to list an item in, for example a Jack Nicklaus commemorative Royal Bank Of Scotland fiver may do better in the "golf" category than in "papermoney", there were so many Nicklaus notes listed at one time that a negative search for "-jack" became essential in the papermoney section to eliminate them. If you are a buyer looking at active auctions don't restrict your use of the search function to the category the item should be listed in, search all of ebay, and internationally. That rare coin you have always wanted may lurk un-noticed in the wrong category, or it may be listed with a spelling error, "Scotish" for "Scottish" for example so search for both or use "scot*" as that search will pick up both.

It's unusual to have a look at the UK papermoney listings without coming across someone offering a "rare withdrawn number rub off " Bank of England fiver. There were indeed faulty fivers whose serial numbers could be rubbed off and they were indeed withdrawn after 3 million had been released but they were treated to cure the problem and the issue continued, this latter fact is conveniently omitted from the note description. A collector looking to add one of these notes to their collection would probably want the first prefix which was HA01 but the ones on ebay usually have a very high prefix that can be found at any bank in England for face value. One seller was asking £150

for four notes and the fuzzy picture made it impossible to read the prefix, HA01 notes are available from dealers for around £15. The less desirable an item the more fluff there will be in the description so fluffery such as, "an asset to any collection", "much sought after", "unique" etc. are often used to draw attention from the fact that the item on offer is the exact opposite, items with such descriptions are best avoided.

It appears that many coin buyers on ebay blindly accept the grade given in an auction description and ignore the fact that the coin illustrated is nowhere near the grade stated, for example a stated grade of "EF" is often accompanied by a picture of a coin only in fine. I would strongly recommend ignoring the stated grade and grade the coin from the picture and if the picture in not good enough to grade the coin then don't bid on it. It's more difficult, if not impossible, to accurately grade a high grade note from a computer screen image so extra vigilance is required to avoid being scammed. I would recommend not bidding on any UK note described as "uncirculated" unless it's a fairly recent issue as the majority of older notes appear to me to have been treated. If a seller of coins or notes only offers uncirculated items ask yourself how can anyone have nothing but uncirculated items for sale unless they overgrade or have "improved" the notes.

Be aware that sellers based in the USA will often give the condition of a UK coin using the USA grading system but give a catalogue value based on the UK grading system, a USA "XF" grade is well below a UK "EF". As they must be aware of the vast difference in the two grading systems such sellers should be avoided. Mention must be made of the USA practice of "slabbing" coins, these are coins that have been graded by a third party grading service and then sealed in a rigid plastic slab. As previously mention is must be remembered that the USA and UK coin grading systems

" . . . Scammers rely on bargain hunters that have thrown common sense out of the window and who ignore the many red flags that should alert them to the bad seller . . . "

are chalk and cheese and if that's not enough the differences between the grading standards of the third party grading companies are also chalk and cheese. Coin collectors in the USA refer to the grading companies are being either top tier, middle tier or bottom feeders and there are endless debates in the internet coin News Groups as to who fits where. This being the case it's even more important to grade a slabbed coin from the picture and pay no attention to the grade on the slab. There are an unbelievable eleven "mint state" grades from "MS60" to "MS70", which is plainly ridiculous. To give one example, an 1893 florin slabbed by the grading company PCGS and graded as "MS66" included the information, "The PCGS MS66 population is just this Single example with NONE certified in ANY finer grade." This implies that the coin is a "condition rarity", something that our coin collecting friends on the other side of the Atlantic are willing to pay a premium price for but the £205 paid for the coin beggars belief, and it had an unattractive mottled tone.

Scammers rely on bargain hunters that have thrown common sense out of the window and who ignore the many red flags that should alert them to the bad seller. Early on in the ebay career of one seller it was clear to me that their coins were definitely in the "too good to be true" category. The coins illustrated were nowhere near the grade stated and the catalogue values they gave were for accurately graded coins, the buyers were at first overjoyed at getting a "bargain" at a fraction of the catalogue value and the feedback left by buyers was mainly positive. Towards the end of their ebay career they offered several modern UK coins described as "matt proofs" that if genuine would have been rare and valuable but from the pictures they seemed to be normal proofs or even non proofs with a dusty tone. The feedback left by the unfortunate buyers confirmed my suspicions and the seller is now "NARU", i.e. Not A Registered User, their account having been cancelled by ebay. Several ebay buyers lost a few hundred pounds each as a result of this bad seller's activities but if they had applied a little common sense it could have been avoided. This "NARU" seller has been replaced in 2007 with a seller with similar techniques, they list an unfeasibly high number of old coins in "uncirculated" condition at "bargain" prices but many coins look odd. The portraits appear to have been treated to give them a cameo effect and most look to have been dipped to removed toning, it will end in tears for their buyers I'm sure.

A UK based seller of antiquities on ebay. co.uk was recently prosecuted for the illegal practice of shill bidding, this is when a seller safeguards the selling price by have friends bid on their items to avoid them being sold too cheaply. It can be useful to do a bidder search to see if a buyer has an usually high percentage of bids places with a single seller, this does not always indicate shill bidding however as the seller just may be a good seller or the best source for a particular collectable.

Ebay are just an auction venue and cannot be expected to vet the many millions of items listed each week, for example I have yet to find a genuine USA silver trade dollar listed by a seller based in China . If you are new to ebay don't learn the hard way and remember that a little common sense can go a long way, if a seller's stock looks too good to be true then it probably is. Why do they sell on ebay to get a fraction of the amount that could be achieved if the coin or note was consigned to one of the major UK auction houses?

This is only my opinion of buying and selling on eBay and other people's experiences may vary. However, I would encourage collectors to visit the auction sites, but be careful. I welcome correspondence on the subject of eBay or other online numismatic activities and I can be contacted at william.mccreath@ntlworld.com.

COINS FOR SALE

£5 + £2 PIECES
1887 £2 BU £425
1902 MP £2 UNC £495
1989 PR. £2 FDC....................£295
2 GUINEAS, GUINEAS, ETC
1738 2 Gn. GVF Rare £995
1716 Gn. NVF/VF £575
1787 Gn. NEF £375
1797 Gn. UNC £650
SOVEREIGNS
1821 GF £295
1847 BU Extra Rare.................£750
1869 BU £275
1875 S BU £350
1879 S Nice BU £350
1885 S BU £295
1894 S BU £140
1894 M BU £140
1894 L Nice BU £150
1895 M BU £140
1896 M BU £140
1896 S BU £175
1897 M NICE BU £140
1898 M BU Scarce £135
1899 M BU £135
1899 L BU Scarce £150
1900 M BU £135
1901 M BU £135
Edward VII .... Many on List
George V .... Many on List
Elizabeth II .... Many on List
HALF SOVS
1818 Nice BU £750
1887 Jub. BU £90
1892 BU £100
1902 MP UNC £140
1905 L Nice BU £90
1906 L BU £85
1907 L BU £85
1908 L BU £85
1910 S Nice BU £225
1910 L BU £85
1913 L BU £68
1915 S BU £80
1915 M BU £125
1925 SA BU £75
1926 SA BU £75
1982 BU GEM £52
2007 ....£52

GOLD PROOF SETS ORIG. R. MINT
BOXES FDC ....On List
USA GOLD.........................On List
FOREIGN GOLD ....On List

CROWNS
1707 E VF 2nd Bust.................£240
1708 EF £135
1844 GF £50
1845 GF £45
1887 NVF................................£18
1887 UNC................................£90
1889 BU £85
1890 BU £110
1893 LVI BU............................£195
1895 LIX BU............................£195
1896 LX BU.............................£250
1900 LXIV UNC/BU................£175
1902 Nice Abt BU....................£125
1928 BU £275
1930 NEF/EF Scarce...............£150
1932 BU Extr. rare £750
1935 BU £15
1935 Spec BU £45
1936 Superb BU £850
1937 Pr. GEM UNC £65
1937 BU £22
1951 Pr. BU.............................£5
1953 BU £5
1960 BU £7
More on List
DOUBLE FLORINS
1887 A BU £65
1887 A ABU £42
1887 R GEM UNC....................£75
1889 VF £18
1890 F/GF £15
HALFCROWNS
1689 Wm & Mary Fine.............£125
1712 F/GF £85
1713 GF £100
1732 NVF.................................£150
1732 GF £125
1739 GFVF+ £350
1746 Lima GF £80
1817 Sm. Hd. NVF £25
1820 L. Hd UNC......................£375
1825 Nice BU £350
1826 VF £45
1826 UNC................................£350
1836 F £15
1887 Jub. BU £38
1888 BU £100
1889 BU £75
1891 BU £140
1893 BU £85
1895 BU £125
1896 BU GEM £150
1897 BU £75

1899 BU £120
1902 BU £120
1909 GF £10
1915 BU £33
1916 BU £38
1918 BU £40
1927 BU £65
1929 BU £25
1938 BU £35
More on list
FLORINS
1849 UNC................................£225
1873 BU GEM £250
1881 BU £275
1885 GVF.................................£45
1886 BU £225
1887 Jub. BU £30
1888 BU £110
1897 BU GEM £85
1898 BU £90
1902 BU £75
1902 MP UNC £70
1903 BU £175
1905 BU Extr. rare £950
1909 Nice ABU........................£225
1909 GF £12
1910 ABU £95
1912 BU £110
1933 BU EF £40
1937 BU £6
More on List
SHILLINGS
Edward Vi GVF £375
1676 Fine £80
1711 UNC................................£350
1734 GF/GVF £75
1743 F £35
1747 Nice UNC........................£350
1758 UNC................................£95
1787 UNC No Hts.....................£85
1787 VF Hts.............................£22
1818 UNC................................£240
1820 BU £85
1821 UNC................................£225
1824 UNC................................£250
More on List

| **SIXPENCES On List** |
| **GROATS, SILVER 1 1/2d On List** |
| **SILVER 3d On List** |
| **MAUNDY SETS On List** |
| **1ds, 1/2, 1/4 On List** |
| **USA Silver Dollars On List** |

**IF YOU WOULD LIKE TO RECEIVE MY FREE SALES LIST
OF ENGLISH, GOLD, SILVER AND COPPER COINS, (A VERY WIDE RANGE
(1200 – 2007). PLEASE WRITE, TELEPHONE OR FAX ME**

41

Talking Tokens

Strictly speaking, a token is any piece of money whose intrinsic value is less than its face value. In that sense, therefore, all modern coins are mere tokens, because their metallic worth is invariably less than their nominal, legal tender value. Until the 19th century, however, most countries issued coins which contained metal up to the value at which they circulated. This applied mainly to gold and silver coins, but it should be noted that Britain's first copper penny and twopence (1797) were so cumbersome because they contained one and two ounces of metal respectively, copper being then valued at a penny an ounce.

The desire for parity between intrinsic and nominal value led to copper coins containing a small plug of silver to bring them up to their full value. The UK abandoned full value in 1816; as a result of the recoinage of that year the gold sovereign became the absolute standard and all silver and copper coins became mere tokens. The difference between real and nominal value widened in subsequent years with the debasement of silver coins and finally the replacement of silver altogether by cupro-nickel and other base alloys. Oddly enough, there have been many instances of small copper or bronze coins in recent years which had a greater intrinsic value than their face value and actually cost twice as much to produce as they were worth in circulation.

" . . . A token is an outward sign or pledge, something given or shown as a guarantee of authority or good faith . . . "

A token is an outward sign or pledge, something given or shown as a guarantee of authority or good faith. The word comes from German *zeichen* and Old English *tacen*, meaning a sign or mark. From this developed the notion of a promise, symbol or keepsake. In the numismatic sense, however, the term is restricted to any coinlike object, either issued by a body other than a government, or something which is used in place of money and can be exchanged for specified goods and services. Broadly speaking, tokens include any unofficial coins supplied by local bodies or occasionally even private individuals and tolerated in general

circulation at times of shortage of government issues of small change.

Tokens go back a surprisingly long way. The earliest issues in base metal with limited local validity were produced by Sicily in the middle of the fifth century BC, the bronze litra being easier to handle than its tiny silver counterpart. Himera was one of the first towns to issue such tokens, but by the end of the century many Sicilian towns had adopted small bronze pieces as token currency, the intrinsic value of which was considerably below the circulating value placed on them by the issuing authorities.

This concept gradually spread to all other parts of the Greek world. Under the Roman Empire, base-metal tokens were issued from the time of Augustus to the late third century AD. Sometimes referred to quasi-autonomous coinage, these pieces were struck mostly in bronze with the nominal value of drachmae or sestertii, and have portraits of local deities instead of the Roman emperor and members of his family. These tokens were struck by every town and city and their range and variety is enormous.

This concept survived the fall of the Roman Empire and many towns in medieval Europe continued to strike small base-metal pieces for use as local currency. They were usually accorded a measure of legality because they were authorised by the royal or imperial government, even if their actual design and metal content were decided by the municipal authorities. In addition to the tokens which served as small change there are other categories of coinlike material which deserve comment.

*17th century tokens come in a
variety of shapes and sizes.*

Jetons (from French *jeter*, to throw) originated in medieval France as counters used on the chequerboard by merchants and bankers as well as royal treasurers to do their monetary calculations. These pieces spread rapidly all over Europe, but found their greatest expression at Nuremberg where, in the hands of Hans Krauwinckel (flourished 1580–1620), they attained the status of an art form and were often produced in thematic sets.

While many jetons were struck in gold or silver and were eventually used (especially in France) as a form of New Year bonus to servants, the vast majority of them were struck in debased silver alloys (billon) or in copper, bronze, brass or pewter. Base-metal Nuremberg jetons, in fact, often circulated as small change in countries where there was a shortage of total lack of government issues of small change. This situation arose in England early in the 14th century, Nuremberg jetons circulating freely until 1335 when they were banned by statute.

English tokens

The first indigenous tokens in England were cast or struck in lead and have been recorded as circulating in 1404. For many years these local farthings and half-farthings were tolerated but had no official sanction. They were certainly well-established in Tudor times and it was not until 1598 that any attempt was made to regulate them. Queen Elizabeth then licensed Bristol to issue lead tokens, to be valid within a ten-mile radius of the city. At the same time, private tokens were expressly forbidden, so that the municipal tokens were given a monopoly. By the end of the Civil War (1649) there was an acute shortage of small change, and illicit tokens, mainly in lead and including pewter, brass, copper or even leather pieces, were revived in England and Wales.

Almost 4,000 types of token were issued in London alone, by tradesmen and shopkeepers of all kinds, and often circulating no farther than the end of the street. As the vast majority were produced before the Great Fire of 1666 they form an invaluable record of London streets and their occupants from this period. Following the introduction of regal copper farthings and halfpence in 1672 these tradesmen's tokens were banned, but they continued in some parts of England until 1674, and survived in Ireland until 1679. By contrast there was virtually no need for tokens in 17th century Scotland because of an abundant supply of copper coinage, and only two Scottish tokens (c. 1668) have so far been recorded.

In many ways tokens benefited the poor, who were no longer compelled to purchase more than they actually required because the smallest coin available was a penny. Tokens were also used as alms, as people would gladly give a farthing but would think twice about giving a halfpenny or penny. For this reason many tokens of the 17th century were inscribed "Remember the Poore", "For the Poore's Advantage" or "For Change & Charitie" or some other pious slogan.

There were even tokens inscribed in verse: "To supply the poore's need is charitie indeed". Other poetic inscriptions include "When you please, I'll change thee", "Although but brass, yet let me pass", "Welcome you be to trade with me" or "Take these that will, I'll change them still".

Eighteenth century tokens

Tokens were revived in the British Isles in 1787 to fill a gap in the regal coinage. Silver pennies for general circulation were only sporadically produced in the reign of George III and none at all were minted after 1786. The dearth of copper halfpence and farthings was even greater as none was minted after 1775. On this occasion the way was led by the Angelsey Copper Mining Company which began striking pennies with the effigy of a Druid on the obverse. This triggered off an immense

*The Parys Mines of
Anglesey produced vast
numbers of "Druid's
Head" tokens. Sold at
DNW July 2006 for
£220.*

deluge of token pennies, halfpennies and farthings. The range was not as great as it had been in the 17th century as fewer individual shopkeepers now issued them.

There was a greater concentration of tokens issued by municipal authorities and the more important merchant companies. On the other hand, the quality of design and execution improved beyond all recognition and latterly they were aimed at the contemporary collector market, with emphasis on heraldry, landmarks, scenery, historic events and portraits of local and national celebrities. These tokens enjoyed a decade of use before they were banned following the introduction of the "Cartwheel" coinage in 1797.

William Upcott's rare Devon 19th century token illustrating Eddystone lighthouse, sold in 2006 by DNW for £220.

Nineteenth century tokens

Silver tokens were issued between 1804 and 1816 as a result of a continuing shortage of silver coins. At first countermarked Spanish dollars and half-dollars were issued but in 1811–12 the Bank of England released silver pieces inscribed BANK TOKEN on the reverse, with the value and date below. The obverse portrayed George III and had his name and titles round the circumference like the proper silver coins. Denominations of 1s6d and 3s were issued; though 9d pieces exist they were only patterns. The Bank of Ireland had silver tokens in the same period, but denominated in a decimal system of 5, 10 and 30 pence, as well as 6 shillings. Many private silver tokens were issued in 1811–12 in denominations from 3d to 5s, mainly by private banks, local authorities and large companies.

Copper or bronze tokens were again issued in the British Isles from 1811 to the 1830s. As no copper subsidiary coins were issued between 1807 and 1821 (no halfpence or pennies until 1825–26) the range of tokens in this period was far greater than ever. Significantly a high proportion of these tokens were now issued by banks rather than by private individuals.

Other types of tokens

Tokens have been produced in most countries at some time or another. Very extensive series, for example, were produced in Canada and Australia before these countries introduced subsidiary coinage. They were also produced on a number of occasions in the USA, from the revolutionary period onwards, and notably during the Hard Times (1834–44) during a shortage of copper cents and half-cents. There was a further spate of local tokens during the Civil War (1861–65), often with patriotic motifs and having a propaganda purpose as well as filling the gap in the coinage. Many countries issued tokens during and after the First World War, every type of material from pasteboard and wood to leather and even rubber being pressed into service. A special category consists of trade dollars issued all over Canada. These are often commemorative or intended as tourist mementoes, but they have a nominal value, redeemable for cash within a certain area and over a fixed period, usually twelve months. They are immensely popular and now have a wide following in North America.

In Britain from the 18th century onwards tokens were often issued by textile mills, collieries, iron foundries and other industrial undertakings in exchange for a day's work. These tokens could only be used to obtain goods from the company stores, and were eventually outlawed by the Truck Act in 1844. Nevertheless they survived in various parts of Britain, often in specific forms of labour. A very prolific series, for example, consists of hop-pickers' tokens, associated mainly with the hopfields of Kent and Sussex. In Scotland, however,

Richard Orchard's Sawbridgeworth token sold for the world record price of £24,400 in 1998.

Images courtesy of DNW and Spink.

fruit-pickers' tokens were also issued by many of the farms in the Clyde Valley and the fruit-growing areas of Perthshire and Angus.

Another vast area consists of the checks and tokens issued by co-operative societies, often in proportion to the money spent by the member in the societies' stores, as a form of dividend. When a certain quantity of checks had been accumulated they could be exchanged for goods or services. The same concept underlay the discount schemes, premium giveaways and trading stamps of more recent items.

Tokens of metal, pasteboard or even plastic have been used as a method of controlling the use of public transport by employees of companies, the Post Office or local authorities, being given out whenever it was necessary for an employee to travel on official business. Such tokens were produced by local authorities or the private companies operating buses, ferries, trams and other services. At the other end of the spectrum are the tokens and passes, often in silver or even gold, or ivory, which were issued to directors of the railway companies to enable them to travel free of charge. Tokens in the same materials, and for the same purpose, were produced for the use of the directors and shareholders of theatres and other places of entertainment, and were often highly ornate in design.

Robert Simpson's rare silver halfcrown ticket used for gambling, sold at DNW, June 2006 for £110.

Gaming tokens

This is another vast field, ranging from the brass halfpenny and penny tokens issued by many pubs and taverns in the 19th century for use in games of chance, to the modern tokens, often in cupro-nickel, bronze or aluminium-bronze, used in one-armed bandits and fruit machines. These tokens range from the fairly utilitarian designs showing perhaps a company name and a unit of value only, to the very elaborate tokens used by casinos and gaming clubs, often with special security features built into their design and composition. Many of the gaming tokens of more recent years have a quasi-commemorative or publicity character.

Hop pickers were usually paid in tokens which are highly collected today.

Dates
on coins

The vast majority of modern coins bear the date prominently on one side. In most cases dates are expressed in modified Arabic numerals according to the Christian calendar and present no problem in identification. There have been a few notable exceptions to this general rule, however. Morocco, for example, has used European numerals to express dates according to the Moslem calendar, so that a coin dated 1321 actually signifies 1903. Dates are almost invariably written from left to right—even in Arabic script which writes words from right to left. An exception, however, occurred in the Philippines quarto of 1822 where the date appeared as 2281, and the "2s" back to front for good measure.

	ARABIC-TURKISH	CHINESE, JAPANESE KOREAN, ANNAMESE (ORDINARY)	CHINESE, JAPANESE KOREAN, ANNAMESE (OFFICIAL)	INDIAN	SIAMESE	BURMESE
1	١	一	壹	٩	๑	၁
2	٢	二	貳	٢	๒	၂
3	٣	三	叄	٣	๓	၃
4	٤	四	肆	٨	๔	၄
5	٥	五	伍	٤	๕	၅
6	٦	六	陸	٦	๖	၆
7	٧	七	柒	٧	๗	၇
8	٨	八	捌	٨	๘	၈
9	٩	九	玖	٩	๙	၉
0	٠			٠	๐	၀
10	١٠	十	拾		๑๐	
100	١٠٠	百			๑๐๐	
1000	١٠٠٠	千				

Dates in Roman numerals have been used since 1234 when this practice was adopted by the Danish town of Roskilde. Such Roman numerals were used sporadically throughout the Middle Ages and in later centuries and survive fitfully to this day. This was the system used in England for the first dated coins, the gold half-sovereigns of Edward VI struck at Durham House in 1548 (MDXLVIII). This continued till 1550 (MDL) but thereafter Arabic numerals were used, beginning with the half-crown of 1551. Notable exceptions of more recent times include the Gothic coinage of Queen Victoria (1847–87).

The first coin with the date in European numerals was a plappart of St Gallen, Switzerland dated 1424, but this was an isolated case. In 1477 Maria of Burgundy issued a guldiner which bore a date on the reverse, in the form of two pairs of digits flanking the crown at the top. The numerals in this instance were true Gothic, an interesting transition between true Arabic numerals and the modified Arabic figures now used in Europe. The Tyrolese guldengroschen of 1484–6 were the first coins to be regularly dated in European numerals and thereafter this custom spread rapidly.

For the numismatist, the problem arises when coins bear a date in the numerals of a different alphabet or computed according to a different era. Opposite is a table showing the basic numerals used in different scripts. The various eras which may be found in coin dates are as listed and explained opposite.

46

Hijra

The era used on Moslem coins dates from the flight of Mohammed from Mecca to Medina on July 15, 622 and is often expressed as digits followed by AH (*Anno Hegirae*). Moslems employ a lunar calendar of twelve months comprising 354 11/30 days. Tipu Sultan of Mysore in 1201 AH (the fifth year of his reign)introduced a new era dating from the birth of Mohammed in AD 570 and using a luni-solar system. Tipu also adopted the Hindu cycle of sixty years (the Tamil Brihaspate Cycle), but changed this two or three years later, from Hijra to Muludi.

Afghan coins used the lunar calendar until 1920 and during 1929–31, but at other times have used the solar calendar. Thus the Democratic Republic began issuing its coins in SH 1358 (1979).

To convert an AH date to the Christian calendar you must translate the Arabic into European numerals. Taking an Arabic coin dated 1320, for example, first deduct 3% (to convert from the Moslem lunar year to our solar year). This gives 39.6 which, rounded up to the nearest whole number, is 40. Deduct 40 from 1320 (1280), then add 622. The answer is 1902.

There have been a few notable exceptions. Thus the Khanian era of Ilkhan Ghazan Mahmud began on 1st Rajab 701 AH (1301). This era used a solar calendar, but was shortlived, being confined to coins of Mahmud and his nephew Abu Said down to year 34 (1333).

The era of Tarikh Ilahi was adopted by the Mughal emperor Akbar in the thirteenth year of his reign (922 AH). This era dated from his accession on 5th Rabi al-Sani 963 AH (February 19, 1556). The calendar had solar months and days but no weeks, so each day of the month had a different name. This system was used by Akbar, Jahangir and Shah Jahan, often with a Hijra date as well.

Saphar

The era of the Caesars began on January 1, 38 BC and dated from the conquest of Spain by Augustus. Its use on coinage, however, seems to have been confined to the marabotins of Alfonso VIII of Castile and was expressed in both Latin and Arabic.

Samvat

The era of Vikramaditya began in 57 BC and was a luni-solar system used in some Indian states. Coins may be found with both Samvat and Hijra dates. Conversion to the Christian date is simple; merely subtract 57 from the Samvat to arrive at the AD date.

Saka

This originated in the southwestern district of Northern India and began in AD 78. As it used the luni-solar system it converts easily by adding 78 to the Saka date.

Nepal

Nepalese coins have used four different date systems. All coins of the Malla kings were dated in Nepal Samvat (NS) era, year 1 beginning in 881. This system was also used briefly by the state of Cooch Behar. Until 1888 all coins of the Gurkha dynasty were dated in the Saka era (SE) which began in AD 78. After 1888 most copper coins were dated in the Vikram Samvat (VS) era from 57 BC. With the exception of some gold coins struck in 1890 and 1892, silver and gold coins only changed to the VS era in 1911, but now this system is used for all coins struck in Nepal. Finally, dates in the Christian era have appeared on some commemorative coins of recent years.

Ethiopian

This era dates from August AD 7, so that EE 1885 is AD 1892. Ethiopian dates are expressed in five digits using Amharic numerals. The first two are the digits of the centuries, the third is the character for 100, while the fourth and fifth are the digits representing the decade and year. On modern coins dates are rendered in Amharic numerals using the Christian era.

Thailand

Thai coins mainly use the Buddhist era (BE) which dates from 543 BC, but some coins have used dates from the Chula-Sakarat calendar (CS) which began in AD 638, while others use a Ratanakosind Sok (RS) date from the foundation of the Chakri dynasty in AD 1781.

Hebrew

The coins of Israel use the Jewish calendar dating from the beginning of the world (Adam and Eve in the Garden of Eden) in 3760 BC. Thus the year 1993 is rendered as 5753. The five millennia are assumed in dates, so that only the last three digits are expressed. 735 therefore equates with AD 1975. Dates are written in Hebrew letters, reading from right to left. The first two characters signify 400 and 300 respectively, totalling 700. The third letter denotes the decades (*lamedh* = 30) and the fourth letter, following the separation mark (") represents the final digit (*heh* = 5). The Jewish year runs from September or October in the Christian calendar.

Dates from the creation of the world

This system was also used in Russia under Ivan IV. The dating system *Anno Mundi* (AM) was established by the Council of Constantinople in AD 680 which determined that the birth of Christ had occurred in 5508 AM. Ivan's coins expressed the date as 7055 (1447).

Dynastic dates

The system of dating coinage according to regnal years is a feature of Chinese and Japanese coins. Chinese coins normally have an inscription stating that they are coins of such and such a reign period (not the emperor's name), and during the Southern Sung dynasty this was joined by the numeral of the year of the reign. This system was continued under the republic and survives in Taiwan to this day, although the coins of the Chinese Peoples Republic are dated in western numerals using the Christian calendar.

Early Japanese coins bore a reference to the era (the title assumed by each emperor on his accession) but, like Chinese coins, could not be dated accurately. From the beginning of the Meiji era (1867), however, coins have included a regnal number. The Showa era, beginning in 1926 with the accession of Hirohito, eventually ran to sixty-three (expressed in western numerals on some denominations, in Japanese ideograms on others) to denote 1988, although the rest of the inscription was in Japanese characters.

Dynastic dates were used on Korean milled coins introduced in 1888. These bore two characters at the top *Kae Kuk* (founding of the dynasty) followed by quantitative numerals. The system dated from the founding of the Yi dynasty in 1392. Curiously enough, some Korean banknotes have borne dates from the foundation of the first dynasty in 2333 BC.

Iran adopted a similar system in 1975, celebrating the 15th anniversary of the Pahlavi regime by harking back to the glories of Darius. The new calendar dated from the foundation of the Persian Empire 2535 years earlier, but was abolished only three years later when the Shah was overthrown.

Political eras

France adopted a republican calendar in 1793 when the monarchy was abolished. Coins were then inscribed L'AN (the year) followed by Roman numerals, but later Arabic numerals were substituted. This continued to the year 14 (1806) but in that year the Emperor Napoleon restored the Christian calendar. The French system was emulated by Haiti whose coins dated from the revolution of 1803. The date appeared as AN followed by a number until AN 31 (1834) on some coins; others had both the evolutionary year and the Christian date from 1828 until 1850 (AN 47). Coins with a date in the Christian calendar appeared only in 1807–9 and then from 1850 onwards.

Mussolini introduced the Fascist calendar to Italy, dating from the seizure of power in October 1922. This system was widely employed on documents and memorials, but was first used on silver 20 lire coins of 1927 and then only in addition to the Christian date and appearing discreetly as Roman numerals. Subsequently it was extended to gold 50 lire and 100 lire coins in 1931 and the subsidiary coinage in 1936, being last used in the year XXI (1943).

Around the
WORLD

Listed here are the names of all the coins of the world, many of which have been around for hundreds of years, others are no longer in use. Some of the denominations have been introduced only recently, whilst others are familiar household words. A number of the names are shared by different countries and a few have even been used by different civilisations.

Abazi Caucusus
Abbasi, Abbassi Afghanistan, Georgia, Persia
Ackey Gold Coast
Adli Altin Ottoman Empire
Afghani Afghanistan

Agnel France
Agora (ot) Israel
Ahmadi Mysore, Yemen
Akce Turkey
Akcheh Turkestan
Albertusdaler Denmark
Albus German States, Swiss Cantons
Altin, Altun Egypt, Turkey
Altinlik Turkey
Altyn, Altynnik Russia
Amani Afghanistan
Amman Cash Mewar Udaipur, Pudukota,   India
Angel England, Scotland, Isle of Man
Angelet France
Angelot France
Angster Lucerne
Anna Burma, India, Pakistan, Kenya, Muscat & Oman
Antoninianus Rome
Ardite Navarre
Argentino Argentina
Ariary Malagasy Republic
As Rome
Asarfi Nepal
Ashrafi Afghanistan, Awadh, Bahawalpur, Egypt,   Hyderabad
Asper Algeria, Egypt, Libya, Trebizond, Tunisia,   Turkey

Asses Luxembourg
At Laos
Atia Portuguese India
Atribuo Frankfurt
Att Cambodia, Laos, Siam (Thailand)
August d'Or Saxony
Augustale Sicily
Aurar (plural **Eyrir**) Iceland
Austral Argentina
Avo Macau, Timor
Bagarone Bologna
Bagattino Venice
Baggliangster Lucerne

Baht Thailand
Baiocco (plural **Baiocchi**) Papal States
Baisa Oman
Baiza Kuwait
Baizah Muscat & Oman
Balboa Panama
Ban (plural **Bani** or **Banu**) Roumania
Banica Croatia
Barbarina Mantua
Barbonaccio Lucca
Barbone Lucca
Barbuda Portugal
Barilla Philippines
Batzen German States, Swiss Cantons
Bawbee Scotland
Bazaruco Portuguese India
Bazaruk Dutch Settlements in India
Belga Belgium

Benduqi   Morocco
Besa (plural Bese)   Ethiopia, Somalia
Beshlik   Soviet Central Asia
Bezant   Byzantine Empire, Cyprus, Jerusalem
Bezzo   Italian States
Bianco (plural Bianchi)   Bologna, Papal States
Biche   French Indian Settlements
Binio   Roman Empire
Bipkwele   Equatorial Guinea
Bir (r)   Ethiopia
Bisti   Caucasia
Bit   Guyana, West Indies
Bitt   Danish Virgin Islands
Black Dog   Nevis
Blaffert   Switzerland
Blanc   France
Blodsklipping   Sweden
Bluzger   Swiss Cantons
Bodle   Scotland
Bogach   Yemen
Bolivar   Venezuela
Boliviano   Bolivia
Bolognino   Papal States
Bonk   Ceylon, Dutch East Indies
Bonnet   Scotland
Boo   Japan
Braspenning   Flanders
Broad   England
Bu   Japan
Budju   Algeria
Buqsha   Yemen Arab Republic
Burbe(ns)   Tunisia

Butut   Gambia
Cache   French Indian Settlements
Cagliareso   Italian States
Calderilla   Spain
Candareen   China
Carbovanetz   Ukraine
Carlin   Sicily
Carlino   Papal States
Carolin   Austria,German States, Sweden
Cash   China, Hong Kong, India, Mysore, Travancore, Turkestan, Vietnam
Cassathaler   German States
Cauri   Guinea
Ceitil   Portugal
Cent   Australia, Bahamas, Barbados, Belize, Bermuda, Botswana, British East Caribbean Territories, British Honduras, British North Borneo, British Virgin Islands, Brunei, Canada, Cayman Island, Ceylon, China, Cochin China, Cocos (Keeling) Islands, Cook Islands, Curacao, Cyprus, Danish West Indies, East Africa, Ethiopia, Fiji, French Indochina, Gilbert and Ellice Islands, Guyana, Hawaii, Hong Kong, Indonesia, Jamaica, Kenya, Kiao Chau (Kiatschau), Kiribati, Laos, Liberia, Malaya, Malaysia, Malta, Mauritius, Netherlands, Netherlands Antilles, Netherlands Indies, New Zealand, Nova Scotia, Panama, Prince Edward Island, Sarawak, Seychelles, Sierra Leone, Singapore, Solomon Islands, South Africa, Sri Lanka, Straits Settlements, Suriname, Swaziland, Tanzania, Trinidad and Tobago, Tuvalu, Uganda, United States of America, Virgin Islands, Zanzibar, Zimbabwe
Centas (plural Centa, Centu)   Lithuania

Centavo   Angola, Argentina, Bolivia, Brazil, Cape Verde Islands, Chile, Colombia, Costa Rica, Cuba, Dominican Republic, Ecuador, El Salvador, Guatemala, Guinea-Bissau, Honduras, Mexico, Mozambique, Nicaragua, Paraguay, Peru, Philippines, Portugal, Portuguese Guinea, Portuguese India, Puerto Rico, St Thomas and Prince Islands, Timor, Venezuela
Centecimo   Bolivia
Cententionalis   Roman Empire
Centesimo   Bolivia, Chile, Dominican Republic, Ethiopia, Italian East Africa, Italy, Panama, Paraguay, San Marino, Somalia, Uruguay, Vatican
Centime   Algeria, Antwerp, Belgian Congo, Belgium, Cambodia, Cameroon, Cochin China, Comoro Islands, Djibouti, France, French Equatorial Africa, French Guiana, French Indochina, French Oceania, French Polynesia, French Somali Coast, French West Africa, Guadeloupe, Guinea, Haiti, Laos, Monaco, Morocco, New Caledonia, Reunion, Senegal, Switzerland, Togo, Tunisia, Vietnam, Westphalia, Yugoslavia, Zaire
Centimo   Costa Rica, Mozambique, Paraguay, Peru, Philippines, Puerto Rico, St Thomas and Prince Islands, Spain, Venezuela

Centu   Lithuania
Chaise   Antwerp, Bavaria, France
Chervonetz (plural **Chervontzy**)   Russia
Chetrum   Bhutan
Cheun   South Korea
Chiao   China, Formosa, Manchukuo
Chi'en   China
Chio   China
Cho-gin   Japan
Chomseh   Yemen
Chon   Korea
Christian d'Or   Denmark
Chuckram   Travancore
Colon   Costa Rica, El Salvador
Condor   Chile, Colombia, Ecuador
Cordoba   Nicaragua
Cornado   Spain
Cornuto   Savoy
Coroa de Prata   Portugal
Coroin   Eire
Corona   Austrian provinces of Italy, Naples
Coronato   Castile, Naples
Couronne d'Or   France
Crocione   Italian States
Crossazzo   Genoa
Crown   Ascension, Australia, Bermuda,
   England, Ghana, Gibraltar, Ireland, Isle of
   Man, Jamaica, Jersey, Malawi, New Zealand,
   Nigeria, Rhodesia, Rhodesia and Nyasaland,
   St Helena, Scotland, Southern Rhodesia,
   Tristan da Cunha, Turks and Caicos Islands

Cruzadinho   Brazil, Portugal
Cruzado   Brazil, Portugal
Cruzeiro   Brazil
Cuartillo, Cuartino   Mexico
Cuarto   Bolivia, Spain
Daalder   Netherlands
DakBler   Danish West Indies, Denmark, Sweden
Dam   Afghanistan, India, Nepal
Daric   Persia
Dauphin   France
Decime   France
Decimo   Argentina, Chile, Colombia, Ecuador,
   Galapagos
Decussis   Roman Republic
Dekadrachm   Syracuse, Hellenistic kingdoms
Dekanummion   Byzantine Empire

Dekobolon   Greece
Demareteion   Syracuse
Demer   France
Demy   Scotland
Denar   Hungary
Denarius   Rome
Denaro   Italian States
Denga   Russia
Dengi   Roumania
Denier   France and colonies, Haiti, Swiss
   Cantons
Denning   Denmark
Deut   Rhineland, Westphalia
Deutschemark   Germany
Dhofari Riyal   Yemen
Diamante   Ferrara
Diamantino   Ferrara
Dicken   Swiss Cantons
Didrachm   Greece
Dime   Canada, Hawaii, USA
Dinar   Afghanistan, Algeria, Bahrain, Hejaz,
   Iraq, Kuwait, Morocco, Persia, Saudi Arabia,
   Serbia, Tunisia, Turkey, Yugoslavia
Diner   Andorra

Dinero   Peru, Spain
Diobol   Greece
Dirham   Jordan, Libya, Morocco, United Arab
   Emirates
Dirhem   Dubai, Iraq, Morocco, Qatar
Dio, Diu   Portuguese India
Disme   USA
Dobla   Genoa, Naples and Sicily
Doblado   Spanish colonies
Doblenca, Doblenga   Aragon, Barcelona
Dobler   Mallorca
Doblon   Chile, Spain, Urugay
Dobra   St Thomas and Prince
Dodekadrachm   Carthage
Doit   Netherlands, Netherlands Indies,
   Indonesia
Dokdo   Junagadh, Kutch, Nawanagar (Indian
   States)
Dollar   Anguilla, Antigua and Barbuda,
   Australia, Bahamas, Belize, Bermuda, Canada,
   Cayman Islands, China, Cocos (Keeling)
   Islands, Cook Islands, East Caribbean
   Territories, Fiji, Great Britain, Grenada,
   Guyana, Hawaii, Hong Kong, Indonesia,

Jamaica, Japan, Kiribati, Liberia, Malaysia, Mauritius, Montserrat, Newfoundland, New Zealand, Panama, St Kitts-Nevis, St Lucia, St Vincent, Scotland, Sierra Leone, Singapore, Solomin Islands, Straits Settlements, Trinidad and Tobago, Tuvalu, USA, Virgin Islands, Western Samoa, Zimbabwe

Dolya   Russia

Dong   Annam, Vietnam
Doppia   Italian States
Doppietta   Sardinia
Double   Guernsey
Dou Dou   French Indochina
Douzain   France
Drachma   Crete, Greece
Dram   Armenia
Dreibatzner   Austria, German States
Dreigroscher   Lithuania, Prussia
Dreiling   German States
Dub   Hyderabad, India
Dubbeltje   Holland
Ducat   Austria, Austrian States, Courland, Czechoslovakia, Denmark, German States, Hungary, Italian States, Liechtenstein, Liege, Netherlands,Poland, Roumania, Sweden, Swiss Cantons, Russia, Yugoslavia
Ducaton   Belgium, Netherlands
Ducatone   Italian States
Dudu   India
Duetto   Italian States
Duit   Ceylon, German States, Netherlands, Netherlands Indies
Dukat   Czechoslovakia, German States, Hungary, Poland, Sweden, Yugoslavia
Duplone   Swiss Cantons
Duro   Spain
Dyak   Nepal
Ecu   Belgium, Bosnia, France, Gibraltar
Ekuele   Equatorial Guinea
Elisabeth d'Or   Russia
Emalangeni   Swaziland
Escalin   Belgium, Guadeloupe, Haiti, Liege, Martinique
Escudillo   Spain
Escudo   Angola, Argentina, Azores, Bolivia, Cape Verde Islands, Central American Republic, Chile, Colombia, Costa Rica, Ecuador, Guadeloupe, Guatemala, Guinea-

Bissau, Madeira, Mexico, Mozambique, Peru, Portugal, Portuguese Guinea/India, St Thomas and Prince Islands, Spain, Timor
Espadin   Portugal
Esphera   Goa
Euro   Austria, Belgium, Finland, France, Germany, Greece, Ireland, Italy, Luxembourg, Monaco, The Netherlands, Portugal, San Marino, Spain, The Vatican
Excelente   Spain
Eyrir (singular **Aurar**) Iceland
Fals   Iraq
Faluce   Ceylon
Falus   Afghanistan, China, India, Iran, Morocco, Turkestan
Fanam   Ceylon, Dutch East Indies, Travancore
Fano   Tranquebar (Danish Indian Settlements)
Fanon   French Indian Settlements
Farthing   Antigua, Ceylon, Great Britain, Isle of Man, Jamaica, Malta, Scotland, South Africa
Fels   Algeria
Fen   People's Republic of China, Manchukuo
Fenig (ow)   Poland
Feoirling   Eire
Ferding   Courland, Livonia
Filiberto   Savoy
Filippo   Italian States
Filler   Hungary
Fils   Bahrain, Iraq, Jordan, Kuwait, South Arabia, United Arab Emirates, Yemen
Fiorino   Italian States
Flitter   South German States
Floirin   Eire
Florin   Australia, Austria, East Africa, Fiji, Great Britain, Hungary, Ireland, Malawi, New Zealand, Rhodesia and Nyasaland, South Africa, Swiss Cantons
Follis   Rome, Byzantine Empire

Forint   Hungary
Franc   Algeria, Belgian Congo, Belgium, Burundi, Cambodia, Cameroon, Central African Republic, Chad, Comoro Islands, Congo, Danish West Indies, Djibouti, Dominican Republic, Ecuador, France, French colonies, Gabon, Guadeloupe, Guinea, Ivory Coast, Katanga, Luxembourg, Madagascar, Malagasy Republic, Mali, Martinique, Mauretania, Monaco, Morocco,

New Caledonia, New Hebrides, Reunion, Ruanda-Urundi, Rwanda, St Pierre and Miquelon, Senegal, Switzerland, Togo, Tunisia, West African States

Francescone   Italian States

Franchi   Switzerland

Franco   Dominican Republic, Ecuador, Italian States, Swiss Cantons

Frang   Luxembourg

Frank(en)   Belgium, Liechtenstein, Saar, Switzerland, Westphalia

Franka Ara   Albania

Frederik d'Or   Denmark

Friedrich d'Or   German States

Fyrk   Sweden

Gabellone   Papal States

Gayah   Sumatra

Gazetta   Venice

Genovino   Genoa, Florence, Venice

Genevoise   Geneva

George Noble   England

Georgstaler   German States

Gersh   Ethiopia

Gigliato   Hungary, Naples, Rhodes

Gigot   Brabant, Flanders

Gin   Japan

Giorgino   Ferrara, Modena

Giovannino   Genoa

Girsh   Hejaz, Nejd, Saudi Arabia, Sudan

Giulio   Italian States

Golde   Sierra Leone

Goldgulden   German States, Swiss Cantons

Goldpfennig   German States

Goryoban   Japan

Gourde   Haiti

Gourmier   Morocco

Gram   Afghanistan

Gramme   Burma

Gramo   Bolivia, Tierra del Fuego

Grana   Italian States

Grano   Italian States, Mexico, Sovereign Order of Malta

Grenadino   Colombia, New Granada

Greschl   Roumania, Transylvania

Grivenka   Russia

Grivennik   Russia

Grivna (plural **Grivny**)   Ukraine

Groat   Great Britain

Groeschl   Bohemia

Groot   Netherlands

Gros   France

Groschel   German States

Groschen   Austria, German States, Poland, Swiss Cantons

Groshen   Austria, German States

Grossetto   Dalmatia, Illyria, Venice

Grosso   Italian States

Grossone   Italian States

Grosspfennig   Pomerania, Rhineland

Grossus   Courland, Poland

Grosz (plural **Grosze** or **Groszy**)   Poland

Grote   German States

Grush   Albania

Guarani   Paraguay

Guerche   Egypt, Saudi Arabia

Guinea   Great Britain, Saudi Arabia

Gulden   Austria, Curacao, German States, Netherlands, Netherlands Indies, Swiss Cantons

Guldiner   Austria, South German States, Swiss Cantons

Gutegroschen   North and Central German States

Guterpfennig   German States

Habibi   Afghanistan

Halala   Saudi Arabia, Yemen

Halbag   Frankfurt

Haler (plural **Halere, Haleru**)   Czechoslovakia, Czech Republic

Halierov   Slovakia

Haller   Swiss Cantons

Hao   China, Vietnam

Hapalua   Hawaii

Hardhead   Scotland

Hardi   France, Turin

Hau   Tonga

Hayrir Altin   Iraq, Turkey

Hekte   Lesbos, Mytilene

Heller   Austria, German States, German East Africa

Helm   England

Henri d'Or   France

Hryvnia   Ukraine

Hsien   China

Hvid   Denmark

Hwan   Korea

Hyperpyron   Byzantine Empire

Ichibu-gin   Japan

Ikilik   Russia

Imadi   Yemen

Imami   Mysore

Imperial   Russia

Isabella   Spain

Ischal   Russia

Ishu Gin   Japan

Jacondale   France
Jawa   Nepal
Jeon   Korea
Jerome d'Or   Westphalia
Jiao   People's Republic of China
Jedid   Egypt
Jefimok (plural **Jefimki**)   Russia
Joachimico   Italy
Joachimik   Poland
Joachimstaler   Bohemia
Joao   Portugal
Johanna   Portugal
Johannes   Portugal
Jokoh   Kelantan, Malaysia
Judenpfennig   Frankfurt
Justo   Portugal
Kapang   Sarawak
Kapeikas   Latvia, Belarus
Karolin   German States
Kas   Danish Indian Settlements
Kasu   Mysore
Kazbeg   Caucasia, Safavid Persia
Khayriya   Egypt
Khoum   Mauretania
Kin   Japan
Kina   Papua New Guinea
Kip   Laos
Koban   Japan
Kobo   Nigeria
Kopec   Poland
Kopejek   Outer Mongolia (Tannu Tuva)
Kopek   Russia
Kori   Kutch**Korona**   Bohemia and Moravia,
   Hungary, Slovakia
Kortling   German States
Korun(a) (plural **Koruny** or **Koruncic**)
   Czechoslo-vakia
Koula   Tonga
Krajczar   Hungary
Kran   Iran, Persia
Kreu(t)zer   Austria, Austrian States,
   Czechoslovakia, German States, Hungary,
   Liechtenstein, Poland, Roumania, Swiss
   Cantons
Krona (plural **Kronor** or **Kronur**)   Iceland,
   Sweden
Krona (plural **Kroner** or **Kronen**)   Austria,
   Denmark, German States, Greenland,
   Liechtenstein, Norway
Kroon(i)   Estonia
Krugerrand   South Africa
Kuna (plural **Kune**)   Croatia
Kupang   Malaysia, Thailand
Kurus   Turkey
Kuta   Congo-Kinshasa, Zaire
Kwacha   Malawi, Zambia
Kwanza   Angola

Kwartnik   Poland
Kyat   Burma, Myanmar
Kyrmis   Russia
Lang   Annam
Laree, Lari, Lariat or Larin   Maldive Islands
Lati, Lats   Latvia
Laurel   England
Lei   Roumania
Lek (plural **Leke** or **Leku**)   Albania
Lempira   Honduras
Leone   Sierra Leone
Leopard   England
Lepton (plural **Lepta**)   Crete, Greece, Ionian
   Islands
Leu (plural **Lei**)   Roumania
Lev(a)   Bulgaria
Li   Manchukuo
Liang   China, Laos
Liard   Belgium, France, Luxembourg
Libra   Peru
Licente   Lesotho
Likuta   Zaire

Lilangeni   Swaziland
Lion   Scotland
Lion d'Or   Austrian Netherlands
Lira (plural **Lire**)   Eritrea, Italian East Africa,
   Italy, San Marino, Syria, Turkey, Vatican
Lira (plural **Lirot**)   Israel
Lisente   Lesotho
Litas (plural **Litai** or **Litu**)   Lithuania
Litra   Sicily, Syracuse
Livre   France, Guadeloupe, Lebanon,
   Martinique, Mauritius, Reunion
Louis d'Argent   France
Louis d'Or   France
Luhlanga   Swaziland
Lumma   Armenia
Lweis   Angola
Mace   China
Macuta   Angola
Magdalon d'Or   Aix-en-Provence, Tarascon
Mahalek   Ethiopia
Mahallak   Harar
Mahbub   Egypt, Ottoman Empire
Mahmudi   Saudi Arabia
Makuta   Zaire
Maloti   Lesotho
Manat   Azerbaijan
Manghir   Crimea
Marabotin   Moorish kingdoms, Southern Spain

Maravedi   Spain
Marchetto   Italian States
Marck   German States
Marengo   France
Mariengroschen   German States
Mark   Germany, German States, German New
   Guinea, Norway, Poland, Sweden
Marka   Estonia
Markka(a)   Finland
Mas   Malaysia
Masriya   Egypt
Masson   Lorraine and Bar
Mat   Burma
Matapan   Venice
Mathbu   Morocco
Maticaes   Mozambique
Matona   Ethiopia
Mattier   German States
Maximilian d'Or   German States
Mazuna   Morocco
Medin   Egypt
Mehmudiye Altin   Ottoman Empire
Meinhard   Austria, German States
Melgarejo   Bosnia

Merk   Scotland
Metica   Mozambique
Meung   Japan
Mil   Cyprus, Hong Kong, Israel, Malta, Palestine
Milan d'Or   Serbia
Miliarense   Byzantine Empire
Milesima   Spain
Millieme   Egypt, Libya
Millime   Tunisia
Milreis   Brazil
Miscals   China
Mohar   Nepal
Mohur   Afghanistan, Bikanir, Cooch Behar,
   Gwalior, Hyderabad, India (Mughal Empire),
   Maldive Islands, Netherlands Indies, Rajkot
Moidore (Moeda de ouro)   Portugal
Momme   Japan
Mon   Japan, Ryukyu Islands
Mongo   Mongolia
Mouton d'Or   France
Mu   Burma
Mun   Korea
Mung   Mongolia
Munzgulden   Swiss Cantons

Muzuna   Algeria
Naira   Nigeria
Nami-sen   Japan
Napoleon   France
Naya Paisa   Bhutan, India
Negotiepenning   Netherlands
Neugroschen   German States
New Pence   Gibraltar, Great Britain, Guernsey,
   Isle of Man, Jersey
Ngultrum   Bhutan
Ngwee   Zambia
Nisar   Afghanistan, India
Nisfiya   Egypt
Noble   Austria, England, Scotland, Isle of Man
Nomisma   Byzantine Empire
Nonsunt   Scotland
Nummion (plural Nummia)   Byzantine Empire
Oban   Japan
Obol   Greece, Ionian Islands
Ochavo   Spain
Octavo   Mexico, Philippines
Omani   Oman
Onca   Mozambique
Oncia   Italian States
Onlik   Crimea
Onluk   Turkey
Onza   Bolivia, Chile, Costa Rica, Mexico
Or   Sweden
Ore   Denmark, Faroe Islands, Greenland,
   Norway, Sweden
Ort(e)   Poland, Prussia
Ortug (plural Ortugar)   Sweden
Ouguiya   Mauretania
Pa'anga   Tonga
Pagoda   India (Madras)
Pahlavi   Iran
Pai   India, Siam (Thailand)
Paisa   Afghanistan, Bhutan, India, Nepal,
   Pakistan
Panchia   India
Pano   Portuguese Africa
Paoli   Italian States
Papetto   Papal States
Para (plural Paras or Parades)   Crimea, Egypt,
   Greece, Iraq, Libya, Nejd, Roumania,
   Saudi Arabia, Serbia, Sudan, Syria, Turkey,
   Walachia, Yugoslavia
Pardao   Portuguese India
Parisis d'Or   France
Pataca   Macau
Pataco   Portugal
Patagon   Belgium
Patrick   Ireland
Pavillon d'Or   France
Pe   Burma, Cambodia
Peca   Portugal
Pengo   Hungary

Penni(a) Finland
Penning(ar) Denmark, Sweden
Penny (plural **Pence**) Australia, Bahamas,
  Barbados, Bermuda, Biafra, British Guiana,
  British East Africa British West Africa, Canada,
  Ceylon, Falkland Islands, Fiji, Gambia,
  Ghana, Gibraltar, Gold Coast, Great Britain,
  Guernsey, Ireland, Isle of Man, Jamaica, Jersey,
  Malawi, Montserrat, New Guinea, New
  Zealand, Nigeria, Rhodesia and Nyasaland, St
  Helena, St Kitts-Nevis, South Africa, Southern
  Rhodesia, Trinidad & Tobago, Tristan da
  Cunha, Zambia
Pentekontalitron Sicily
Pentekontedrachm Hellenistic kingdoms
Pentenummion Byzantine Empire
Perper(a) Montenegro
Pesa German East Africa
Peseta Andorra, Equatorial Guinea, Peru, Spain
Pesewa Ghana
Peso Argentina, Bolivia, Cambodia, Chile,
  Colombia, Costa Rica, Cuba, Dominican
  Republic, El Salvador, Guatemala, Guinea-
  Bissau, Honduras, Mexico, Netherlands
  Antilles, Nicaragua, Paraguay, Peru,
  Philippines, Puerto Rico, Uruguay, Venezuela
Pessa Yemen (Lahej), Zanzibar
Petermannchen Trier
Pfennig(e) Austria, Bohemia, Germany, German
  States, Poland, Swiss Cantons
Pfenning Austrian States, German States
Philippeioi Macedon
Phoenix Greece
Piastra Italian States
Piastre Annam, Cambodia, Cochin China,
  Cyprus, Denmark, Egypt, French Indochina,
  Hejaz, Iraq, Khmer, Lebanon, Libya, Nejd,
  Saudi Arabia, Syria, Sudan, Tonkin, Tunisia,
  Turkey, Vietnam, Yemen
Piataltynny Russia
Picciolo Sovereign Order of Malta
Piccolo Italian States
Pice Bhutan, Ceylon, East Africa, India, Kenya,
  Malaysia

Pinto Portugal
Piso Philippines
Pistole France, German States, Ireland,
  Scotland, Swiss Cantons

Pitis Brunei, Java, Sumatra, Siam
Plack Scotland
Plappart Switzerland
Poisha Bangladesh
Poltina Russia
Poltura Hungary, Roumania
Poludenga Russia
Polupoltinnik Russia
Polushka Russia
Pond Transvaal
Pound Ascension, Australia, Biafra, Cyprus,
  Egypt, Falkland Islands, Ghana, Gibraltar,
  Great Britain, Guernsey, Iran, Isle of Man,
  Israel, Jersey, Malta, Nigeria, Rhodesia, St
  Helena, South Arabia, South Africa, Sudan,
  Syria
Protea South Africa
Pruta(ot) Israel
Puffin Lundy
Pul Afghanistan, China, Turkestan
Pula Botswana
Puli Caucasia
Pultorak Poland
Pya(t) Burma
Pysa Zanzibar
Qindar(ka) Albania
Qiran Afghanistan
Qirsh Egypt
Quadrans Roman Republic
Quan Annam
Quart Gibraltar, Swiss Cantons
Quart d'Ecu France
Quartenses Silesia
Quartillo Spain
Quartinho Portugal
Quarto Ecuador, Mexico, Philippines, Spain
Quartuncia Rome
Quaternio Rome
Quattrino Italian States
Qepiq Azerbaijan
Quetzal Guatemala
Quinarius Rome
Quint USA
Quinto di Scudo Papal States
Rand South Africa
Rappen Switzerland
Rasi Netherlands Indies
Real(es) Argentina, Bolivia, Central American
  Republic, Chile, Colombia, Costa Rica,
  Dominican Republic, Ecuador, El Salvador,
  Venezuela
Real Batu Indonesia
Reichsmark Germany
Reichspfennig Germany
Reichsthaler Germany
Reis Angola, Azores, Brazil, Madeira,
  Mozambique, Portugal, Portuguese India

Reisedaler   Denmark
Rentenmark   Germany
Rentenpfennig   Germany
Reul   Eire
Rial   Iran, Morocco, Muscat and Oman, Oman,
Persia, Yemen Arab Republic
Rider   Scotland
Riel   Kampuchea
Rigsbankdaler   Denmark
Rigsbankskilling   Denmark
Rigsdaler,   Denmark, Norway
Rigsmontskilling   Denmark
Rijder   Friesland, Guelderland, United Provinces
Rijksdaalder   Netherlands
Riksdaler   Sweden
Riksdaler Riksmynt   Sweden
Riksdaler Specie   Sweden
Rin   Japan
Ringgit   Malaysia
Rio   Japan
Rixdollar   Ceylon
Riyal   Iran, Iraq, Saudi Arabia, United Arab
Emirates, Yemen Arab Republic
Rose Noble   England
Rouble   Russia, USSR
Royal d'Or   France
Royalin(er)   Tranquebar, Danish Indian
Settlements
Rub   Ethiopia
Rubel   German occupation of Russia
Rubiya   Egypt
Ruble   Poland, Transnistria
Rublis   Latvia
Rufiyaa   Maldive Islands
Rumi Altin   Ottoman Empire
Rupee   Afghanistan, Andaman Islands, Bhutan,
Burma, China, Cocos Keeling Islands, India,
Iran, Kenya, Mauritius, Nepal, Pakistan, Saudi
Arabia, Seychelles, Sri Lanka, Tanzania, Tibet,
United Arab Emirates, Yemen
Rupia   Portuguese India, Somalia
Rupiah   Indonesia
Rupie   German East Africa
Ruspone   Italian States
Ryal   England, Hejaz, Iran, Muscat and Oman,
Nejd, Oman, Persia, Quaiti State, Saudi
Arabia, Yemen, Zanzibar
Ryo   Japan
Rytterpenning   Denmark, Hanseatic League
Saidi   Oman
Saiga   Merovingian Empire
Salung   Siam (Thailand)
Salut d'Or   France
Sampietrino   Papal States
Sanar   Afghanistan
Sanese   Siena
Santa Croce   Italian States

Santim(at)   Morocco
Santims (plural **Santimi** or **Santimu**)   Latvia
Sapeque   Annam, Cochin China, French
Indochina
Sar   Sinkiang
Sarrazzino   Crusader kingdoms
Satang   Siam (Thailand)
Sceat   Anglo-Saxon England
Scellino   Somalia
Schilling   Austria, German States, Poland,
Swiss Cantons
Schoter   Breslau, Silesia
Schwaren   German States
Scilling   Eire
Scudo   Bolivia, Italian States, Mexico, Malta,
Papal States, Peru, San Marino
Sechsling   German States
Semis   Rome
Semuncia   Rome
Sen   Brunei, Cambodia, Indonesia, Irian Barat,
Japan, Kampuchea, Malaysia, Riau Lingga,
West New Guinea
Sene   Samoa
Sengi   Zaire
Seniti   Tonga
Sent   Estonia
Sente   Lesotho
Senti   Estonia, Somalia, Tanzania
Sentimo   Philippines
Serebrnik   Bulgaria
Sertum   Bhutan
Sesena   Spain
Sesino   Italian States
Sestertius   Rome
Sestino   Italian States
Shahi   Afghanistan, Iran, Turkestan
Sheqal(im)   Israel
Shilingi   Tanzania
Shilling   Australia, Biafra, British West Africa,
Canada, Cyprus, East Africa, Fiji, Gambia,
Ghana, Great Britain, Grenada, Guernsey,
Ireland, Isle of Man, Jamaica, Jersey, Kenya,
Malawi, Malta, New Guinea, New Zealand,
Nigeria, Scotland, Somalia, South Africa,
Trinidad and Tobago, Uganda, Zambia
Sho   Nepal, Tibet
Shokang   Tibet
Shu   Japan
Siglos   Achaemenid Empire
Sik   Siam (Thailand)
Silbergroschen   German States, Luxembourg
Silbergulden   South Germany
Skar   Tibet
Skilling   Danish West Indies, Denmark,
Norway, Sweden
Skillingrigsmont   Denmark
Skot   Prussia, Silesia
Sol(es)   Argentina, Belgium, Bolivia, France,

Haiti, Luxembourg, Mauritius, Peru, Reunion, Switzerland, Windward Islands

Soldo (plural **Soldi**)   Italian States, Swiss Cantons, Papal States, Yugoslavia

Solidus   Argentina, Bolivia, Peru, Rome

Solot   Siam

Som   Kyrgyzstan

Somalo   Somalia

Sosling   Denmark

Sou   Canada, French colonies, Guadeloupe, Mauritius, Reunion, Spain

Souverain d'Or   Austrian Netherlands

Sovereign   Australia, Canada, England, Falkland Islands, India, Isle of Man, Saudi Arabia, South Africa, United Kingdom

Sovrano   Italian States

Speciedaler   Denmark, Norway

Species Ducat   Denmark

Srang   Tibet

Stater   Greece

Stella   USA

Stiver   British Guiana, Ceylon, Demerara and Essequibo, Dutch East Indies, Netherlands

Stotinka   Bulgaria

Stuber   German States

Stuiver   Curacao, Dutch East Indies, Netherlands, Netherlands Antilles

Styca   Northumbria

Styver   Sweden

Su   South Vietnam

Sucre   Ecuador, Galapagos

Sueldo   Bolivia, Spain

Sukus   Indonesia

Sultani   Algeria, Libya, Tunisia

Surre Altin   Ottoman Empire

Syli   Guinea

Tackoe   Gold Coast

Tael   China, Laos

Taka   Bangladesh

Tala   Samoa, Tokelau

Talar(a)   Poland

Talaro   Ethiopia

Taler   German States, Poland, Swiss Cantons

Talirion   Greece

Tallero   Ethiopia, Italian States, Ragusa

Tambac-tron   Annam

Tambala   Malawi

Tamlung   Siam

Tanga   Portuguese India

Tangka   Tibet

Tanka   Nepal

Tankah   Burma

Tarin   Naples, Sicily

Taro (plural **Tari**)   Italian States, Malta

Tek Altin   Ottoman Empire

Tenga   China, Bokhara, Turkestan

Ternar   Poland

Tester   England

Testern   British East Indies

Testone   Italian States

Testoon   England

Tetartemorion   Greece

Tetarteron   Byzantine Empire

Tetradrachm   Greece

Tetrobol   Greece

Thaler   Austria, Austrian States, Courland, Czechoslovakia, German States, Hungary, Liechtenstein, Poland, Roumania, Switzerland

Thebe   Botswana

Theler   Frankfurt

Thistle Crown   England

Thistle Merk   Scotland

Thistle Noble   Scotland

Thrymsa   Anglo-Saxon England

Tical   Cambodia, Thailand

Tien   Annam, Vietnam

Tilla   Afghanistan, Sinkiang, Turkestan

Timasha   Afghanistan

Tostao   Portugal

Toea   Papua New Guinea

Tola   India, Nepal

Tolar   Slovenia

Toman   Iran, Persia, Azerbaijan

Tornese   Italian States

Tournois   France

Trade Dollar   Great Britain, Japan, USA

Trah   Malaysia

Tremissis   Rome, Byzantine Empire, Franks, Lombards, Visigoths

Tressis   Rome

Triens   Rome

Trihemiobol   Greece

Triobol   Greece

Tritartemorion   Greece

Tughrik   Mongolia

Turner   Scotland

Tympf   Poland

Tyyn   Kyrgyzstan

Unghero   Italian States

Unicorn   Scotland

Unit   Scotland, French West Africa

Unite   England

Van   Vietnam

Vatu   Vanuatu

Veld Pond   South African Republic

Venezolano   Venezuela

Vereinstaler   Austria-Hungary, German States

Victoriate   Rome

Vierer   Swiss Cantons

Glossary of
coin terms

In this section we list all the terms commonly encountered in numismatics or in the production of coins.

Abbey Coins Medieval coins struck in the abbeys, convents and other great religious houses which were granted coinage rights. These coins were often used also by pilgrims journeying from one monastery to another.

Abschlag (German for "discount") A *restrike* from an original die.

Accolated Synonym for *conjoined* or *jugate* and signifying two or more profiles overlapping.

Acmonital Acronym from *Aciaio Monetario Italiano*, a stainless steel alloy used for Italian coins since 1939.

Adjustment Reduction of metal in a *flan* or *blank* to the specified weight prior to striking, accomplished by filing down the face. Such file marks often survived the coining process and are occasionally met with in coins, especially of the 18th century.

Ae Abbreviation for the Latin *Aes* (bronze), used for coins made of brass, bronze or other copper alloys.

Aes Grave (Latin for heavy bronze) Heavy circular coins first minted at Rome in 269 BC.

Aes Rude (Latin for rough bronze) Irregular lumps of bronze which gradually developed into ingots of uniform shape and were the precursors of coins in Rome.

Aes Signatum (Latin for signed bronze) Bronze ingots of regular size and weight, bearing marks of authority to guarantee their weight (289–269 BC).

Agonistic (Greek) Term for coins issued to commemorate, or pertaining to, sporting events.

Alliance Coinage struck by two or more states acting together and having common features of design or inscription.

Alloy Coinage metal composed of two or more metallic elements.

Altered Deliberately changed, usually unofficially, with the aim of increasing the numismatic value of a coin, medal or note. This applies particularly to dates, where a common date may be altered to a rare date by filing or re-engraving one of the digits.

Aluminium (American *Aluminum*) Silvery lightweight metal, developed commercially in the late 19th century for commemorative medals, but used for tokens and emergency money during the First World War and since 1940 widely used in subsidiary coinage.

Aluminium-bronze Alloy of aluminium and copper. Hard-wearing and gold-coloured, it is now widely used in tokens and subsidiary coinage.

Amulet Coin or medal believed to have talismanic qualities, such as warding off disease and bad luck. Many Chinese and Korean pieces come into this category. See also *Touchpiece*.

Androcephalous Heraldic term for creatures with a human head.

Anepigraphic Coins or medals without a legend.

Annealing Process of heating and cooling applied to metal to relieve stresses and prepare it for striking into coins.

Annulet Small circle often used as an ornament or spacing device in coin inscriptions.

Antimony Brittle white metal, chemical symbol *Sb*, virtually impractical as a coinage metal but used for the Chinese 10 cents of Kweichow, 1931. Alloyed with tin, copper or lead, it produces the white metal popular as a medallic medium.

Antoniniani Silver coins minted in Imperial Rome. The name derives from the Emperor Caracalla (Marcus Aurelius Antoninus) in whose reign they were first struck. The silver content was progressively reduced and by the last issue (AD 295) they were reduced to *billon*.

Ar Abbreviation for Latin *Argentum* (silver), used for coins struck in this metal.

Assay Mark Mark applied to a medal struck in precious metal by an assayer or assay office as a guarantee of the fineness of the metal.

Assignat Type of paper money used in France

1789–96, representing the land assigned to the holders.

Attribution Identification of a coin by characteristics such as issuing authority, date or reign, mint, denomination, metal, and by a standard reference.

Au Abbreviation for *aurum* (Latin for gold), denoting coins of this metal.

AU Abbreviation for "About Uncirculated", often found in catalogues and dealers' lists to describe the condition of a numismatic piece.

Autodollar Name given to the silver yuan issued by Kweichow, 1928, and having a contemporary motor car as the obverse motif.

Auxiliary Payment Certificate Form of paper money intended for use by American military personnel stationed in overseas countries. See also *Baf* and *Scrip*.

Babel Note Nickname given to the paper money of the Russian Socialist Federated Soviet Republic (1919) because it bore the slogan "workers of the world unite" in seven languages, a reference to the biblical tower of Babel.

Baf Acronym from British Armed Forces, the popular name for the vouchers which could only be exchanged for goods in service canteens from 1945 onwards.

Bag Mark Minor scratch or abrasion on an otherwise uncirculated coin, caused by coins in mint bags knocking together.

Banknote Form of paper money issued by banks and usually promising to pay the bearer on demand in coin of the realm.

Barbarous Imitation of Greek or Roman coins by the Celtic and Germanic tribes who lived beyond the frontiers of the civilised world.

Base Non-precious metals or alloys.

Bath Metal Inferior bronze alloy, named after the English city where it was used for casting cannon. Used by William Wood of Bristol for Irish and American tokens and by Amos Topping for Manx coins of 1733/4.

Beading Ornamental border found on the raised rim of a coin.

Behalfszahlungsmittel German term for auxiliary payment certificates used in occupied Europe from 1939 to 1945.

Bell Metal Alloy of copper and tin normally used for casting bells, but employed for the subsidiary coinage of the French Revolutionary period.

Billon Silver alloy containing less than 50 per cent fine silver, usually mixed with copper. In Spain this alloy was known as *vellon*.

Bi-metallic Coins struck in two separate metals or alloys. Patterns for such coins exist from the 19th century but actual coins with a centre of one metal surrounded by a ring of another did not appear till 1982 (Italy, San Marino and Vatican). Canada introduced coins with a tiny plaque inset in a second metal (1990). See also *Clad*, *Plugged* and *Sandwich*.

Bi-metallism Monetary system in which two metals are in simultaneous use and equally available as legal tender, implying a definite ratio between the two. A double standard of gold and silver, with a ratio of 16:1, existed till the mid-19th century.

Bingle American term for a trade token, more specifically the US government issue of tokens for the Matacuska, Alaska colonization project, 1935.

Birthday Coins Coins celebrating the birthday of a ruler originated in Roman Imperial times, notably the reigns of Maximianus (286–305) and Constantinus I (307–37). Birthday talers were issued by many German states, and among recent examples may be cited coins marking the 70th, 80th and 90th birthdays of Gustaf Adolf VI of Sweden, 80th and 90th birthday coins from the British Commonwealth for the Queen Mother, and coins honouring Queen Elizabeth, the Duke of Edinburgh and the Prince of Wales.

Bit Term denoting fragments of large silver coins, cut up and circulating as fractional values. Spanish dollars were frequently broken up for circulation in the American colonies and the West indies. Long bits and short bits circulated at 15 and 10 cents respectively, but the term came to be equated with the Spanish real or eighth peso, hence the American colloquialism "two-bit" signifying a quarter dollar.

Black Money English term for the debased silver deniers minted in France which circulated freely in England until they were banned by government decree in 1351.

Blank Piece of metal, cut or punched out of a roller bar or strip, and prepared for striking to produce coins. Alternate terms are *flan* and *planchet*.

Blundered Inscription Legend in which the lettering is jumbled or meaningless, indicating

"Breeches" money, so-called from the reverse design!

A "Cartwheel" penny, so called because of its cumbersome size.

the illiteracy of the tribes who copied Greek and Roman coins.

Bonnet Piece Scottish gold coin, minted in 1539–40. The name is derived from the obverse portraying King James V in a large, flat bonnet.

Bon Pour French for "good for", inscribed on Chamber of Commerce brass tokens issued in 1920–7 during a shortage of legal tender coinage.

Bouquet Sou Canadian copper token halfpenny of 1837 deriving its name from the nosegay of heraldic flowers on the obverse.

Box Coin Small container formed by *obverse* and *reverse* of two coins, hollowed out and screwed together.

Bracteate (Latin *bractea*, a thin piece of metal) Coins struck on blanks so thin that the image applied to one side appears in reverse on the other. First minted in Erfurt and Thuringia in the 12th century, and later produced elsewhere in Germany, Switzerland and Poland till the 14th century.

Brass Alloy of copper and zinc, widely used for subsidiary coinage. The term was also formerly used for bronze Roman coins, known numismatically as first, second or third brass.

Breeches Money Derisive term given by the Royalists to the coinage of the Commonwealth, 1651, the conjoined elongated oval shields on the reverse resembling a pair of breeches.

Brockage Mis-struck coin with only one design, normal on one side and *incuse* on the other. This occurs when a coin previously struck adheres to the die and strikes the next blank to pass through the press.

Broken Bank-note Note issued by a bank which has failed, but often applied more generally to banknotes which have been demonetised.

Bronze Alloy of copper and tin, first used as a coinage metal by the Chinese c. 1000 BC. Often used synonymously with copper, though it

should be noted that bronze only superseded copper as the constituent of the base metal British coins in 1860.

Bull Neck Popular term for the coins of King George III, 1816–17.

Bullet Money Pieces of silver, *globular* in shape, bearing various *countermarks* and used as coins in Siam (Thailand) in the 18th and 19th centuries.

Bullion Precious metal in bars, ingots, strip or scrap (i.e. broken jewellery mounts, watch-cases and plate), its weight reckoned solely by weight and fineness, before being converted into coin.

Bullion Coin A coin struck in platinum, gold or silver, whose value is determined solely by the prevailing market price for the metal as a commodity. Such coins do not generally have a nominal face value, but include in their inscriptions their weight and fineness. Good examples of recent times include the Krugerrand (South Africa), the Britannia (UK), the Maple Leaf (Canada), Libertad (Mexico), the Nugget (Australia) and the Eagle (USA).

Bun Coinage British coins of 1860–94 showing Queen Victoria with her hair in a bun.

Bungtown Coppers Derisive term (from Anglo-American slang *bung*, to swindle or bribe) for halfpence of English or Irish origin, often counterfeit, which circulated in North America towards the end of the colonial period.

Carat (American *Karat*) Originally a unit of weight for precious stones, based on carob seeds (ceratia), it also denotes the fineness or purity of gold, being 1/24th part of the whole. Thus 9 carat gold is .375 fine and 22 carat, the English sovereign standard, is .916 fine. Abbreviated as ct or kt.

Cartwheel Popular term for the large and cumbersome penny and twopenny pieces of 1797 weighing one and two ounces, struck by Matthew Boulton at the Soho Mint, Birmingham.

Cased Set Set of coins in mint condition, housed in the official case issued by the mint. Formerly leather cases with blue plush or velvet lining were used, but nowadays many sets are encapsulated in plastic to facilitate handling.

Cash (from Portuguese *caixa*, Hindi *kasu*). Round piece of bronze or brass with a square hole in the centre, used as subsidiary coinage in China for almost 2000 years, till the early 12th century. In Chinese these pieces were known as *Ch'ien* or *Li* and strung together in groups of 1000 were equivalent to a silver tael.

Cast Coins Coins cast from molten metals in moulds. This technique, widespread in the case of early commemorative medals, has been used infrequently in coins, the vast majority of which are struck from *dies*. Examples of cast coins include the Chinese cash and the Manx coins of 1709.

Check A form of *token* given as a means of identification, or issued for small amounts of money or for services of a specific nature.

Cheque (American *Check*) A written order directing a bank to pay money.

Chop (Hindi, to seal). Countermark, usually consisting of a single character, applied by Chinese merchants to precious metal coins and ingots as a guarantee of their weight and fineness. Coins may be found with a wide variety of chop marks and the presence of several different marks on the same coin considerably enhances its interest and value. See also *Shroff mark*.

Christmas Coins issued as Christmas gifts date from the Middle Ages when the Venetian Doges struck *Osselle* as presents for their courtiers. In modern times, however, the custom has developed only since the late 1970s, several countries having issued attractive coins at Christmas since then.

Cistophori (Greek for chest bearing) a generic term for the coins of Pergamum with an obverse motif of a chest showing a serpent crawling out of the half-opened lid. Cistophori became very popular all over Asia Minor in the 3rd and 2nd centuries BC and were struck also at mints in Ionia, Phrygia, Lydia and Mysia.

Clad Coins Coins with a core of one alloy, covered with a layer or coating of another. US half dollars from 1965 to 1970, for example, had a core of 21 per cent silver and 79 per cent copper, bonded to outer layers of 80 per cent silver and 20 per cent copper. More recently, however, coins usually have a body in a cheap alloy, with only a thin cladding of a more expensive material, such as the British 1p and 2p coins of stainless steel with a copper cladding, introduced late in 1992.

Clash Marks Mirror image traces found on a coin which has been struck from a pair of dies, themselves damaged by having been struck together without a blank between.

Clipped Coins Precious metal coins from which small amounts have been removed by clipping the edges. It was to prevent this that *graining* and *edge inscriptions* were adopted.

Cob Crude, irregularly shaped silver piece, often with little more than a vestige of die impressions, produced in the Spanish American mints in the 16th–18th centuries.

Coin Piece of metal, marked with a device, issued by government authority and intended for use as money.

Collar Retaining ring within which the *dies* for the *obverse* and *reverse* operate. When the *blank* is struck under high pressure between the dies the metal flows sideways and is formed by the collar, taking up the impression of *reeding* or *edge inscription* from it.

Commemorative Coin, medal, token or paper note issued to celebrate a current event or the anniversary of a historic event or personality.

Communion Token Token, cast in lead, but later struck in pewter, brass, bronze or white metal, issued to members of a congregation to permit them to partake of the annual communion service in the Calvinist and Presbyterian churches. John Calvin himself is said to have invented the communion token in 1561 but they were actually referred to in the minutes of the Scottish General Assembly in 1560. Later they were adopted by the Reformed churches in many parts of Europe. They survived in Scotland till the early years of this century. Each parish had its own tokens, often bearing the names or initials of individual ministers, with dates, symbols and biblical texts.

Conjoined Term denoting overlapped profiles of two or more rulers (e.g. William and Mary).

Contorniate (from Italian *contorno*, edge). Late 4th and 5th century Roman bronze piece whose name alludes to the characteristic grooving on the edges.

Contribution Coins Coins struck by Bamberg, Eichstatt, Fulda and other German cities in the 1790s during the First Coalition War against the French Republic. The name alludes to the fact that the bullion used to produce the coins necessary to pay troops was raised by contribution from the Church and the public.

Convention Money Any system of coinage agreed by neighbouring countries for mutual acceptance and interchange. Examples include the Amphictyonic coins of ancient Greece, and the Austrian and Bavarian talers and gulden of 1753–1857 which were copied by other south German states and paved the way for the German Monetary union.

Copper Metallic element, chemical symbol *Cu*, widely used as a coinage medium for 2,500 years. Pure or almost pure copper was used

A typical communion token from Scotland.

for subsidiary coinage in many countries till the mid-19th century, but has since been superseded by copper alloys which are cheaper and more durable: *bronze* (copper and tin), *brass* (copper and zinc), *Bath metal* or *bell metal* (low-grade copper and tin), *aluminium-bronze* (copper and aluminium), *potin* (copper, tin, lead and silver) or *cupro-nickel* (copper and nickel). Copper is also alloyed with gold to give it its reddish hue, and is normally alloyed with silver in coinage metals. When the copper exceeds the silver content the alloy is known as *billon*.

Copperhead Popular term for a copper *token* about the size and weight of an American cent which circulated in the USA during the Civil War (1861–65) during a shortage of subsidiary coinage. Many different types were produced, often of a political or patriotic nature.

Coppernose Popular name for the debased silver shillings of Henry VIII. Many of them were struck in copper with little more than a silver wash which tended to wear off at the highest point of the obverse, the nose on the full-face portrait of the king.

Counter A piece resembling a coin but intended for use on a medieval accountancy board or in gambling. See also *jeton*.

Counterfeit Imitation of a coin, token or banknote intended for circulation to deceive the public and defraud the state.

Countermark Punch mark applied to a coin some time after its original issue, either to alter its nominal value, or to authorise its circulation in some other country.

Cowrie Small shell (*Cypraea moneta*) circulating as a form of primitive currency from 1000 BC (China) to the present century (East and West Africa) and also used in the islands of the Indian and Pacific Oceans.

Crockard Debased silver imitation of English pennies produced in the Netherlands and imported into England in the late 13th century. Edward I tried to prevent their import then, in 1299, allowed them to pass current as halfpennies. As they contained more than a halfpenny worth of silver this encouraged their trading in to be melted down and they disappeared from circulation within a year. Sometimes known as *pollards*. See also *Lushbourne*.

Crown Gold Gold of 22 carat (.916) fineness, so called on account of its adoption in 1526 for the English gold crown. It has remained the British standard gold fineness ever since.

Cumberland Jack Popular name for a counter or medalet of sovereign size, struck unofficially in 1837 in brass. The figure of St George was replaced by the Duke of Cumberland on horseback with the inscription "To Hanover" a reference to the unpopular Duke of Cumberland, uncle of Queen Victoria, who succeeded to the Hanoverian throne since Victoria, as a female, was debarred by Salic law from inheritance.

Cupellation (Latin *cupella*, a little cup). Process by which gold and silver were separated from lead and other impurities in their ores. A cupel is a shallow cup of bone-ash or other absorbent material which, when hot, absorbs any molten material that wets its surface. Lead melts and oxidises with impurities into the cupel, whereas gold and silver remain on the cupel. Cupellation is also used in assaying the fineness of these precious metals.

Cupro-nickel Coinage alloy of 75 per cent copper and 25 per cent nickel, now widely used as a base metal substitute for silver. A small amount of zinc is added to the alloy in modern Russian coins.

Currency Coins, tokens, paper notes and other articles intended to pass current in general circulation as money.

Current Coins and paper money still in circulation.

Cut Money Coins cut into smaller pieces to provide correspondingly smaller denominations. The cross on many medieval coins assisted the division of silver pennies into halfpence and farthings. Spanish dollars were frequently divided into *bits* which themselves became units of currency in America and the West Indies.

Darlehnskassen (German for "state loan notes"). Paper money issued during the First World War in an abortive bid to fill the shortage of coinage in circulation. These low-denomination notes failed to meet demand and were superseded by local issues of small *Notgeld* in 1916.

Debasement The reduction in the precious metal content of the coinage, widely practised since time immemorial by governments for economic reasons. British coins, for example, were debased from sterling (.925 fine) silver to .500 in 1920 and from silver to cupro-nickel in 1947.

Decimalisation A currency system in which the principal unit is subdivided into ten, a hundred, or a thousand fractions. Russia was the first country to decimalise, in 1534 when the rouble of 100 kopeks was introduced, but it was not till 1792 that France adopted the franc of 100 centimes and 1793 when the USA introduced the dollar of 100 cents. Most European countries decimalised their currency in the 19th century. Britain toyed with the idea, introducing the florin or tenth of a pound in 1849 as the first step, but did not complete the process till 1971. The last countries to decimalise were Malta and Nigeria, in 1972 and 1973 respectively.

Demidiated Heraldic term to describe the junction of two armorial devices, in which only half of each is shown.

Demonetisation The withdrawal of coins or paper money from circulation and declaring them to be worthless.

Device Heraldic term for the pattern or emblem on coins or paper notes.

Die Hardened piece of metal bearing a mirror image of the device to be struck on one side of a coin or medal.

Die Proof An impression, usually pulled on soft carton or India paper, of an *intaglio* engraving of a banknote, usually taken during the progress of the engraving to check the detail. Banknote proofs of this nature usually consist of the portrait or some detail of the design, such as the border, rather than the complete motif.

Dodecagonal Twelve-sided, a term applied to the nickel-brass threepence of Great Britain, 1937–67.

Dump Any primitive coin struck on a very thick *flan*, but more specifically applied to the circular pieces cut from the centre of Spanish dollars, countermarked with the name of the colony, a crown and the value, and circulated in New South Wales at 15 pence in 1813. See *Holey Dollar*.

Duodecimal Currency system based on units of twelve, i.e. medieval money of account (12 denarii = 1 soldo) which survived in Britain as 12 pence to the shilling as late as 1971.

Ecclesiastical Coins Coins struck by a religious authority, such as an archbishop, bishop, abbot, prior or the canons of a religious order. Such coins were common in medieval times but survived as late as the early 19th century, the bishops of Breslau (1817) and Gurk (1823) being the last prelates to exercise coinage rights. Coins were struck by authority of the Pope at Rome till 1870 but since 1929 coinage has been struck at the Italian state mint on behalf of the Vatican.

Edge Inscription Lettering on the edge of a coin or medal to prevent clipping. Alluding to this, the Latin motto *Decus et Tutamen* (an ornament and a safeguard) was applied to the edge of English milled coins in the reign of Charles II.

Edge Ornament An elaboration of the *graining* found on many milled coins to prevent clipping, taking the form of tiny leaves, florets, interlocking rings, pellets and zigzag patterns. In some cases the ornament appears between layers of more conventional reeding.

EF Abbreviation for Extremely Fine.

Effigy An image or representation of a person, normally the head of state, a historical personage, or an allegorical figure, usually on the *obverse* or "heads" side of a coin or medal.

Electrotype A reproduction of a coin or medal made by an electrolytic process.

Electrum Alloy of gold and silver, sometimes called white gold, used for minting the staters of Lydia, 7th century BC, and other early European coins.

Elongated Coin An oval *medalet* created by passing a coin, such as an American cent, between rollers under pressure with the effect of squeezing it out and impressing on it a souvenir or commemorative motif.

Emergency Money Any form of money used in times of economic and political upheaval, when traditional kinds of currency are not available. Examples include the comparatively crude silver coins issued by the Royalists during the *Civil War* (1642–49), *obsidional* money, issued in time of siege, from Tyre (1122) to Mafeking (1900), the *Notgeld* issued by many German towns (1916–23), *encased money, fractional currency, guerrilla notes, invasion, liberation* and *occupation money* from the two World Wars and minor campaigns. Among the more recent examples may be cited the use of sweets and cheques in Italy (1976–77) and the issue of coupons and vouchers in many of the countries of the former Soviet Union pending the introduction of their own distinctive coins and notes.

Enamelled Coins Coins decorated by enamelling the obverse and reverse motifs in contrasting colours was an art practised by many jewellers in Birmingham and Paris in the 19th century, and revived in Europe and America in the 1970s.

Encased Money Postage and revenue stamps enclosed in small metal and mica-faced discs, circulated as small change in times of emergency. The practice was invented by John Gault, a Boston sewing-machine salesman, during the American Civil War (1862). The face of the stamp was visible through the transparent window, while the back of the disc was embossed with firms' advertisements. This practice was revived during and after the First World War when there was again a shortage of small coins. Encased stamps have also been recorded from France, Austria, Norway, Germany and Monaco. See also under *Stamp Money*.

Engrailing Technical term for the close serrations or vertical bars round the edge of a coin, applied as a security device.

Engraving The art of cutting lines or grooves in plates, blocks or dies. Numismatically this takes the form of engraving images into the face of the dies used in striking coins, a process which has now been almost completely superseded by *hubbing* and the use of *reducing machinery*. In the production of paper money, *intaglio* engraving is still commonly practised. In this process the engraver cuts the design into a steel die and the printing ink lies in the grooves. The paper is forced under great pressure into the grooves and picks up the ink, and this gives banknotes their characteristic ridged feeling to the touch. Nowadays many banknotes combine traditional intaglio engraving with multicolour lithography or photogravure to defeat the would-be counterfeiter.

Epigraphy The study of inscriptions, involving the classification and interpretation of coin legends, an invaluable adjunct to the study of a coin series, particularly the classical and medieval coins which, in the absence of dates and mintmarks, would otherwise be difficult to arrange in chronological sequence.

Erasion The removal of the title or effigy of a ruler from the coinage issued after his or her death. This process was practised in imperial Rome, and applied to the coins of Caligula, Nero and Geta, as part of the more general practice of *damnatio memoriae* (damnation of the memory) ordered by the Senate.

Error Mistakes on coins and paper money may be either caused at the design or engraving stage, or as a result of a fault in the production processes. In the first category come mis-spellings in legends causing, in extreme cases, *blundered inscriptions*, or anachronisms or inaccuracies in details of the design. In the second, the most glaring error is the mule caused by marrying the wrong dies. Faulty alignment of dies can cause obverse and reverse to be out of true. Although many coins are issued with obverse and reverse upside down in relation to each other, this can also occur as an error in coins where both sides should normally be facing the same way up. Other errors caused at the production stage include striking coins in the wrong metal or with the wrong *collar* thus creating a different edge from the normal.

Essay (From the French *essai*, a trial piece). The term is applied to any piece struck for the purposes of examination, by parliamentary or financial bodies, prior to the authorisation of an issue of coins or paper money. The official nature of these items distinguishes them from *patterns*, which denote trial pieces often produced by mints or even private individuals bidding for coinage contracts.

Evasion Close copy or imitation of a coin, with sufficient deliberate differences in the design or inscription to avoid infringing counterfeit legislation. A good example is the imitation of Sumatran coins by European merchants, inscribed SULTANA instead of SUMATRA.

Exergue Lower segment of a coin or medal, usually divided from the rest of the *field* by a horizontal line, and often containing the date, value, ornament or identification symbols.

Exonumia Generic term for numismatic items not authorised by a government, e.g. *patterns, tokens, medalets* or *model coins.*

F Fine

Face The surface of a coin, medal or token, referred to as the *obverse* or the *reverse*. The corresponding faces of a paper note are more correctly termed *verso* and *recto*, but the coin terms are often

An example of a "Facing" portrait on the obverse of a medallion of Henry Simms, 1901. Actual size 360mm.

Facing Term for the portrait, usually on the obverse, which faces to the front instead of to the side (profile).

Fantasy Piece of metal purporting to be the coinage of a country which does not exist. Recent examples include the money of Atlantis and the Hutt River Province which declared its independence of Western Australia.

FDC Abbreviation for *Fleur de Coin*, a term denoting the finest possible condition of a coin.

Fiat Money Paper notes issued by a government but not redeemable in coin or bullion.

Field Flat part of the surface of a coin or medal, between the *legend*, the *effigy* and other raised parts of the design.

Fillet Heraldic term for the ribbon or headband on the effigy of a ruler or allegorical figure.

Find Term applied to an archaeological discovery of one or more coins. A large quantity of such material is described as a *hoard*.

Flan Alternative name for *blank* or *planchet*, the piece of metal struck between dies to produce a coin or medal.

Forgery An unauthorised copy or imitation, made with the intention of deceiving collectors. Forgeries intended to pass current for real coins or notes are more properly called *counterfeits*.

Fractional Currency Emergency issue of small-denomination notes by the USA in 1863–5, following a shortage of coins caused by the Civil War. This issue superseded the *Postage Currency* notes, but bore the inscription "Receivable for all US stamps", alluding to the most popular medium of small change at that time. Denominations ranged from 3c to 50c.

Franklinium Cupro-nickel alloy developed by the Franklin Mint of Philadelphia and used for coins, medals and gaming tokens since 1967.

Freak An *error* or *variety* of a non-recurring type, usually caused accidentally during production.

Frosting Matt surface used for the high relief areas of many proof coins and medals, for greater contrast with the mirrored surface of the field.

Funeral Money Imitations of banknotes, used in China and Latin America in funeral ceremonies.

Geat (Git) Channel through which molten metal is ducted to the mould. Cast coins and medals often show tiny protrusions known as geat marks.

Ghost Faint image of the design on one side of a coin visible on the other. Good examples were the British penny and halfpenny of George V, 1911–27, the ghosting being eliminated by the introduction of a smaller effigy in 1928.

Globular Coins struck on very thick *dumps* with convex faces. The term is applied to some Byzantine coins, and also the *bullet money* of Siam (Thailand).

Godless (or *Graceless*) Epithet applied to any coin which omits the traditional reference to the deity, e.g. the British florin of 1849 which omitted D.G. (*Dei Gratia*, "by the Grace of God").

Gold Precious metal, chemical symbol and numismatic abbreviation *Au*, from the *Latin Aurum*, used as a coinage medium from the 7th century BC till the present day. The purity of gold is reckoned in *carats* or a decimal system. Thus British gold sovereigns are 22 carat or .916 fine. Medieval coins were 23.5 carat or .995 fine, and some modern bullion coins are virtually pure gold, denoted by the inscription .999. Canadian maple leaves are now struck in "four nines" gold and bear the inscription .9999.

Goodfor Popular name for token coins and *emergency money* made of paper or card, from the inscription "Good for" or its equivalent in other languages (e.g. French *Bon pour* or Dutch *Goed voor*) followed by a monetary value. They have been recorded from Europe, Africa and America during times of economic crises or shortage of more traditional coinage.

Gothic Crown Popular name for the silver crown issued by the United Kingdom (1847–53), so-called on account of its script (more properly Old English, rather than Gothic).

Grain The weight of a single grain of wheat was taken as the smallest unit of weight in England. The troy grain was 1/5760 of a pound, while the avoirdupois grain was 1/7000 pound, the former being used in the weighing of precious metals and thus employed by numismatists in weighing coins. A grain is 1/480 troy ounce or 0.066 gram in the metric system.

Graining Term sometimes used as a synonym for the *reeding* on the edge of milled coins.

Gripped Edge Pattern of indentations found on the majority of American cents of 1797, caused by the milling process. Coins of the same date with a plain edge are rather scarcer.

Guerrilla Money Money issued in areas under the control of guerrillas and partisans during wartime range from the *veld ponds* of the Boers (1900–2) to the notes issued by the Garibaldi Brigade in Italy and the anti-fascist notes of Tito's forces in Yugoslavia. The most prolific issues were those produced in Luzon, Mindanao and Negros Occidental by the Filipino resistance during the Japanese occupation (1942–5).

Guilloche French term signifying the intricate pattern of curved lines produced by the rose engine and used as a security feature in the production of banknote, cheques, stocks and share certificates.

Gun Money Emergency coinage of Ireland (1689–91) minted from gunmetal, a type of bronze used in the casting of cannon. All denominations of James II, from the sixpence to the crown, normally struck in silver, were produced in this base metal.

Gutschein German word for voucher or coupon, denoting the paper money used aboard ships of the Imperial Navy during the First World War. The last issue was made at Scapa Flow, 1918–19, during the internment of the High Seas Fleet.

Hammered Term denoting coins produce by the traditional method of striking a *flan* laid on an anvil with a hammer. A characteristic of hammered coins is their uneven shape which tended to encourage *clipping*. This abuse was gradually eliminated by the introduction of the screw press in the 15th century and the mechanisation of coining processes in the course of the 16th and 17th centuries.

Hard Times Token Copper piece the size of the large cent, issued in the USA, 1834–44, during a shortage of coins caused by the collapse of

"Hard Times" tokens issued by the New York and Harlem Railroad Company.

the Bank of the United States, the panic of 1837 and the economic crisis of 1839, the landmarks in the period known as the Hard Times. Banks suspended *specie* payments and the shortage of coinage was filled by tradesmen's tokens. Many of these were more in the nature of satirical *medalets* than circulating pieces.

Hat Piece   Alternative name for the *bonnet piece* of James VI of Scotland, 1591.

Hell Notes   Imitation paper money used in Chinese funeral ceremonies and buried with the dead to pay for services in the next world.

Hoard   Accumulation of coins concealed in times of economic or political upheaval and discovered, often centuries later.   Under English common law, such hoards are subject to th law of *treasure trove* if they contain precious metal.

Hog Money   Popular name for the early coinage of Bermuda, issued about 1616. The coins were minted in brass with a silver wash and circulated at various values from twopence to a shilling. They derived their name from the hog depicted on the obverse, an allusion to the pigs introduced to the island in 1515 by Juan Bermudez.

Holed   Term denoting two different categories: (a) coins which have been pierced for suspension as a form of jewellery or talisman, and (b) coins which have a hole as part of their design.   In the latter category come the Chinese *cash* with a square hole, and numerous issues of the 19th and 20th centuries from many countries, with the object of reducing weight and metal without sacrificing overall diameter.

Holey Dollar   Spanish silver peso of 8 reales with the centre removed. The resultant ring was counter-marked "New South Wales" and dated 1813, with "Five Shillings" on the reverse, and placed into circulation during a shortage of British coin. The centre, known as a *dump*, was circulated at 15 pence.

Hub   Heavy circular piece of steel on which the *die* for a coin or medal is engraved.   The process of cutting the die and transferring the master die, by means of intermediary *punches*, to the die from which the coins will be struck, is known as hubbing.   Soft steel is used in the preliminary process, and after the design has been transferred, the hub is hardened by chemical action.

Hybrid   Alternative name for a *mule*.

Imitation Money   Also known as play money or toy money, it consists of coins and notes produced for games of chance (like Monopoly), children's toy shops and post offices, as tourist souvenirs, or for political satire (e.g. the shrinking pound or dollar). See also *funeral money, hell notes, model coins* and *skit notes*.

Imprint   Inscription on a paper note giving the name of the printer.

Incuse   Impression which cuts into the surface of a coin or medal, as opposed to the more usual raised relief. Many of the earliest coins, especially those with a device on one side only, bear an incuse impression often in a geometric pattern. An incuse impression appears on one side of the coins, reflecting the image on the other side. Few modern coins have had an incuse design, notable examples being the American half and quarter eagle gold coins of 1908–29 designed by Bela Pratt. Incuse inscriptions on a raised rim, however, are more common, and include the British *Cartwheel* coins of 1797 and the 20p coins since 1982.

Inflation Money   Coins produced as a result of inflation date back to Roman times when bronze minimi, little bigger than a pinhead, circulated as denari.   Nearer the present day inflation has had devastating effects on the coinge and banknotes of Germany (1921–3), Austria (1923), Poland (1923), Hungary (1945–6), Greece (1946) and many Latin American countries since the 1980s. Hungary holds the record for the highest value of any note ever issued — one thousand million adopengos, which is written as 20,000,000,000,000,000,000,000,000,000 pengos.

Ingot   Piece of precious metal, usually cast in a mould, and stamped with the weight and fineness.   though mainly used as a convenient method of storing bullion, ingots have been used as currency in many countries, notably Russia and Japan.

Inlay   Insertion into the surface of a coin or medal of another substance for decorative effect. e.g. Poland Amber Trade Routes 20zl (amber), Isle of Man Queen Mother centenery (pearl) and various coins incorporating rubies or diamonds.

Intaglio   Form of *engraving* in which lines are cut into a steel die for the recess-printing of banknotes.

Intrinsic   The net metallic value of a coin, as distinguished from the nominal or face value.

Iron   Metal, chemical symbol Fe (from Latin

Ferrum), used as a primitive form of currency from classical times onwards. Iron spits (obeliskoi) preceded the obol as the lowest unit of Greek coinage, a handful of six spits being worth a drachma (from *drassomai*, "I grasp"). Cast iron coins were issued in China as a substitute for copper *cash*. Many of the emergency token issues of Germany during the First World War were struck in iron. Iron coins were issued by Bulgaria in 1943. See also *Steel*.

Ithyphallic (Greek for "erect penis"). Term descriptive of coins of classical Greece showing a satyr.

Janiform Double profiles back to back, after the Roman god Janus.

Jeton (From French *jeter*, to throw). Alternative term for *counter*, and used originally on the chequerboard employed by medieval accountants. Nuremberg was the most important centre for the production of medieval jetons, often issued in lengthy portrait series. In modern parlance the term is often synonymous with *token*, though more specifically confined to pieces used in vending equipment, parking meters, laundromats, telephones and urban transport systems in many European countries. Apart from security, removing the temptation of vandals to break into the receptacles, the main advantage of such pieces is that they can be retariffed as charges increase, without any alteration in their design or composition, a method that is far cheaper than altering costly equipment to take larger coins.

Jubilee Head The effigy of Queen Victoria by Joseph Boehm adopted for British coinage after the 1887 Golden Jubilee.

Jugate (From Latin *jugum*, a yoke). Alternative to *accolated* or *conjoined* to denote overlapping profiles of rulers.

Key Date Term describing the rarest in a long-running series of coins with the dates changed at annual intervals.

Kipperzeit German term meaning the time of clipped money, denoting the period during and after the Thirty Years War (1618–48) in which debased and clipped money was in circulation.

Klippe Rectangular or square pieces of metal bearing the impression of a coin. Coins of this type were first struck in Sweden in the 16th century and were subsequently produced in many of the German states. The idea has been revived in recent years as a medium for striking commemorative pieces.

Knife Money Cast bronze pieces, with an elongated blade and a ring at one end to facilitate stringing together in bunches, were used as currency in China from the 9th century BC until the 19th century.

Kreditivsedlar (Swedish for "credit notes"). The name given to the first issue of paper money made in the western world. Paper money of this type was the brainchild of Johan Palmstruch at Riga in 1652, but nine years elapsed before it was implemented by the Stockholm Bank. The notes were redeemable in copper *platmynt*.

Laureate Heraldic term for a laurel wreath, often framing a state emblem or shown, in the Roman fashion, as a crown on the ruler's forehead.

Leather Money Pieces of leather embossed with an official device have been used as money on various occasions, including the sieges of Faenza and Leiden and in the Isle of Man in the 15th and 16th centuries. Several towns in Austria and Germany produced leather tokens during and after the First World War.

Legal Tender Coins or paper money which are declared by law to be current money and which tradesmen and shopkeers are obliged to accept in payment for goods or services. (See *Money and the Law*).

Legend The inscription on a coin or medal.

Liberation Money Paper money prepared for use in parts of Europe and Asia, formerly under Axis occupation. Liberation notes were used in France, Belgium and the Netherlands in 1944–5, while various Japanese and Chinese notes were overprinted for use in Hong Kong when it was liberated in 1945. Indian notes overprinted for use in Burma were issued in 1945–6 when that country was freed from Japanese occupation.

Ligature (From Latin *ligatus*, bound together). Term denoting the linking of two letters in a *legend*, e.g. Æ and Œ.

Long Cross Coinage Type of coinage introduced by King Henry III in 1247, deriving its name from the reverse which bore a cross whose arms extended right to the edge to help safeguard the coins against *clipping*. This remained the style of the silver penny, its fractions and multiples, till the reign of Henry VII, and vestiges of the long cross theme can be seen in the silver coins throughout the remaining years of the Tudor period.

Love Token A coin which has been altered by smoothing one or both surfaces and engraving initials, dates, scenes, symbols of affection and messages thereon.

Lushbourne English word for base pennies of inferior silver, said to have emanated from Luxembourg, from which the name derived. These coins were first minted under John the Blind who adopted the curious spelling of his name EIWANES in the hope that illiterate English merchants might confuse it with EDWARDVS and thus be accepted as coin issued in the name of Edward III. Lushbournes were also minted by Robert of Bethune, William I of Namur and the bishops of Toul during the mid-14th century.

Lustre The sheen or bloom on the surface of an uncirculated coin resulting from the centrifugal flow of metal caused by striking.

Magnimat Trade name used by VDM (*Verein Deutscher Metallwerke*) for a high-security alloy containing copper, nickel and magnetised steel. First used for the 5 deutschemark coin of 1975, it has since been adopted for other high-value coins in Germany and other countries.

Manilla Copper, bronze or brass rings, sometimes shaped like horseshoes and sometimes open, with flattened terminals, used as currency in West Africa until recent years.

Matrix Secondary die for a coin or medal, produced from the master die by means of an intermediate punch. In this way dies can be duplicated from the original cut on the reducing machine.

Matt or Matte Finely granulated surface or overall satin finish to proof coins, a style which was briefly fashionable at the turn of the century. The Edward VII proof set of 1902 is a notable example. In more recent years many issues produced by the Franklin Mint have been issued with this finish.

Maundy Money Set of small silver coins, in denominations of 1, 2, 3 and 4 pence, distributed by the reigning British monarch to the poor and needy on Maundy Thursday. The custom dates back to the Middle Ages, but in its present form, of distributing pence to as many men and women as the years in the monarch's age, it dates from 1666. At first ordinary silver pennies and multiples were used but after they went out of everyday use distinctive silver coins were produced specifically for the purpose from the reign of George II (1727–60) onwards. For centuries the ceremony took place in Westminster Abbey but since 1955 other venues have been used in alternate years.

Medal (French *medaille*, Italian *medaglia*, from Latin *metallum*). A piece of metal bearing devices and legends commemorating an event or person, or given as an award. Military medals date from the 16th and 17th centuries, but were not generally awarded to all ranks till the 19th century. Commemora-tive medals can be traced back to Roman times, but in their present form they date from the Italian Renaissance when there was a fashion for large cast portrait medals.

Medalet A small medal, generally 25mm or less in diameter.

Medallion Synonym for medal, but usually confined to those with a diameter of 50mm or more.

Milling Process denoting the mechanical production of coins, as opposed to the handmade technique implied in *hammering*. It alludes to the use of watermills to drive the machinery of the screw presses and blank rollers developed in the 16th century. As the even thickness and diameter of milled coins permitted a security edge, the term milling is popularly, though erroneously, used as a synonym for *graining* or *reeding*.

Mint The place in which coins and medals are produced. Mint condition is a term sometimes used to denote pieces in an uncirculated state.

Mint Set A set of coins or medals in the package or case issued by the mint. See also *year set*.

Mintmark A device appearing on a coin to denote the place of minting. Athenian coins of classical times have been recorded with up to 40 different marks, denoting individual workshops. In the 4th century AD the Romans adopted this system to identify coins struck in provincial mints. This system was widely used in the Middle Ages and survives in France and Germany to this day. Initials and symbols are also used to identify mints, especially where the production of a coin is shared between several different mints. From 1351 onwards symbols were adopted in England to denote periods between trials of the *Pyx*, and thus assist the proper chronological sequence of coins, in an era prior to the adoption of dating. These mintmarks continued into the 17th century, but gradually died out as the use of dates became more widespread. See also *countermark* and *privy mark*.

Mionnet Scale Scale of nineteen diameters covering all sizes of coins belonging to the classical period, devised by the French numismatist, Theodore-Edme Mionnet (1770–1842) during the compilation of his fifteen-volume catalogue of the numismatic collection in the Bibliotheque Nationale in Paris.

Mirror Finish The highly polished surface of proof coins.

Misstrike A coin or medal on which the impression has been struck off-centre.

Model Coin Tiny pieces of metal, either reproducing the designs of existing coins (used as play money by children) or, more specifically, denoting patterns produced by Joseph Moore and Hyam Hyams in their attempts to promote an improved subsidiary coinage in 19th century Britain. These small coins were struck in bronze with a brass or silver centre and were designed to reduce the size of the existing cumbersome range of pence, halfpence and farthings.

Modified Effigy   Any coin in which the profile on the obverse has been subtly altered. Examples include minor changes in the Victorian Young Head and Old Head effigies and the George V profile by Sir Bertram Mackennal.

Money Order   Certificate for a specified amount of money, which may be transmitted by post and encashed at a money order office or post office. This system was pioneered by Britain and the United States in the early 19th century and is now virtually worldwide. The term is now confined to certificates above a certain value, the terms *postal order* and *postal note* being used for similar certificates covering small amounts.

Mule   Coin whose obverse is not matched with its official or regular reverse. Mules include the erroneous combination of dies from different reigns, but in recent years such hybrids have arisen in mints where coins for several countries are struck. Examples include the Coronation Anniversary crowns combining Ascension and Isle of Man dies and the 2 cent coins with Bahamas and New Zealand dies. *Restrikes* of rare American coins have been detected in which the dated die has been paired with the wrong reverse die, e.g. the 1860 restrike of the rare 1804 large cent.

Mute   An *anepigraphic* coin, identifiable only by the devices struck on it.

Nail Mark   Small indentation on ancient coins. The earliest coins of Asia Minor developed from the electrum *dumps* which merchants marked with a broken nail as their personal guarantee of value, the ancient counterpart of the *chop* marks used in China and Japan.

NCLT Coins   Abbreviation for "Non Circulating Legal Tender", a term devised by modern coin catalogues to denote coins which, though declared *legal tender*, are not intended for general circulation on account of their precious metal content or superior finish.

Nicked Coin   Coin bearing a tiny cut or nick in its edge. Silver coins were tested by this method, especially in the reign of Henry I (1100–35) when so many base silver pennies were in circulation. Eventually people refused to accept these nicked coins a problem which was only overcome when the state decreed that all coins should have a nick in them.

Nickel   Metallic element, chemical symbol *Ni*, a hard white metal relatively resistant to tarnish, and extensively used as a cheap substitute for silver. It was first used for the American 5 cent coin in 1866, hence its popular name which has stuck ever since, although nowadays the higher denominations are minted in an alloy of copper and nickel. Although best known as a silver substitute, nickel was widely used in Jamaica (1869–1969) for halfpence and pennies and in British West Africa for the tiny 1/10th pennies (1908–57). Pure nickel was used for French francs and German marks, but usually it is alloyed with copper or zinc to produce *cupro-nickel* or nickel brass.

Notaphily   Hybrid word from Latin *nota* (note) and Greek philos (love), coined about 1970 to denote the branch of numismatics devoted to the study of paper money.

Notgeld   German word meaning emergency money, applied to the *tokens*, in metals, wood, leather and even ceramic materials, issued during the First World War when coinage disappeared from circulation. These tokens were soon superseded by low-denomination paper money issued by shops and businessmen in denominations from 10 to 50 pfennige and known as *kleine Notgeld* (small emergency money). These notes were prohibited in September 1922 but by that time some 50,000 varieties are thought to have been issued. Inflation raced out of control and the government permitted a second issue of local notes, known as *large Notgeld*, as the denominations were in thousands, and latterly millions, of marks. Some 3,600 types appeared in 1922 and over 60,000 in 1923 alone. These mementoes of the German hyperinflation ceased to circulate in 1924 when the currency was reformed.

Numismatics   The study of coins, medals and other related fields, a term derived from the Latin *numisma* and Greek *nomisma* (money).

Obsidional Currency   (From Latin *obsidium*, a siege). Term for *emergency money* produced by the defenders of besieged towns and cities. These usually took the form of pieces of silver plate, commandeered for the purpose, crudely marked with an official device and the value. Instances of such seige coinage have been recorded from the 12th to the 19th centuries.

Obverse   The "heads" side of a coin or medal, generally bearing the effigy of the head of state or an allegorical figure.

Off Metal   Term denoting a piece struck in a metal other than the officially authorisied or issued alloy. This originally applied to *patterns* which were often struck in lead or copper instead of gold and silver as trial pieces or to test the dies; but in recent years it has applied to collectors' versions, e.g. proofs in platinum, gold or silver of coins normally issued in bronze or cupro-nickel.

Overdate   One or more digits in a date altered by superimposing another figure. Alterations of this kind, by means of small hand punches, were made to dated dies so that they could be used in years other than that of the original manufacture. Coins with overdates invariably show traces of the original digit.

Overstrike   Coin, token or medal produced by using a previously struck pieces as a flan. The Bank of England dollar of 1804 was overstruck on Spanish pieces of eight, and examples showing traces of the original coins are worth a good premium.

Paduan   Name given to imitations of medals and bogus coins produced in Italy in the 16th century, and deriving from the city of Padua where forgeries of bronze sculpture were produced for the antique market.

Patina   Oxidation forming on the surface of metallic objects. So far as coins and medals are concerned, this applies mainly to silver, brass, bronze and copper pieces which may acquire oxidation from the atmosphere, or spectacular patination from salts in the ground in which they have been buried. In extreme forms patina leads to verdigris and other forms of rust which corrode the surface, but in uncirculated coins it may be little more than a mellowing of the original *lustre*. Coins preserved in blue velvet presentation cases often acquire a subtle toning from the dyes in the material.

Pattern   Piece resembling a coin or medal, prepared by the mint to the specifications or on the authorisation of the coin-issuing authority, but also applied to pieces produced by mints when tendering for coinage or medal contracts. Patterns may differ from the final coins as issued in the type of alloy used (*off metal*) but more often they differ in details of the design.

Pellet   Raised circular ornament used as a spacing device between words and abbreviations in the *legend* of coins and medals. Groups of pellets were also used as ornaments in the angles of the cross on the reverse of English silver pennies.

Piece de Plaisir   (French for "fancy piece"). Term given to coins struck in a superior precious metal, or to a superior finish, or on a much thicker flan than usual. See *off metal*, *piedfort* and *proof*.

A piedfort £1 coin compared to one of a normal flan.

Piedfort (Piefort)   Piece struck with coinage dies on a *flan* of much more than normal thickness. This practice originated in France in the late

16th century and continues to the present day. In recent years it has been adopted by mints in Britain and other countries as a medium for collectors' pieces.

Pile   Lower die incorporating the obverse motif, used in striking coins and medals. See also *trussel*.

Planchet   French term used as an alternative for *blank* or *flan*.

Plaque or **Plaquette**   Terms sometimes used for medals struck on a square or rectangular flan.

Plaster   Cast taken from the original model for a coin or medal sculpted by an artist, and used in modern reducing machines in the manufacture of the master *die*.

Plated Coins   Coins stuck in base metal but given a wash of silver or some other precious metal. This expedient was adopted in inflationary times, from the Roman Republic (91 BC) till the Tudor period. American cents of 1943 were struck in steel with a zinc coating, and more recently *clad* coins have produced similar results.

Platinum   The noblest of all precious metals, platinum has a higher specific gravity than gold and a harder, brighter surface than silver. Until an industrial application was discovered in the mid-19th century, it was regarded as of little value, and was popular with counterfeiters as a cheap substitute for gold in their forgeries which, with a light gold wash, could be passed off as genuine. It was first used for circulating coins in Russia (the chief source of the metal since 1819) and 3, 6 and 12 rouble coins were mined at various times between 1828 and 1845. In recent years platinum has been a popular metal for limited-edition proof coins.

Platmynt   (Swedish for "plate money"). Large copper plates bearing royal cyphers and values from half to ten dalers produced in Sweden between 1643 and 1768. They represented laudable attempts by a country rich in copper to produce a coinage in terms of its silver value, but the net result was far too cumbersome to be practical. The weight of the daler plate, for example, ranged from 766 grams to 1.1kg, and special carts had to be devised to transport them!

Plugged Coins   Coins struck predominantly in one metal, but containing a small plug of another. This curious practice may be found in the farthings of Charles II (1684–85) and the halfpence or farthings of James II (1685–87), which were struck in tin, with a copper plug, to defeat forgers.

Pollard   Alternative name for *crockard*.

Porcelain Money   Tokens made of porcelain circulated in Thailand from the late 18th century till 1868. The Meissen pottery struck tokens in 1920–22 as a form of small *Notgeld*, using reddish-brown Bottger stoneware and white *bisque* porcelain. These ceramic tokens circulated in various towns of Saxony.

Postage Currency Small paper notes in denominations of 5, 10, 25 and 50 cents, issued by the US federal government in 1862–63, were thus inscribed and had reproductions of postage stamps engraved on them — five 5c stamps on the 25c and five 10c stamps on the 50c notes. The earliest issue even had perforations in the manner of stamps, but this unnecessary device was soon done away with. See also *stamp money*.

Postal Notes or Orders Low-value notes intended for transmission by post and encashable at post offices. Introduced by Britain in 1883, they were an extension of the earlier *money order* system, and are now issued by virtually every country.

Potin (French for pewter). Alloy of copper, tin, lead and silver used as a coinage metal by the Celtic tribes of eastern Gaul at the beginning of the Christian era.

Privy Mark Secret mark incorporated in the design of a coin or medal to identify the minter, or even the particular die used. The term is also used more loosely to denote any small symbol or initials appearing on a coin other than a *mint mark*, and is sometimes applied to the symbols associated with the trial of the *Pyx* found on English coins.

Prize Coins Coins of large size and value struck primarily as prizes in sporting contests. this principle dates from the late 5th century BC when Syracuse minted decadrachms as prizes in the Demareteian Games. The most notable example in modern times is the lengthy series of talers and five-franc coins issued by the Swiss cantons since 1842 as prizes in the annual shooting festivals, the last of which honoured the Lucerne contest of 1939.

Profile A side view of the human face, widely used as a coinage effigy.

Proof Originally a trial strike testing the *dies*, but now denoting a special collectors' version struck with dies that have been specially polished on *flans* with a mirror finish. Presses operating at a very slow speed, or multi-striking processes, are also used.

Propaganda Notes Paper money containing a political slogan or a didactic element. During the Second World War forgeries of German and Japanese notes were produced by the Allies and additionally inscribed or overprinted with slogans such as "Co-Prosperity Sphere—What is it worth?" (a reference to the Japanese occupied areas of SE Asia). Forged dollars with anti-American propaganda were airdropped over Sicily by the Germans in 1943 and counterfeit pounds with Arabic propaganda over Egypt in 1942–43. Various anti-communist organisations liberated propaganda forgeries of paper money by balloon over Eastern Europe during the Cold War period.

Provenance Mark Form of *privy mark* denoting the source of the metal used in coins. Examples include the plumes or roses on English coins denoting silver from Welsh or West of England mines, and the elephant or elephant and castle on gold coins denoting bullion imported by the African Company. Coins inscribed VIGO (1702–03) or LIMA (1745–46) denote bullion seized from the Spaniards by Anglo-Dutch privateers and Admiral Anson respectively. Other provenance marks on English coins include the letters EIC and SSC, denoting bullion imported by the East India Company or the South Sea Company.

Pseudo Coins Derisory term coined in recent years to signify pieces of precious metal, often struck in *proof* versions only, aimed at the international investment market. Many of these pieces, though bearing a nominal face value, are not *legal tender* in the countries purporting to issue them and in many cases they go straight from the overseas mint where they are produced to coin dealers in America and western Europe, without ever appearing in the so-called country of origin. See also *NCLT coins*.

Punch or Puncheon Intermediate *die* whereby working dies can be duplicated from the master die, prior to the striking of coins and medals.

Pyx Box in which a specimen from every 15 pounds troy weight of gold and every 60 pounds of silver minted in England is kept for annual trial by weight and assay. Many of the *mintmarks* on English coins of the 14th–17th centuries were in use from one trial to the next and still exist today and can therefore be used to date them.

Reducing Machinery Equipment designed on the pantographic principle for transferring the image from a *plaster* to a *hub* and reducing it to the size of the actual coin or medal. The image is transferred by means of a stylus operating rather like a gramophone needle, but working from the centre to the outer edge.

Reeding Security edging on coins, consisting of close vertical ridges. As a rule, this appears all round the edge but some coins, e.g. New Zealand's 50c (1967) and the Isle of Man's £1 (1978) have segments of reeding alternating with a plain edge, to help blind and partially sighted persons to identify these coins.

Re-issue A coin or note issued again after an extended lapse of time.

Relief   Raised parts of the *obverse* and *reverse* of coins and medals, the opposite of *incuse*.

Remainder   A note from a bank or issuing authority which has never been circulated, due to inflation, political changes or bank failure. Such notes, some-times in partial or unfinished state (e.g. missing serial numbers or signatures), are generally unloaded on to the numismatic market at a nominal sum and provide a good source of inexpensive material for the beginner.

Restrike   Coin, medal or token produced from *dies* subsequent to the original use. Usually restrikes are made long after the original and can often be identified by marks caused by damage, pitting or corrosion of the dies after they were taken out of service.

Retrograde   Term describing inscriptions running from left to right, or with the letters in a mirror image, thought to arise from unskilled die-cutters failing to realise that inscriptions have to be engraved in negative form to achieve a positive impression.   Retrograde inscriptions are common on ancient Greek coins, but also found on Roman and Byzantine coins.

Reverse   The side of a coin or medal regarded as of lesser importance;   in colloquial parlance, the "tails" side.

Saltire   Heraldic term for a cross in the shape of an X.

Sandwich   Coin *blank* consisting of thin outer layers in one alloy bonded to a core in another. See *clad coins*.

Sceat   (Anglo-Saxon for "treasure", or German *Schatz*).   Money of account in Kent early in the 7th century as the twelfth part of a shilling or Merovingian gold tremissis. As a silver coin, it dates from about AD 680–700 and weighed about 20 grains, putting it on par with the Merovingian denier or penny. Sceats spread to other parts of England in the 8th century but tended to decline in weight and value, but from about 760 it was gradually superseded by the silver penny minted under Offa and his successors.

Scissel   The clippings of metal left after a *blank* has been cut. Occasionally one of these clippings accidentally adheres to the blank during the striking process, producing characteristic crescent-shaped flaws on the finished coin.

Scrip   Paper money of restricted validity or circulation, e.g. *Bafs* and other military scrip used in canteens and post exchanges.

Scyphate   (Greek *scypha*, a skiff or small boat).   Byzantine coin with a concave *flan*.

Sede Vacante   (Latin for "Vacant See").   Coins struck at *ecclesiastical mints* between the death of a prelate and the election of his successor are often thus inscribed. This practice originated at Rome in the 13th century and spread to every part of Europe.

Seignorage or Seigneurage   Royalty or percentage paid by persons bringing *bullion* to a mint for conversion into coin, but nowadays synonymous with the royalty paid by mints in respect of the precious metal versions of coins sold direct to collectors.   It arises from the medieval right of the king to a small portion of the proceeds of a mint, and amounted to a tax on moneying. It has also been applied to the money accruing to the state when the coinage is re-issued in an alloy of lesser fineness, as, for example, the debased sovereigns of Henry VIII in 20 instead of 23 carat gold, the king's treasury collecting the difference.

Series   Term applied to sets of medals of a thematic character, which first became fashionable in the early 18th century. Jean Dassier pioneered the medallic series in the 1720s with his set of 72 medals portraying the rulers of France till Louis XV. The idea was developed by J. Kirk, Sir Edward Thomason, J. Mudie and A. J. Stothard in Britain, and by Moritz Fuerst and Amedee Durand in Europe. The fashion died out in the 19th century, but has been revived in America and Europe since 1964.

Serrated   Having a notched or toothed edge, rather like a cogwheel.   Coins of this type, struck in *electrum*, an alloy of silver and gold, are known from Carthage in the 2nd century BC, and some silver denarii of Rome in the 2nd century AD also come into this category.

Sexagesimal System   Monetary system in which the principal unit is divided into 60 parts. The oldest system in the Western world was based on the gold talent of 60 minae and the mina of 60 shekels.   In medieval Europe 60 groschen were worth a fine mark; in England from 1551, the silver coinage was based on the crown of 60 pence, and in the south German states till 1873 the gulden was worth 60 kreuzers.

Shin Plasters   Derisory term originally applied to the Continental currency notes issued during the American War of Independence, the fractional currency of the Civil War period and also the low-denomination notes of Canada between 1870 and 1935, but often applied indiscriminately to any other low-denomination, small-format notes.

Short Cross Coinage   Term for the silver coinage introduced by Henry II in 1180 and minted till 1247 at which time it was replaced by the *Long Cross* type. The termination of the arms of the cross on the reverse well within the circumference encouraged the dishonest practice of *clipping*.

Shroff Mark   A *countermark* applied by Indian

bankers or merchants to attest the full weight and purity of coins. See also *chop*.

Siege Money See *Obsidional Currency*

Silver Precious metal, chemical symbol *Ag*, numismatic abbreviation *Ar*, from Latin *Argentum*, widely used as a coinage metal from the 6th century BC to the present day.

Sterling silver denotes an alloy of .925 fine silver with .075 copper. Fine silver alloys used over the past 2,500 years have ranged from .880 to .960 fine, but base silver has also been all too common. British coins from 1920 to 1946 were struck in .500 fine silver, while alloys of lesser fineness are known as *billon* or *vellon*. Silver alloyed with gold produces a metal called *electrum*, used for the earliest coinage of the western world, the staters of Lydia in the 7th century BC. Since 1970 silver as a medium for circulating coinage has almost virtually disappeared, yet the volume of silver coins for sale to collectors has risen considerably in recent years.

Skit Note Piece of paper masquerading as a banknote. It differs from a *counterfeit* in that its design parodies that of a genuine note, often for political, satirical or advertising reasons. Others were produced as April Fools' Day jokes or a form of Valentine (e.g. the Bank of Lovers). In recent years they have been produced as advertising gimmicks, or as coupons permitting a discount off the list price of goods.

Slug Popular name for the $50 gold pieces produced by private mints in California in the mid-19th century. The term is also applied nowadays to *tokens* intended for use in gaming machines.

Spade Guinea Name given to the guineas of George III issued between 1787 and 1799 because the shield on the reverse design resembled the shape of a spade. In Victorian times the spade guinea was extensively copied in brass for gaming counters.

Spade Money Cast bronze pieces resembling miniature spades and other agricultural implements, used as money and derived from the actual implements which had previously been used in barter. Often referred to as *Pu* or *Boo* money.

Specie Financial term denoting money in the form of precious metals (silver and gold), usually struck as coin, as opposed to money in the form of paper notes and bills of exchange. It occurs in the name of some European coins (e.g. *speciedaler*, *speciestaler* and *speciesducat*) to denote the use of fine silver or gold.

Specimen Generally used to denote a single piece, but more specifically applying to a coin in a special finish, less than *proof* in quality but

superior to the general circulating version. It also denotes paper notes intended for circulation between banks or for press publicity and distinguished from the generally issued version by zero serial numbers, punch holes or a security endorsement.

Spintriae Metal tokens produced in Roman imperial times, with erotic motifs, thought to have been tickets of admission to brothels.

Spit Copper or iron rod used as a primitive form of currency in the Mediterranean area. The Greek word *belos* meant a spit, dart or bolt, and from this came the word *obolos* used for a coin worth a 6th of a drachma.

Stamp Money Both postage and revenue (fiscal) stamps have circulated as money during shortages of coins, from the American Civil War onwards. *Encased postage stamps* were used in the USA, 1861–62, before they were superseded by *Postage Currency* notes, but the same expedient was adopted by many countries during and immediately after the First World War. Stamps affixed to special cards have circulated as money in Rhodesia (now Zimbabwe) in 1900, the French colonies and Turkey during the First World War, in Spain during the Civil War (1936–39) and the Philippines during the Second World War. Stamps printed on thick card, with an inscription on the reverse signifying their parity with silver coins, were issued in Russia (1917–18) and also in Armenia, the Crimea and the Ukraine (1918–20). During the Second World War Ceylon (now Sri Lanka) and several Indian states issued small money cards with contemporary stamps printed on them.

Steel Refined and tempered from *iron*, and used in chromed or stainless versions as a coinage metal in the 20th century. Zinc-coated steel cents were issued by the USA (1943) but in the form known as *acmonital* (nickel steel) it has been extensively used by Italy since 1939. Other alloys of nickel and steel have been used for coins of the Philippines (1944–45) and Roumania since 1963. Chrome steel was used by France for 5 centime coins in 1961–64. Copper-clad steel is now extensively used for subsidiary coins formerly struck in bronze.

Sterling Word of uncertain origin denoting money of a standard weight and fineness, and hence the more general meaning of recognised worth. The traditionally accepted derivation from the Easterlings, north German merchants who settled in London in the 13th century and produced silver pennies of uniform fineness, is unlikely as the term has been found in documents a century earlier. A more plausible explanation is from Old English *steorling* ("little coin with a star"), alluding to Viking pennies with this device, or even as a diminutive of *stater*. Sterling silver denotes silver of .925 fineness.

Stone Money   Primitive currency in the form of large stone discs, used in West Africa in the pre-colonial period, and in the Pacific island of Yap (now Micronesia) as recently as 1940.

Striation   A pattern of alternate light and dark parallel marks or minute grooves on the surface of a coin or medal. In the latter case it is sometimes done for textural effect, but in coins it may result from faulty *annealing*. Deliberate ridging of the surface, however, was a distinctive feature of Japanese *koban* and *goryoban* coins of 1736–1862.

Styca   Name given to the debased silver *sceats* of Northumbria in the 8th century.

Tael   Chinese unit of weight corresponding to the European ounce and sometimes referred to as a liang. It was a measure of silver varying between 32 and 39 grams. In the 19th century it served as *money of account*, 100 British or Mexican trade dollars being worth 72 tael. The term has also been loosely applied to the Chinese silver yuan, although this was worth only .72 tael, or 7 mace and 2 candareens (10 candareens = 1 mace; 10 mace = 1 tael).

Thrymsa   Early Anglo-Saxon gold coin based on the Merovingian tremissis or third-solidus, current in Kent, London and York about AD 63–75.

Tical   Unit of weight in Thailand, first appearing as coins in the form of crudely shaped *bullet money* current from the 14th till the late 19th centuries. When European-style coins were introduced in 1860 the word was retained as a denomination (32 solot = 16 atts = 8 peinung or sio = 4 songpy or sik = 2 fuang= 1 salung or quarter-tical. The currency was decimalised in 1909 (100 satangs = 1 tical), and the tical was superseded by the baht about 1950.

Tin   Metallic element, chemical symbol Sn (from Latin *Stannum*). Because of its unstable nature and tendency to oxidise badly when exposed to the atmosphere, it is unsatisfactory as a coinage metal, but has been used on several occasions, notably in Malaya, Thailand and the East Indies. In was also used for British halfpence and farthings, 1672–92.

Token   Any piece of money whose nominal value is greater than its intrinsic value is, strictly speaking, a token or promise. Thus most of the coins issued since 1964 can be regarded in this light, but numismatists reserve the term for a piece of limited validity and circulation, produced by tradesmen, chambers of commerce and other organisations during times of a shortage of government coinage. The term is also loosely applied to metal tickets of admission, such as *communion tokens*, or *jetons* and *counters* intended for games of chance. Tokens with a nominal value may be produced for security reasons to lessen the possibility of theft from milk bottles, vending machines, telephones, parking meters and transport facilities. Tokens exchangeable for goods have been issued by co-operative societies and used in prisons and internment camps in wartime. In addition to the traditional coinage alloys, tokens have been produced in ceramics, plastics, wood, stout card, leather and even rubber, in circular, square or polygonal shapes.

Tombac   Type of brass alloy with a high copper content, used in coinage requiring a rich golden colour. It is, in fact, a modern version of the *aurichalcum* used by the Romans. It was used for the Canadian 5-cent coins of 1942–43, while 5- and 10-pfennig coins of Germany have a tombac cladding on a steel core.

Touchpiece   Coin kept as a lucky charm, but more specifically the medieval gold angel of England which was worn round the neck as an antidote to scrofula, otherwise known as king's evil, from the belief that the reigning monarch possessed the power of healing by touch. The ceremony of touching for king's evil involved the suspension of an angel round the victim's neck, hence the prevalence of these coins pierced for suspension.

Trade Coins   Coins widely used as a medium of international trade, often far beyond the boundaries of the country issuing them. The earliest examples were the Aiginetan turtles and Athenian tetrdrachms of the classical period. In the Middle Ages the English *sterling* was widely prized on account of its silver purity. Arab dinars and Italian florins were popular as gold coins in late-medieval times, while the British gold sovereign has been the preferred gold coin of modern times. The Maria Theresa silver thaler of Austria, with its date frozen at 1782, has been minted widely down to the present time for circulation in the Near and Middle East as a trade coin. Trade dollars were minted by Britain, the USA, the Netherlands and Japan to compete with the Spanish, and later the Mexican, peso or 8-reales coins as a trading medium in the Far East.

Transport Tokens   Coin-like pieces of metal, plastic or card, issued by companies and corporations to employees and exchangeable for rides on municipal transport systems, date from the mid-19th century. In more recent times similar tokens have been used in many countries to activate turnstiles in buses, trams and rapid-transit railway systems.

Treasury Note   Paper money worth 10 shillings or one pound, issued by the British Treasury on the outbreak of the First World War when *specie* payments were suspended, and continuing till 1928 when the Bank of England took over responsibility for note-issuing.

Treasure Trove   Articles of precious metal concealed in times of economic or political upheaval and discovered years (often centuries) later are deemed by law to be treasure trove (from the French word *trouve*, found). For further details see *Money and the Law*.

Trial Plate   Plate of the same metal as the current coinage against which the fineness and quality of the coins produced are compared and tested.

Troy Weight   System of weights derived from the French town of Troyes whose standard pound was adopted in England in 1526. It continued in Britain till 1879 when it was abolished, with the exception of the troy ounce and its decimal parts and multiples, which were retained for gold, silver, platinum and precious stones. The troy ounce of 480 grains is used by numismatists for weighing coins.

Truncation   Stylised cut at the base of a coinage effigy, sometimes containing a die number, engraver's initials or *mintmark*.

Trussel   Reverse die in *hammered* coinage, the opposite of the *pile*.

Type   Principal motif on a coin or medal, enabling numismatists to identify the issue.

Type Set   A set of coins comprising one of each coin in a particular series, regardless of the actual date of issue.

Uncirculated   Term used in grading coins to denote specimens in perfect condition, with original mint lustre. In recent years the term "Brilliant Uncirculated" has been adopted (abbreviated as BUnc or BU).

Uniface   Coin, medal or token with a device on one side only.

Variety   Variation in, or modification of type, effigy, motif or inscription.

Vecture   Term (mainly US) for a *transport token*.

Veiled Head   The effigy of Queen Victoria by Thomas Brock adopted for British coinage after 1893—often referred to as the "Old Head" coinage.

The Veld Pond   (Dutch for "field pound"). Gold coin struck by the Boer guerrillas at Pilgrims Rest in 1902, in imitation of the British sovereign.

Vellon   Spanish form of *billon*.

VF   Abbreviation for Very Fine, used to describe the state of a coin or medal.

VG   Abbreviation for Very Good.

Vignette   Strictly speaking the pictorial element of a paper note shading off into the surrounding unprinted paper rather than having a clearly defined border or frame; but nowadays applied generally to the picture portion of a banknote, as opposed to portrait, armorial or numeral elements.

Vis-à-Vis   (French for "face to face"). Term describing coins with double portraits of rulers, their profiles or busts facing each other. A good example is the English coinage of Philip and Mary, 1554–58.

Wampum   Barter currency of the North American Indians, composed of shells of *Venus mercenaria* strung together to form belts or "fathoms" worth 5 shillings. Wampum were tariffed variously from three to six to the English penny in the American colonies till 1704.

White Gold   Alternative term for *electrum*.

Wire Money   Primitive currency of the Maldive Islands in the form of lengths of silver wire known as lari, from which the modern currency unit *laree* is derived. The term was also applied to English coins of the 18th century in which the numerals of value were exceptionally thin, resembling wire.

Wooden Coins   Thin pieces of wood used as tokens are known from many parts of China and Africa, and as small *Notgeld* from Austria and Germany during the First World War. Wooden nickels is the somewhat contradictory name given to tokens of a commemorative nature, widely popular in the USA since 1930.

Year set.   A set of coins issued annually by a mint. It often contains specimens not generally released for circulation in that year.

Young Head   Profile of Queen Victoria sculpted by William Wyon for the Guildhall Medal of 1837 and subsequently utilised for British coins struck from 1837 to 1860 (copper) and 1887 (silver and gold).

Zinc   Metallic element, chemical symbol *Zn*, widely used, with copper, as a constituent of brass. Alloyed with copper to form *tombac*, it was used for Canadian 5-cent coins (1942–43) and, coated on steel, it was used for American cents (1943). Zinc was used for *emergency coinage* in Austria, Belgium, Luxembourg and Germany (1915–18) and in Germany and German-occupied countries during the Second World War. Since then alloys of copper, nickel and zinc have been used for coinage in Eastern Europe, and an alloy of zinc with titanium has been developed in the 1970s as a potential substitute for *bronze* in subsidiary coinage.

Mintmarks
of the world

The following is a list of the initials and symbols denoting mints. In many cases, notably the Royal Mint, no mintmark was used on either British coins or those struck on behalf of other countries. Conversely many countries have only used one mintmark, that of one or other of the leading private mints.

It should be noted that the mintmarks of the main private mints have been recorded on the coins of the following countries:

H (Heaton, later the Birmingham Mint):
Australia, Bolivia, British Honduras, British North Borneo, British West Africa, Bulgaria, Canada, Ceylon, Chile, Colombia, Costa Rica, Cyprus, Dominican Republic, East Africa, Ecuador, Egypt, El Salvador, Finland, French Indochina, Great Britain, Greece, Guatemala, Guernsey, Haiti, Hong Kong, Iran, Israel, Italy, Jamaica, Jersey, Liberia, Malaya and British Borneo, Mauritius, Mombasa, Mozambique, Newfoundland, Nicaragua, Poland, Roumania, Sarawak, Serbia, Siam, Straits Settlements, Uruguay and Venezuela.

FM (Franklin Mint, Philadelphia): Bahamas, Belize, British Virgin Islands, Cayman Islands, Cook Islands, Guyana, Jamaica, Liberia, Malaysia, Malta, Panama, Papua New Guinea, Philippines, Solomon Islands, Trinidad and Tobago.

PM (Pobjoy Mint, Sutton, Surrey): Ascension, Bosnia, Cook Islands, Gibraltar, Isle of Man, Liberia, Macau, Niue, Philippines, St Helena, Senegal, Seychelles, Tonga and Tristan da Cunha.

ALBANIA
L	London
R	Rome
V	Valona

ARGENTINA
BA	Buenos Aires
Bs	Buenos Aires
B.AS	Buenos Aires
JPP	Jose Policarpo Patino
M	Mendoza
PNP	Pedro Nolasco Pizarro

PP	Pedro Nolasco Pizarro
PTS	Potosi
R	Rioja
RA	Rioja
SE	Santiago del Estero
SoEo	Santiago del Estero
TN	Tucuman

AUSTRALIA
A	Perth
D	Denver
H	Heaton (1912–16)
I	Bombay (1942–43)
I	Calcutta (1916–18)
M	Melbourne
P	Perth
PL	Royal Mint, London
S	Sydney
S	San Francisco (1942–43)
Dot before and after PENNY and I on obverse	Bombay (1942–43)
Dot before and after HALFPENNY and I on obverse	Bombay (1942–43)
Dot before and after PENNY	Bombay (1942–43)
Dot after HALFPENNY	Perth
Dot before SHILLING	Perth (1946)
Dot above scroll on reverse	Sydney (1920)
Dot below scroll on reverse	Melbourne (1919–20)
Dot between designer's initials KG	Perth (1940–41)
Dot after AUSTRALIA	Perth (1952–53)

AUSTRIA
A	Vienna (1765–1872)
AH–AG	Carlsburg, Transylvania (1765–76)
AH–GS	Carlsburg (1776–80)
A–S	Hall, Tyrol (1765–74)
AS–IE	Vienna (1745)
AW	Vienna (1764, 1768)
B	Kremnitz (1765–1857)
B–L	Nagybanya (1765–71)

B–V	Nagybanya (1772–80)
C	Carlsburg (1762–64)
C	Prague (1766–1855)
C–A	Carlsburg (1746–66)
C–A	Vienna (1774–80)
CG–AK	Graz (1767–72)
CG–AR	Graz (1767)
C–K	Vienna (1765–73)
CM	Kremnitz (1779)
CVG–AK	Graz (1767–72)
CVG–AR	Graz (1767)
D	Graz (1765–72), Salzburg (1800–09)
E	Carlsburg (1765–1867)
EC–SK	Vienna (1766)
EvM–D	Kremnitz (1765–74)
EvS–AS	Prague (1765–73)
EvS–IK	Prague (1774–80)
F	Hall (1765–1807)
FH	Hall
G	Graz (1761–63)
G	Gunzburg (1764–79)
G	Nagybanya (1766–1851)
G–K	Graz (1767–72)
G–R	Graz (1746–67)
GTK	Vienna (1761)
H	Hall (1760–80)
H	Gunzburg (1765–1805)
H–A	Hall (1746–65)
H–G	Carlsburg (1765–77)
H–S	Carlsburg (1777–80)
IB–FL	Nagybanya (1765–71)
IB–IV	Nagybanya (1772–80)
IC–FA	Vienna (1774–80)
IC–IA	Vienna (1780)
IC–SK	Vienna (1765–73)
I–K	Graz (1765-67)
I–K	Vienna (1767)
IZV	Vienna (1763–65)
K	Kremnitz (1760–63)
K–B	Kremnitz (1619–1765)
K–D	Kremnitz (1765)
K–M	Kremnitz (1763–65)
M	Milan (1780–1859)
N	Nagybanya (1780)
N–B	Nagybanya (1630–1777, 1849)
O	Oravicza (1783–1816)
P	Prague (1760–63)
P–R	Prague (1746–67)
PS–IK	Prague (1774–80)
S	Hall (1765–80), Schmollnitz (1763–1816)
S–C	Gunzburg (1765–74)
SC–G	Gunzburg (1765)
S–F	Gunzburg (1775–80)
S–G	Gunzburg (1764–65)
S–IE	Vienna (1745)
SK–PD	Kremnitz (1774–80)
TS	Gunzburg (1762–88)

V	Venice (1805–66)
VC–S	Hall (1774–80)
VS–K	Prague (1774–80)
VS–S	Prague (1765–73)
W	Vienna (1748–63)
W–I	Vienna (1746–71)

BAHAMAS
FM	Franklin Mint
JP	John Pinches

BELGIUM
A	Vienna
B	Kremnitz
C	Prague
E	Carlsburg
F	Hall
G	Nagybanya
H	Gunzburg
hand	Antwerp
lion	Bruges

BELIZE (British Honduras)
FM	Franklin Mint
H	Heaton (1912–16)

BOLIVIA
H	Heaton (1892–1953)
P, PTR, PTS	Potosi

BRAZIL
A	Berlin (1913)
B	Bahia (1714–1831)
C	Cuiaba (1823–33)
G	Goias (1823–33)
M	Minas Gerais (1823–28)
P	Pernambuco
R	Rio de Janeiro (1703–1834)
RS	Rio de Janeiro (1869)
SP	Sao Paulo (1825–32)

BRITISH NORTH BORNEO (Sabah)
H	Heaton (1882–1941)

BRITISH WEST AFRICA
G	JR Gaunt, Birmingham
H	Heaton, Birmingham (1911–57)
K	King's Norton
KN	King's Norton
SA	Pretoria

BULGARIA
A	Berlin
BP	Budapest
Heaton	Heaton, Birmingham (1881–1923)
KB	Kormoczbanya
cornucopia	Paris
thunderbolt	Poissy

CANADA

C	Ottawa
H	Heaton (1871–1907)
maple leaf	Ottawa (on coins struck after the year inscribed on them)

CENTRAL AMERICAN REPUBLIC

CR	San Jose (Costa Rica)
G	Guatemala
NG	Guatemala
T	Tegucigalpa (Honduras)

CEYLON

H	Heaton (1912)

CHILE

A	Agustin de Infante y Prado (1768–72)
AJ	The above and Jose Maria de Bobadilla (1800–01)
D	Domingo Eizaguirre
DA	Domingo Eizaguirre and Agustin de Infante (1772–99)
BFF	Francisco Rodriguez Brochero
FJJF	Brochero and Jose Maria de Bobadilla (1803–17)
H	Heaton (1851)
J	Jose Larraneta (1749–67)
So	Santiago
VA	Val Distra

COLOMBIA

A	Paris
B	Bogota
BA	Bogota
B.B	Bogota
H	Heaton (1912)
M	Medellin
NR	Nuevo Reino
NoRo	Nuevo Reino
P	Popayan
PN, Pn	Popayan
SM	Santa Marta

COSTA RICA

CR	San Jose (1825–1947)
HBM	Heaton (1889–93)
S	San Domingo
SD	San Domingo

COURLAND

ICS	Justin Carl Schroder
IFS	Johan Friedrich Schmickert

CYPRUS

H	Heaton (1881–2)

DENMARK

FF	Altona
KM	Copenhagen Altona (1842)
crown	Copenhagen
heart	Copenhagen
orb	Altona (1839–48)

Other letters are the initials of mintmasters and moneyers

DOMINICAN REPUBLIC

HH	Heaton (1888–1919)

EAST AFRICA

A	Ackroyd & Best, Morley
H	Heaton (1910–64)
I	Bombay
K	Kynoch (IMI)
KN	King's Norton
SA	Pretoria

ECUADOR

BIRM^MH	Heaton (1915)
BIRMING-HAM	Heaton (1899–1900, 1928)
D	Denver
H	Heaton (1890, 1909, 1924–5)
HEATON BIRMING-HAM	Heaton (1872–95)
HF	Le Locle
LIMA	Lima
Mo	Mexico
PHILA	Philadelphia
QUITO	Quito
SANTIAGO	Santiago de Chile

EGYPT

H	Heaton (1904–37)

EL SALVADOR

CAM	Central American Mint, San Salvador
H	Heaton (1889–1913)
Mo	Mexico
S	San Francisco

FIJI

S	San Francisco

FINLAND

H	Heaton (1921)
heart	Copenhagen (1922). Since then coins have been struck at Helsinki without a mintmark.

Initials of mintmasters:

S	August Soldan (1864–85)
L	Johan Lihr (1885–1912)
S	Isaac Sundell (1915–47)

L	V. U. Liuhto (1948)	AGP	Cleve, Rhineland (1742–43)
H	Uolevi Helle (1948–58)	AK	Dusseldorf, Julich-Berg (1749–66)
S	Allan Soiniemi (1958–75)	ALS	Berlin (1749)
SH	Soiniemi & Heikki Halvaoja (1967–71)	B	Bayreuth, Franconia (1796–1804)
K	Timo Koivuranta (1977, 1979)	B	Breslau, Silesia (1750–1826)
KN	Koivuranta and Antti Neuvonen (1978)	B	Brunswick, Brunswick (1850–60)
KT	Koivuranta and Erja Tielinen (1982)	B	Brunswick, Westphalia (1809–13)
KM	Koivuranta and Pertti Makinen (1983)	B	Dresden, Saxony (1861–72)
N	Reino Nevalainen (1983)	B	Hannover, Brunswick (1860–71)
		B	Hannover, East Friesland (1823–25)

FRANCE

A	Paris (1768)	B	Hannover, Hannover (1821–66)
AA	Metz (1775–98)	B	Hannover, Germany (1866-78)
B	Rouen (1786–1857)	B	Regensburg, Regensburg (1809)
B	Beaumont le Roger (1943–58)	B	Vienna, Germany (1938–45)
BB	Strasbourg (1743–1870)	BH	Frankfurt (1808)
C	Castelsarrasin (1914, 1942–46)	B–H	Regensburg, Rhenish Confederation (1802–12)
CC	Genoa (1805)		
CL	Genoa (1813–14)	C	Cassel, Westphalia (1810–13)
D	Lyons (1771–1857)	C	Clausthal, Brunswick
G	Geneva (1796–1805)	C	Clausthal, Westphalia (1810–11)
H	La Rochelle (1770–1837)	C	Dresden, Saxony (1779–1804)
L	Limoges (1766–1837)	C	Frankfurt, Germany (1866–79)
K	Bordeaux (1759–1878)	CHI	Berlin (1749–63)
L	Bayonne (1761–1837)	CLS	Dusseldorf, Julich-Berg (1767–70)
M	Toulouse (1766–1837)	D	Aurich, East Friesland (1750–1806)
MA	Marseilles (1787–1857)	D	Dusseldorf, Rhineland (1816–48)
N	Montpellier (1766–93)	D	Munich, Germany (1872)
O	Riom	E	Dresden, Germany (1872–87)
P	Dijon	E	Koenigberg, East Prussia (1750–98)
Q	Perpignan (1777–1837)	E	Muldenhutte, Germany (1887–1953)
R	Royal Mint, London (1815)	EC	Leipzig, Saxony (1753–63)
R	Orleans (1780–92)	EGN	Berlin (1725–49)
T	Nantes (1739–1835)	F	Dresden, Saxony (1845–58)
U	Turin (1814)	F	Magdeburg, Lower Saxony (1740–1806)
V	Troyes	F	Cassel, Hesse-Cassel (1803–07)
W	Lille (1759–1857)	F	Stuttgart, Germany (1872)
X	Amiens (1740)	FW	Dresden, Saxony (1734–63)
&	Aix en Provence (1775)	G	Dresden, Saxony (1833–44, 1850–54)
9	Rennes	G	Glatz, Silesia (1807–09)
cow	Pau (1746–93)	G	Karlsruhe, Germany (1872)
flag	Utrecht (1811–14)	G	Stettin, Pomerania (1750–1806)
crowned R	Rome (1811–14)	GK	Cleve (1740–55)
thunderbolt	Poissy (1922-24)	GN	Bamberg, Bamberg
star	Madrid (1916)	H	Darmstadt, Germany (1872–82)

In addition, French coins include symbols denoting the privy marks of Engravers General (Chief Engravers since 1880) and Mint Directors.

		H	Dresden, Saxony (1804–12)
		HK	Rostock, Rostock (1862–64)
		I	Hamburg, Germany (1872)
		IDB	Dresden, Prussian occupation (1756–59)
		IEC	Dresden, Saxony (1779–1804)

GERMANY

The first name gives the location of the mint, and the second name of the country or state issuing the coins.

		IF	Leipzig, Saxony (1763–65)
A	Amberg, Bavaria (1763–94)	IGG	Leipzig, Saxony (1716–34, 1813–32)
A	Berlin (1850)	J	Hamburg, Germany (1873)
A	Clausthal, Hannover (1832–49)	J	Paris, Westphalia (1808–09)
AE	Breslau, Silesia (1743–51)	L	Leipzig, Saxony (1761–62)
		MC	Brunswick, Brunswick (1813–14, 1820)
		PM	Dusseldorf, Julich-Berg (1771–83)
		PR	Dusseldorf, Julich-Berg (1783–1804)

S	Dresden, Saxony (1813–32)
S	Hannover, Hannover (1839–44)
S	Schwabach, Franconia (1792–94)
SGH	Dresden, Saxony (1804–12)
ST	Strickling, Blomberg (1820–40)

GREAT BRITAIN

A	Ashby (1645)
B	Nicolas Briot (1631–39)
B	Bridgnorth (1646)
B	Bristol (1696)
Br	Bristol (1643–45)
C	Chester (1696)
CARL	Carlisle (1644–45)
CC	Corfe Castle (1644)
CHST	Chester (1644)
CR	Chester (1644)
E	Southwark (1547–49)
E	Exeter (1696)
E	Edinburgh (1707–13)
E*	Edinburgh (1707–09)
H	Heaton, Birmingham (1874–1919)
HC	Hartlebury Castle (1646)
K	London (1547–49)
KN	King's Norton
N	Norwich (1696)
OX	Oxford (1644–45)
OXON	Oxford (1644)
PC	Pontefract (1648–49)
SC	Scarborough (1644–45)
SOHO	Birmingham (1797–1806)
T	Canterbury (1549)
TC	Bristol (1549)
WS	Bristol (1547–49)
Y	Southwark (1551)
boar	Shrewsbury (1643–44)
book	Aberystwyth (1638–42)
bow	Durham House (1548–49)
castle	Exeter (1644–45)
crown	Aberystwyth Furnace (1648–49)
plume	Shrewsbury (1642)
plume	Oxford (1642–46)
plume	Bristol (1643–46)

Other symbols and marks on the hammered coins of Great Britain are usually referred to as Initial Marks. Complete listings of these marks appear in a number of specialist publications.

GREECE

A	Paris
B	Vienna
BB	Strasbourg
H	Heaton (1921)
K	Bordeaux
KN	King's Norton
owl	Aegina (1828–32)
owl	Athens (1838-55)
thunderbolt	Poissy

GUATEMALA

CG	Guatemala City (1733-76)
G	Guatemala City (1776)
H	Heaton (1894–1901)
NG	Nueva Guatemala (1777)

GUERNSEY

H	Heaton (1855–1949)

HAITI

A	Paris
HEATON	Heaton (1863)

HONDURAS

A	Paris (1869–71)
T	Tegucigalpa (1825–62)

HONG KONG

H	Heaton (1872–1971)
KN	King's Norton

HUNGARY

A	Vienna
B	Kremnitz
BP	Budapest
CA	Vienna
G	Nagybanya
GN	Nagybanya
GYF	Carlsburg
HA	Hall
K	Kremnitz
KB	Kremnitz
NB	Nagybanya
S	Schmollnitz
WI	Vienna

INDIA

B	Bombay (1835-1947)
C	Calcutta (1835-1947)
I	Bombay (1918)
L	Lahore (1943-45)
M	Madras (1869)
P	Pretoria (1943-44)
diamond	Bombay
dot in diamond	Hyderabad
split diamond	Hyderabad
star	Hyderabad

IRAN

H	Heaton (1928–29)

IRAQ

I	Bombay

ISRAEL

H	Heaton (1951–52)
star of David	Jerusalem

ITALY AND STATES

B	Bologna
B/I	Birmingham (1893–4)
FIRENZE	Florence
H	Heaton (1866–67)
KB	Berlin
M	Milan
N	Naples
OM	Strasbourg
R	Rome
T	Turin
V	Venice
ZV	Venice
anchor	Genoa
eagle head	Turin

JAMAICA

C	Ottawa
FM	Franklin Mint
H	Heaton (1882–1916)

JERSEY

H	Heaton (1877)

KENYA

C/M	Calcutta
H	Heaton (1911–64)

LIBERIA

B	Berne
FM	Franklin Mint
H	Heaton (1896–1906)
PM	Pobjoy Mint

LIECHTENSTEIN

A	Vienna
B	Berne
M	Munich

LUXEMBOURG

A	Paris
H	Gunzburg
anchor	Paris
angel	Brussels
caduceus	Utrecht
double eagle	Brussels
sword	Utrecht

MALAYSIA

B	Bombay
FM	Franklin Mint
H	Heaton (1955–61)
I	Calcutta (1941)
I	Bombay (1945)
KN	King's Norton
W	James Watt, Birmingham

MAURITIUS

H	Heaton (1877–90)
SA	Pretoria

MEXICO

A, As	Alamos
C, CN	Culiacan
CA, CH	Chihuahua
Ce	Real del Catorce
D, Do	Durango
Eo	Tlalpam
GA	Guadalajara
GC	Guadelupe y Calvo
Go	Guanajuato
Ho	Hermosillo
M, Mo	Mexico City
Mo	Morelos
MX	Mexico City
O, OA, OKA	Oaxaca
Pi	San Luis Potosi
SLPi	San Luis Potosi
TC	Tierra Caliente
Z, Zs	Zacatecas

MONACO

A	Paris
M	Monte Carlo
clasped hands	Cabanis
thunderbolt	Poissy

MOZAMBIQUE

H	Heaton (1894)
R	Rio

NETHERLANDS AND COLONIES
Austrian Netherlands (1700-93)

H	Amsterdam
S	Utrecht
W	Vienna
hand	Antwerp
head	Brussels
lion	Bruges

Kingdom of the Netherlands

B	Brussels (1821–30)
D	Denver (1943–45)
P	Philadelphia (1941–45)
S	Utrecht (1816–36)
S	San Francisco (1944–45)
Sa	Surabaya
caduceus	Utrecht

NICARAGUA

H	Heaton (1880–1916)
NR	Leon de Nicaragua

NORWAY

hammers	Kongsberg

PANAMA
CHI	Valcambi
FM	Franklin Mint

PERU
AREQ, AREQUIPA	Arequipa
AYACUCHO	Ayacucho
CUZCO, Co	Cuzco
L, LM, LR	Lima
LIMAE	Lima
PASCO	Pasco
Paz, Po	Pasco
P	Lima (1568-70)
P	Philadelphia
S	San Francisco

PHILIPPINES
BSP	Bangko Sentral Pilipinas
D	Denver (1944–45)
FM	Franklin Mint
M, MA	Manila
PM	Pobjoy Mint
S	San Francisco (1903–47)
5 point star	Manila

POLAND
AP	Warsaw (1772–74)
CI	Cracow (1765–68)
EB	Warsaw (1774–92)
EC	Leipzig (1758–63)
FF	Stuttgart (1916–17)
FH	Warsaw (1815–27)
FS	Warsaw (1765–68)
FWoF	Dresden (1734–64)
G	Cracow (1765–72)
H	Heaton (1924)
IB	Warsaw (1811–27)
IGS	Dresden (1716–34)
IP	Warsaw (1834–43)
IS	Warsaw (1768–74)
JGG	Leipzig (1750–53)
JS	Warsaw (1810–11)
KG	Warsaw (1829–34)
MV, MW	Warsaw
arrow	Warsaw (1925–39)
Dot after date	Royal Mint (1925)
8 torches	Paris (1924)

ROUMANIA
B	Bucharest (1879–85)
C	Bucharest (1886)
H	Heaton (1867–1930)
HUGUENIN	Le Locle
J	Hamburg
KN	King's Norton
V	Vienna

W	Watt, Birmingham
thunderbolt	Poissy

RUSSIA
AM	Annensk (1762–96)
BM	Warsaw (1825–55)
bM	St Petersburg (1796)
C–M	Sestroretsk (1762–96)
CM	Souzan (1825–55)
E–M	Ekaterinburg (1762–1810)
KM	Kolpina (1810)
K–M	Kolyvan (1762–1810)
MM, M–M	Moscow (1730–96)
MMD	Moscow (1730–96)
MW	Warsaw (1842–54)
NM	Izhorsk (1811–21)
SP	St Petersburg (1798–1800)
SPB	St Petersburg (1724–1915)
SPM	St Petersburg (1825–55)
T–M	Feodosia (1762–96)

SAN MARINO
M	Milan
R	Rome

SIAM
(Thailand)	H Heaton (1898)

SOUTH AFRICA
SA	Pretoria

SPAIN
B	Burgos
B, BA	Barcelona
Bo	Bilbao
C	Catalonia
C	Cuenca
C	Reus
CA	Zaragoza
G	Granada
GNA	Gerona
LD	Lerida
J, JA	Jubia
M, MD	Madrid
P	Palma de Majorca
PpP, PL, PA	Pamplona
S, S/L	Seville
Sr	Santander
T, To, Tole	Toledo
TOR:SA	Tortosa
V, VA, VAL	Valencia
crowned C	Cadiz
crowned M	Madrid
aqueduct	Segovia
crowned shield	Tarragona
pomegranate	Granada
quartered shield	Palma
scallop	Coruna

SPAIN *continued*

stars:

3 points	Segovia
4 points	Jubia
5 points	Manila
6 points	Madrid
7 points	Seville (1833)
8 points	Barcelona (1838)
wavy lines	Valladolid

SURINAM

P	Philadelphia
S	Sydney
caduceus	Utrecht

SWITZERLAND

A	Paris
AB	Strasbourg
B	Berne
B	Brussels (1874)
BA	Basle
BB	Strasbourg
S	Solothurn

URUGUAY

H	Heaton (1869)

UNITED STATES OF AMERICA

C	Charlotte, North Carolina
Cc	Carson City, Nevada
D	Dahlonega, Georgia (1838–61)
D	Denver, Colorado (1906)
O	New Orleans
P	Philadelphia
S	San Francisco
W	West Point

VENEZUELA

A	Paris
H	Heaton (1852)
HEATON	Heaton (1852–63)

YUGOSLAVIA (including former Serbia)

A	Paris
H	Heaton (1883–84)
KOBHNUA, A.D.	Kovnica
V	Vienna
thunderbolt	Poissy

The Reducing Room at the Royal Mint, Tower Hill in the 1930s.

Coin
inscriptions

This alphabetical listing is confined to inscriptions found on coins, mainly in the form of mottoes or of a commemorative nature. Names of rulers are, for the most part, excluded. Where the inscription is in a language other than English a translation is given, followed by the name of the issuing country or authority in parentheses.

A Deo et Caesare From God and the Emperor (Frankfurt).

A Domino Factum est Istud et est Mirabile in Oculis Nostris This is the Lord's doing and it is marvellous in our eyes (England, Mary).

A Solo Iehova Sapientia From God alone comes true wisdom (Wittgenstein).

Ab Inimicis Meis Libera Me Deus Free me from enemies (Burgundy).

Ad Legem Conventionis According to the law of the Convention (Furstenberg).

Ad Normam Conventionis According to the standard of the Convention (Prussia).

Ad Palmam Pressa Laeturo Resurgo Pressed to the palm I rise more joyfully (Wittgenstein).

Ad Usam Luxemburgi CC Vallati For the use of the besieged Luxembourgers (Luxembourg siege coins).

Adiuva Nos Deus Salutaris Noster Help us, O God, our Saviour (Lorraine).

Adventus Optimi Principis The coming of the noblest prince (Papacy).

Aes Usibus Aptius Auro Bronze in its uses is more suitable than gold (Brazil).

Aeternum Meditans Decus An ornament intended for all time (Alencon).

Aliis Inserviendo Consumor I spend my life devoted to others (Brunswick-Wolfenbuttel).

Alles Mit Bedacht All with reflection (Brunswick).

Amor Populi Praesidium Regis The love of the people is the king's protection (England, Charles I).

Ang Fra Dom Hib & Aquit (King) of England and France, Lord of Ireland and Aquitaine (England, Edward III).

Anno Regni Primo In the first year of the reign (Britain, edge inscription on crowns).

Apres les Tenebres la Lumiere After the shadows, the light (Geneva).

Archangelus Michael Archangel Michael (Italy, Grimoald IV).

Ardua ad Gloriam Via Struggles are the way to glory (Waldeck).

Arte Mea Bis Iustus Moneta Lud Iust By my art I am twice the just coin of King Louis (France, 1641).

Aspera Oblectant Wild places delight (Nassau-Weilburg).

Aspice Pisas Sup Omnes Specio Behold the coin of Pisa, superior to all (Pisa).

Audiatur Altera Pars Let the other part be heard (Stavelot).

Auf Gott Trawe Ich In God I trust (Brunswick).

Ausen Gefaesen der Kirchen und Burger From the vessels of the Church and citizens (Frankfurt siege, 1796).

Auspicio Regis et Senatus Angliae By authority of the king and parliament of England (East India Company).

Auxilio fortissimo Dei With the strongest help of God (Mecklenburg).

Auxilium de Sanctio Aid from the sanctuary (Papacy).

Auxilium Meum a Dno Qui Fecit Celum e Terram My help comes from God who made heaven and earth (Portugal).

Beata Tranquillatis Blessed tranquillity (Rome, Licinius II).

Beatus Qui Speravit in dom Blessed is he who has hoped in the Lord (Mansfeld).

Benedic Haereditati Tuae Blessings on your inheritance (Savoy).

Benedicta Sit Sancta Trinitas Blessed be the Holy Trinity (Albon).

Benedictio Domini Divites Facit The blessing of the Lord makes the rich (Teschen).

Benedictus Qui Venit in Nomine Domini Blessed is he who comes in the name of the Lord (Flanders).

Beschaw das Ziel Sage Nicht Viel Consider the matter but say little (Quedlinburg).

Besser Land und Lud Verloren als ein Falscher Aid Geschworn Better to lose land and wealth than swear a false oath (Hesse).

Bey Gott ist Rath und That With God is counsel and deed (Mansfeld).

Britanniarum Regina Queen of the Britains (Britain, Victoria).

Britt Omn Rex King of all the Britains (i.e. Britain and the overseas dominions) (Britain, 1902–52).

Cal et Car Com de Fugger in Zin et Norn Sen & Adm Fam Cajetan and Carl, Counts of Fugger in Zinnenberg and Nordendorf, Lords and Administrators of the Family (Empire, Fugger).

Candide et Constanter Sincerely and steadfastly (Hesse-Cassel).

Candide sed Provide Clearly but cautiously (Osterwitz).

Candore et Amore With sincerity and love (Fulda).

Candore et Constantia With sincerity and constancy (Bavaria).

Capit Cath Ecclesia Monasteriensis Chapter of the Cathedral Church of Munster (Munster).

Capit Eccle Metropolit Colon Chapter of the Metropolitan Church of Cologne (Cologne).

Capitulum Regnans Sede Vacante Chapter governing, the See being vacant (Eichstadt).

Carola Magna Ducissa Feliciter Regnante Grand Duchess Charlotte, happily reigning (Luxembourg).

Carolus a Carolo Charles (I) to Charles (II) (England).

Cedunt Prementi Fata The fates yield to him who presses (Ploen, Hese-Cassel).

Charitate et Candore With charity and sincerity (East Frisia).

Charta Magna Bavariae The Great Charter of Bavaria (Bavaria).

Christo Auspice Regno I reign under the auspices of Christ (England, Charles I).

Christus Spes Una Salutis Christ is our one hope of salvation (Cleve).

Chur Mainz Electoral Principality of Mainz (Mainz).

Circumeundo Servat et Ornat It serves and decorates by going around (Sweden).

Civibus Quorum Pietas Coniuratione Die III Mai MDCCXCI Obrutam et Deletam Libertate Polona Tueri Conabatur Respublica Resurgens To the citizens whose piety the resurgent commonwealth tried to protect Poland overturned and deprived of liberty by the conspiracy of the third day of May 1791 (Poland).

Civitas Lucemborgiensis Millesimum Ovans Expletannum Completing the celebration of a thousand years of the city of Luxembourg (Luxembourg).

Civium Industria Floret Civitas By the industry of its people the state flourishes (Festival of Britain crown, 1951).

Cluniaco Cenobio Petrus et Paulus Peter and Paul from the Abbey of Cluny (Cluny).

Comes Provincie Fili Regis Francie Court of Provence and son of the King of France (Provence).

Communitas et Senatus Bonon City and senate of Bologna (Bologna).

Concordia Fratrum The harmony of the brothers (Iever).

Concordia Patriae Nutrix Peace, the nurse of the fatherland (Waldeck).

Concordia Res Parvae Crescunt Little things increase through harmony (Batavian Republic).

Concordia Res Parvae Crescunt, Discordia Dilabuntur By harmony little things increase, by discord they fall apart (Lowenstein-Wertheim-Virneburg).

Concordia Stabili With lasting peace (Hildesheim).

Confidens Dno Non Movetur He who trusts in God is unmoved (Spanish Netherlands).

Confidentia in Deo et Vigilantia Trust in God and vigilance (Prussian Asiatic Company).

Confoederato Helvetica Swiss Confederation (Switzerland)

Conjuncto Felix Fortunate in his connections (Solms).

Conservator Urbis Suae Saviour of his city (Rome, 4th century).

Consilio et Aequitate With deliberation and justice (Fulda).

Consilio et Virtutis With deliberation and valour (Hesse-Cassel).

Constanter et Sincere Steadfastly and sincerely (Lautern).

Crescite et Multiplicamini Increase and multiply (Maryland).

Cristiana Religio Christian religion (Germany, 11th century).

Crux Benedicat May the cross bless you (Oldenburg).

Cuius Cruore Sanati Sumus By His sacrifice are we healed (Reggio).

Cultores Sui Deus Protegit God protects His followers (England, Charles I).

Cum Deo et Die (Jure) With God and the day (Wurttemberg).

Cum Deo et Jure With God and the law (Wurttemberg).

Cum Deo et Labore With God and work (Wittgenstein).

Cum His Qui Orderant Pacem Eram Pacificus With those who order peace I was peaceful (Zug).

Curie Bonthon to so Doulo Protect his servant, o Lord (Byzantine Empire).

Custos Regni Deus God is the guardian of the kingdom (Naples and Sicily).

Da Gloriam Deo et Eius Genitrici Marie Give glory to God and His mother Mary (Wurttemberg).

Da Mihi Virtutem Contra Hostes Tuos Give me

valour against mine enemies (Netherlands, Charles V).

Dat Wort is Fleis Gworden   The word is made flesh (Muster).

Date Caesaris Caesari et Quae Sunt Dei Deo   Render unto Caesar the things that are Caesar's and unto God the things that are God's (Stralsund).

De Oficina . . .   From the mint of . . . (France, medieval).

Decreto Reipublicae Nexu Confoederationis Iunctae Die V Xbris MDCCXCII Stanislao Augusto Regnante   By decree of the state in conjunction with the joint federation on the fifth day of December 1792, Stanislaus Augustus ruling (Poland).

Decus et Tutamen   An ornament and a safeguard (Britain, pound).

Deducet Nos Mirabiliter Dextera Tua   Thy right hand will guide us miraculously (Savoy).

Denarium Terrae Mariae   Penny of Maryland (Maryland).

Deo Conservatori Pacis   To God, preserver of peace (Brandenburg-Ansbach).

Deo OM Auspice Suaviter et Fortiter sed Luste nec Sibi sed Suis   Under the auspices of God, greatest and best, pleasantly and bravely but justly, not for himself but for his people (Speyer).

Deo Patriae et Subditio   For God, fatherland and neighbourhood (Mainz).

Der Recht Glaubt In Ewig Lebt   Who believes in right will live in eternity (Linange-Westerburg).

Der Rhein ist Deutschlands Strom Nicht Deutschlands Grenze   The Rhine is Germany's River not Germany's Frontier.

Deum Solum Adorabis   You will venerate God alone (Hesse).

Deus Constituit Regna   God establishes kingdoms (Ni jmegen).

Deus Dat Qui Vult   God gives to him who wishes (Hanau-Munzenberg).

Deus et Dominus   God and Lord (Rome, 3rd century).

Deus in Adiutorium Meum Intende   God stretch out in my assistance (France).

Deus Providebit   God will provide (Lowenstein-Wertheim-Virneburg).

Deus Refugium Meum   God is my refuge (Cleve).

Deus Solatium Meum   God is my comfort (Sweden).

Dextera Domini Exaltavit Me   The right hand of God has raised me up (Modena, Spain).

Dextra Dei Exalta Me   The right hand of God exalts me (Denmark).

Dieu et Mon Droit   God and my right (Britain, George IV).

Dilexit Dns Andream   The Lord delights in St Andrew (Holstein).

Dilexit Dominus Decorem Iustitiae   The Lord is pleased with the beauty of justice (Unterwalden).

Dirige Deus Gressus Meos   O God, direct my steps (Tuscany, Britain, Una £5).

Discerne Causam Meam   Distinguish my cause (Savoy).

Divina Benedictiae et Caesarea Iustitia   Sacrifice of blessings and imperial justice (Coblenz).

Dn Ihs Chs Rex Regnantium   Lord Jesus Christ, King of Kings (Rome, Justinian II).

Dns Ptetor Ms Z Lib'ator Ms   The Lord is my protector and liberator (Scotland, David II).

Dominabitur Gentium et Ipse   He himself will also be lord of the nations (Austrian Netherlands).

Domine Conserva Nos in Pace   O Lord preserve us in peace (Basle, Mulhausen).

Domine Elegisti Lilium Tibi   O Lord Thou hast chosen the lily for Thyself (France, Louis XIV).

Domine ne in Furore Tuo Arguas Me   O Lord rebuke me not in Thine anger (England, Edward III).

Domine Probasti Me et Congnovisti Me   O Lord Thou hast tested me and recognised me (Mantua).

Domini est Regnum   The Kingdom is the Lord's (Austrian Netherlands).

Dominus Deus Omnipotens Rex   Lord God, almighty King (Viking coins).

Dominus Mihi Adiutor   The Lord is my helper (Spanish Netherlands).

Dominus Providebit   The Lord will provide (Berne).

Dominus Spes Populi Sui   The Lord is the hope of his people (Lucerne).

Donum Dei ex Fodinis Vilmariens   A gift of God from the Vilmar mines (Coblenz).

Duce Deo Fide et Justicia   By faith and justice lead us to God (Ragusa).

Dum Praemor Amplior   I increase while I die prematurely (Savoy).

Dum Spiro Spero   While I live, I hope (Pontefract siege coins).

Dum Totum Compleat Orbem   Until it fills the world (France, Henri II).

Dura Pati Virtus   Valour endures hardships (Saxe-Lauenburg).

Durae Necessitatis   Through force of necessity (Bommel siege, 1599).

Durum Telum Necessitas   Hardship is a weapon of necessity (Minden).

Dux et Gubernatores Reip Genu   Duke and governors of the republic of Genoa (Genoa).

E Pluribus Unum   One out of more (USA).

Eccl S. Barbarae Patronae Fodin Kuttenbergensium Duo Flor Arg Puri   The church of St Barbara, patron of the Kuttensberg mines, two florins of pure silver (Hungary).

Een en Ondelbaer Sterk   One and indivisible (Batavian Republic).

Eendracht Mag Macht   Unity makes strength (Belgium, South African Republic).

Einigkeit Recht und Freiheit Union, right and freedom (Germany).

Electorus Saxoniae Administrator Elector and administrator of Saxony (Saxony).

Elimosina Alms (France, Pepin).

Ep Fris & Ratisb Ad Prum Pp Coad Aug Bishop of Freising and Regensburg, administrator of Pruem, prince-provost, co-adjutant bishop of Augsburg (Trier).

Equa Libertas Deo Gratia Frat Pax in Virtute Tua et in Domino Confido I believe in equal liberty by the grace of God, brotherly love in Thy valour and in the Lord (Burgundy).

Equitas Iudicia Tua Dom Equity and Thy judgments O Lord (Gelderland).

Espoir Me Conforte Hope comforts me (Mansfeld).

Espreuve Faicto Par Lexpres Commandement du Roy Proof made by the express commandment of the King (France, piedforts).

Et in Minimis Integer Faithful even in the smallest things (Olmutz).

Ex Auro Argentes Resurgit From gold it arises, silver again (Sicily).

Ex Auro Sinico From Chinese gold (Denmark).

Ex Flammis Orior I arise from the flames (Hohenlohe-Neuenstein-Ohringen).

Ex Fodinis Bipontio Seelbergensibus From the Seelberg mines of Zweibrucken (Pfalz-Birkenfeld).

Ex Metallo Novo From new metal (Spain).

Ex Uno Omnis Nostra Salus From one is all our salvation (Eichstadt, Mulhouse).

Ex Vasis Argent Cleri Mogunt Pro Aris et Focis From the silver vessels of the clergy of Mainz for altars and for hearths (Mainz).

Ex Visceribus Fodinse Bieber From the bowels of the Bieber mine (Hanau-Munzenberg).

Exaltabitur in Gloria He shall be exalted in glory (England, quarter nobles).

Exemplum Probati Numismatis An example of a proof coin (France, Louis XIII piedforts).

Exemtae Eccle Passau Episc et SRI Princ Prince Bishop of the freed church of Passau, prince of the Holy Roman Empire (Passau).

Expectate Veni Come, o expected one (Roman Britain, Carausius).

Extremum Subidium Campen Kampen under extreme siege (Kampen, 1578).

Exurgat Deus et Dissipentur Inimici Eius Let God arise and let His enemies be scattered (England, James I).

Faciam Eos in Gentem Unam I will make them one nation (England, unites and laurels).

Faith and Truth I will Bear unto You (UK £5, 1993).

Fata Consiliis Potiora The fates are more powerful than councils (Hesse-Cassel).

Fata Viam Invenient The fates will find a way (Gelderland).

Fecit Potentiam in Brachio Suo He put power in your forearm (Lorraine).

Fecunditas Fertility (Naples and Sicily).

Fel Temp Reparatio The restoration of lucky times (Rome, AD 348).

Felicitas Perpetua Everlasting good fortune (Rome, Constantius II).

Felix coniunctio Happy Union (Brandenburg-Ansbach).

Fiat Misericordia Tua Dne Let Thy mercy be O Lord (Gelderland).

Fiat Voluntas Domini Perpetuo Let the goodwill of the Lord last for ever (Fulda).

Fidei Defensor Defender of the Faith (Britain).

Fidelitate et Fortitudine With fidelity and fortitude (Batthyani).

Fideliter et Constanter Faithfully and steadfastly (Saxe-Coburg-Gotha).

Fidem Servando Patriam Tuendo By keeping faith and protecting the fatherland (Savoy).

Filius Augustorum Son of emperors (Rome, 4th century).

Fisci Iudaici Calumnia Sublata The false accusation of the Jewish tax lifted (Rome, Nerva).

Florent Concordia Regna Through harmony kingdoms flourish (England, Charles I and II).

Fortitudo et Laus Mea Dominu Fortitude and my praise in the Lord (Sardinia).

Free Trade to Africa by Act of Parliment *(Sic)* (Gold Coast).

Friedt Ernehrt Unfriedt Verzehrt Peace nourishes, unrest wastes (Brunswick).

Fulgent Sic Littora Rheni Thus shine the banks of the Rhine (Mannheim).

Fundator Pacis Founder of peace (Rome, Severus).

Gaudium Populi Romani The joy of the Roman people (Rome, 4th century).

Gen C Mar VI Dim Col USC & RAMAI Cons & S Conf M General field marshal, colonel of the only dragoon regiment, present privy councillor of both their sacred imperial and royal apostolic majesties, and state conference minister (Batthyani).

Gerecht und Beharrlich Just and steadfast (Bavaria).

Germ Hun Boh Rex AAD Loth Ven Sal King of Germany, Hungary and Bohemia, Archduke of Austria, Duke of Lorraine, Venice and Salzburg (Austria).

Germ Jero Rex Loth Bar Mag Het Dux King of Germany, Jerusalem, Lorraine and Bar, Grand Duke of Tuscany (Austrian Netherlands).

Germania Voti Compos Germany sharing the vows (Brandenburg-Ansbach).

Gloria ex Amore Patriae Glory from love of country (Denmark).

Gloria in Excelsis Deo Glory to God in the highest (France, Sweden).

Gloria Novi Saeculi The glory of a new century (Rome, Gratian).

God With Us (England, Commonwealth).

Godt Met Ons God with us (Oudewater).

Gottes Freundt der Pfaffen Feindt God's friend, the Pope's enemy (Brunswick, Christian).

Gratia Dei Sum Id Quod Sum By the grace of God, I am what I am (Navarre).

Gratia Di Rex By the grace of God, king (France, 8th century).

Gratitudo Concivibus Exemplum Posteritati Gratitude to fellow Citizens, an example to posterity (Poland).

Gud och Folket God and the people (Sweden).

Hac Nitimur Hanc Tuemur With this we strive, this we shall defend (Batavian Republic).

Hac Sub Tutela Under this protection (Eichstadt).

Haec Sunt Munera Minerae S Antony Eremitae These are the rewards of the mine of St Antony the hermit (Hildesheim).

Hanc Deus Dedit God has given this (Pontefract siege coins).

Hanc Tuemur Hac Nitimur This we defend, by this we strive (Batavian Republic).

Has Nisi Periturus Mihi Adimat Nemo Let no one remove these (Letters) from me under penalty of death (Commonwealth, edge inscription).

Henricus Rosas Regna Jacobus Henry (united) the roses, James the kingdoms (England and Scotland, James VI and I).

Herculeo Vincta Nodo Bound by a Herculean fetter (Savoy).

Herr Nach Deinem Willen O Lord Thy will be done (Palatinate, Erbach).

Herre Gott Verleich Uns Gnade Lord God grant us grace (Brunswick).

Hic Est Qui Multum Orat Pro Populo Here is he who prays a lot for the people (Paderborn).

Hir Steid te Biscop Here is represented the bishop (Gittelde).

His Ventis Vela Levantur By these winds the sails are raised up (Hesse-Cassel).

Hispaniarum Infans Infante of Spain and its dominions (Spain).

Hispaniarum et Ind Rex King of Spain and the Indies.

Hispaniarum Rex King of Spain (Spain).

Hoc Signo Victor Eris With this sign you will be victor (Rome, Vetranio).

Honeste et Decenter Honestly and decently (Nassau-Idstein).

Honi Soit Qui Mal y Pense Evil to him who evil thinks (Britain, George III).

Honni Soit Qui Mal y Pense (Hesse-Cassel).

Hospitalis et S Sepul Hierusal Hospital and Holy Sepulchre of Jerusalem (Malta).

Hun Boh Gal Rex AA Lo Wi et in Fr Dux King of Hungary, Bohemia and Galicia, Archduke of Austria, Dalmatia, Lodomeria, Wurzburg and Duke in Franconia (Austria).

Hung Boh Lomb et Ven Gal Lod III Rex Aa King of Hungary, Bohemia, Lombardo-Venezia, Galicia, Lodomeria and Illyria, Archduke of Austria (Austria).

Ich Dien I serve (Aberystwyth 2d, UK 2p).

Ich Getrawe Got in Aller Noth I trust in God in all my needs (Hesse-Marburg).

Ich Habe Nur Ein Vaterland und das Heisst Deutschland I have only one fatherland and that is called Germany (Germany).

Ielithes Penniae Penny of Gittelde (Gittelde, 11th century).

Iesus Autem Transiens Per Medium Illorum Ibat But Jesus, passing through the midst of them, went His way (England, Scotland, Anglo-Gallic).

Iesus Rex Noster et Deus Noster Jesus is our king and our God (Florence).

Ihs Xs Rex Regnantium Jesus Christ, King of Kings (Byzantine Empire).

Ihsus Xristus Basileu Baslie Jesus Christ, King of Kings (Byzantine Empire).

Imago Sanch Regis Illustris Castelle Legionis e Toleto The image of Sancho the illustrious king of Castile, Leon and Toledo.

In Casus Per Vigil Omnes In all seasons through vigil (Wertheim).

In Deo Meo Transgrediar Murum In my God I shall pass through walls (Teschen).

In Deo Spes Mea In God is my hope (Gelderland).

In Domino Fiducia Nostra In the Lord is our trust (Iever).

In Equitate Tua Vivificasti Me In thy equity Thou hast vivified me (Gelderland).

In God We Trust (USA).

In Hoc Signo Vinces In this sign shalt thou conquer (Portugal).

In Honore Sci Mavrici Marti In honour of the martyr St Maurice (St Maurice, 8th century).

In Manibus Domini sortes Meae In the hands of the Lord are my fates (Mainz siege, 1688–9).

In Memor Vindicatae Libere ac Relig In memory of the establishment of freedom and religion (Sweden).

In Memoriam Conjunctionis Utriusque Burgraviatus Norice In memory of the union of both burgraviates in peace (Brandenburg-Ansbach).

In Memorian Connub Feliciaes Inter Princ Her Frider Carol et Dub Sax August Louis Frider Rodas D 28 Nov 1780 Celebrati In memory of the most happy marriage between the hereditary prince Friedrich Karl and the Duchess of Saxony Augusta Louisa Frederika, celebrated on 28 Nov 1780 (Schwarzburg-Rudolstadt).

In Memorian Felicisssimi Matrimonii In memory of the most happy marriage (Wied).

In Memoriam Pacis Teschinensis Commemorating the Treaty of Teschen (Brandenburg-Ansbach).

In Nomine Domini Amen In the name of the Lord amen (Zaltbommel).

In Omnem Terram Sonus Eorum In to all the land

their shall go sound (Chateau Renault, Papal States).

In Silencio et Spe Fortitudo Mea In silence and hope is my fortitude (Brandenburg-Kustrin).

In Spe et Silentio Fortitudo Mea In hope and silence is my fortitude (Vianen).

In Te Domine Confido In you O Lord I place my trust (Hesse).

In Te Domine Speravi In You, O Lord, I have hoped (Gurk).

In Terra Pax Peace in the land (Papacy).

In Via Virtuti Nulla Via There is no way for virtue on the way. (Veldenz).

Ind Imp, Indiae Imperator, Imperatrix Emperor (Empress) of India (Britain).

India Tibi Cessit India has yielded to thee (Portuguese India).

Infestus Infestis Hostile to the troublesome (Savoy).

Inimicos Eius Induam Confusione As for his enemies, I shall clothe them in shame (Sardinia, England, Edward VI).

Insignia Capituli Brixensis The badge of the chapter of Brixen (Brixen).

Isti Sunt Patres Tui Verique Pastores These are your fathers and true shepherds (Papacy).

Iudicium Melius Posteritatis Erit Posterity's judgment will be better (Paderborn).

Iure et Tempore By right and time (Groningen).

Iusques a Sa Plenitude As far as your plenitude (France, Henri II).

Iuste et Constanter Justly and constantly (Paderborn).

Iustirt Adjusted (Hesse-Cassel).

Iustitia et Concordia Justice and harmony (Zurich).

Iustitia et Mansuetudine By justice and mildness (Bavaria, Cologne).

Iustitia Regnorum Fundamentum Justice is the foundation of kingdoms (Austria).

Iustitia Thronum Firmat Justice strengthens the throne (England, Charles I).

Iustus Non Derelinquitur The just person is not deserted (Brandenburg-Calenberg).

Iustus Ut Palma Florebit The just will flourish like the palm (Portugal).

L Mun Planco Rauracorum Illustratori Vetustissimo To L Municius Plancus the most ancient and celebrated of the Rauraci (Basle).

Landgr in Cleggov Com in Sulz Dux Crum Landgrave of Klettgau, count of Sulz, duke of Krumlau (Schwarzburg-Sonderhausen).

Latina Emeri Munita Latin money of Merida (Suevi).

Lege et Fide By law and faith (Austria).

Lex Tua Veritas Thy law is the truth (Tuscany).

Liberta Eguaglianza Freedom and equality (Venice)

Libertad en la Ley Freedom within the law (Mexico).

Libertas Carior Auro Freedom is dearer than gold (St Gall).

Libertas Vita Carior Freedom is dearer than life (Kulenberg).

Libertas Xpo Firmata Freedom strengthened by Christ (Genoa).

Liberte, Egalite, Fraternite Liberty, equality, fraternity (France).

Lucerna Pedibus Meis Verbum Est Thy word is a lamp unto mine feet (England, Edward VI).

Lumen ad Revelationem Gentium Light to enlighten the nations (Papacy).

L'Union Fait la Force The union makes strength (Belgium)

Macula Non Est in Te There is no sin in Thee (Essen).

Magnus ab Integro Saeculorum Nascitur Ordo The great order of the centuries is born anew (Bavaria).

Mandavit Dominus Palatie hanc Monetam Fiert The lord of the Palatine ordained this coin to be made (Balath).

Manibus Ne Laedar Avaris Lest I be injured by greedy hands (Sweden).

Mar Bran Sac Rom Imp Arcam et Elec Sup Dux Siles Margrave of Brandenburg, archchamberlain of the Holy Roman Empire and elector, senior duke of Silesia (Prussia).

Maria Mater Domini Xpi Mary mother of Christ the Lord (Teutonic Knights).

Maria Unxit Pedes Xpisti Mary washes the feet of Christ (France, Rene d'Anjou).

Mater Castrorum Mother of fortresses (Rome, Marcus Aurelius).

Matrimonio Conjuncti Joined in wedlock (Austria).

Me Coniunctio Servat Dum Scinditur Frangor The relationship serves me while I am being torn to pieces (Lowenstein-Wertheim).

Mediolani Dux Duke of Milan (Milan).

Mediolani et Man Duke of Mantua and Milan (Milan).

Memor Ero Tui Iustina Virgo I shall remember you, o maiden Justina (Venice).

Merces Laborum Wages of work (Wurzburg).

Mirabilia Fecit He wrought marvels (Viking coinage).

Misericordia Di Rex King by the mercy of God (France, Louis II).

Mo Arg Ord Foe Belg D Gel & CZ Silver coin of the order of the Belgian Federation, duchy of Guelder-land, county of Zutphen (Guelderland).

Moneta Abbatis Coin of the abbey (German ecclesiastical coins, 13th–14th centuries).

Moneta Argentiae Ord Foed Belgii Holl Silver coin of the federated union of Belgium and Holland (Batavian Republic).

Mo No Arg Con Foe Belg Pro Hol New silver coin of the Belgian Federation, province of Holland (Holland).

Mo No Arg Pro Confoe Belg Trai Holl New silver coin of the confederated Belgian provinces, Utrecht and Holland (Batavian Republic).

Mon Lib Reip Bremens Coin of the free state of Bremen (Bremen).

Mon Nova Arg Duc Curl Ad Norma Tal Alb New silver coin of the duchy of Courland, according to the standard of the Albert thaler (Courland).

Mon Nov Castri Imp New coin of the Imperial free city of . . . (Friedberg).

Moneta Bipont Coin of Zweibrucken (Pfalz-Birkenfeld-Zweibrucken).

Monet Capit Cathedr Fuld Sede Vacante Coin of the cathedral chapter of Fulda, the see being vacant (Fulda).

Moneta in Obsidione Tornacensi Cusa Coin struck during the siege of Tournai (Tournai, 1709).

Moneta Livosesthonica Coin of Livonia (Estonia).

Moneta Nov Arg Regis Daniae New silver coin of the king of Denmark (Denmark).

Moneta Nova Ad Norman Conventionis New coin according to the Convention standard (Orsini-Rosenberg).

Moneta Nova Domini Imperatoris New coin of the lord emperor (Brunswick, 13th century).

Moneta Nova Lubecensis New coin of Lubeck.

Moneta Nova Reipublicae Halae Suevicae New coin of the republic of Hall in Swabia.

Moneta Reipublicae Ratisbonensis Coin of the republic of Regensburg.

Nach Alt Reichs Schrot und Korn According to the old empire's grits and grain (Hesse).

Nach dem Conventions Fusse According to the Convention's basis (German Conventionsthalers).

Nach dem Frankf Schlus According to the Frankfurt standard (Solms).

Nach dem Schlus der V Staend According to the standard of the union (Hesse).

Navigare Necesse Est It is necessary to navigate (Germany).

Nec Aspera Terrent Nor do difficulties terrify (Brunswick).

Nec Cito Nec Temere Neither hastily nor rashlly (Cambrai).

Nec Numina Desunt Nor is the divine will absent (Savoy).

Nec Temere Nec Timide Neither rashly nor timidly (Danzig, Lippe).

Necessitas Legem Non Habet Necessity has no law (Magdeburg).

Nemo Me Impune Lacessit No one touches me with impunity (UK, Scottish pound edge inscription).

Nihil Restat Reliqui No relic remains (Ypres).

Nil Ultra Aras Nothing beyond the rocks (Franque-mont).

No Nobis Dne Sed Noi Tuo Da Gloriam Not to us, o Lord but to Thy name be glory given (France, Francis I).

Nobilissimum Dom Ac Com in Lipp & St Most noble lord and count in Lippe and Sternberg (Schaumburg-Lippe).

Nomen Domini Turris Fortissima The name of the Lord is the strongest tower (Frankfurt).

Non Aes Sed Fides Not bronze but trust (Malta).

Non Est Mortale Quod Opto What I desire is not mortal. (Mecklenburg).

Non Mihi Sed Populo Not to me but to the people (Bavaria).

Non Relinquam Vos Orphanos I shall not leave you as orphans (Papacy).

Non Surrexit Major None greater has arisen (Genoa, Malta).

Nullum Simulatum Diuturnum Tandem Nothing that is feigned lasts long (Wittgenstein).

Nummorum Famulus The servant of the coinage (England, tin halfpence and farthings).

Nunquam Retrorsum Never backwards (Brunswick-Wolfenbuttel).

O Crux Ave Spes Unica Hail, o Cross, our only hope (England half-angels, France, Rene d'Anjou).

O Maria Ora Pro Me O Mary pray for me (Bavaria).

Ob Cives Servatos On account of the rescued citizens (Rome, Augustus).

Oculi Domini Super Iustos The eyes of the Lord look down on the just (Neuchatel).

Omnia Auxiliante Maria Mary helping everything (Schwyz).

Omnia Cum Deo Everything with God (Reuss-Greiz).

Omnia cum Deo et Nihil Sine Eo Everthing with God and nothing without Him (Erbach).

Omnis Potestas a Deo Est All power comes from God (Sweden).

Opp & Carn Dux Comm Rittb SCM Cons Int & Compi Mareschal Duke of Troppau and Carniola, count of Rietberg, privy councillor of his sacred imperial majesty, field marshal (Liechtenstein).

Opp & Carn . . . Aur Velleris Eques Duke of Troppau . . . knight of the Golden Fleece (Liechtenstein).

Opportune Conveniently (Savoy).

Optimus Princeps Best prince (Rome, Trajan).

Opulentia Salerno Wealthy Salerno (Siculo-Norman kingdom).

Pace et Iustitia With peace and justice (Spanish Netherlands).

Pacator Orbis Pacifier of the world (Rome, Aurelian).

Palma Sub Pondere Crescit The palm grows under its weight (Waldeck).

Pater Noster Our Father (Flanders, 14th century).

Pater Patriae Farther of his country (Rome, Caligula).

Patria Si Dreptul Meu The country and my right (Roumania).

Patrimon Henr Frid Sorte Divisum   The heritage of Heinrich Friedrich divided by lot (Hohenlohe-Langenberg).

Patrimonia Beati Petri   The inheritance of the blessed Peter (Papacy).

Patrona Franconiae   Patron of Franconia (Wurzburg).

Pax Aeterna   Eternal peace (Rome, Marcus Aurelius).

Pax et Abundantia   Peace and plenty (Burgundy, Gelderland).

Pax Missa Per Orbem   Peace sent throughout the world (England, Anne).

Pax Petrus   Peace Peter (Trier, 10th century).

Pax Praevalet Armis   May peace prevail by force of arms (Mainz).

Pax Quaeritur Bello   Peace is sought by war (Commonwealth, Cromwell).

Pecunia Totum Circumit Orbem   Money goes round the whole world (Brazil).

Per Aspera Ad Astra   Through difficulties to the stars (Mecklenburg-Schwerin).

Per Angusta ad Augusta   Through precarious times to the majestic (Solms-Roedelheim, a pun on the name of the ruler Johan August).

Per Crucem Tuam Salva Nos Christe Redemptor   By Thy cross save us, O Christ our Redeemer (England, angels).

Per Crucem Tuam Salva Nos Xpe Redemt   By Thy cross save us, O Christ our Redeemer (Portugal, 15th century).

Perdam Babillonis Nomen   May the name of Babylon perish (Naples).

Perennitati Iustissimi Regis   For the duration of the most just king (France, Louis XIII).

Perennitati Principis Galliae Restitutionis   For the duration of the restoration of the prince of the Gauls (France, Henri IV).

Perfer et Obdura Bruxella   Carry on and stick it out, Brussels (Brussels siege, 1579–80).

Perpetuus in Nemet Vivar   Hereditary count in Nemt-Ujvar (Batthanyi).

Pietate et Constantia   By piety and constancy (Fulda).

Pietate et Iustitia   By piety and justice (Denmark).

Plebei Urbanae Frumento Constituto   Free distribu-tion of grain to the urban working-class established (Rome, Nerva).

Pleidio Wyf Im Gwlad   True am I to my country (UK, Welsh pound edge inscription).

Plus Ultra   Beyond (the Pillars of Hercules) (Spanish America).

Point du Couronne sans Peine   Point of the crown without penalty (Coburg).

Pons Civit Castellana   The bridge of the town of Castellana (Papacy).

Populus et Senatus Bonon   The people and senate of Bologna (Bologna).

Post Mortem Patris Pro Filio   For the son after his father's death (Pontefract siege coins).

Post Tenebras Lux   After darkness light (Geneva).

Post Tenebras Spero Lucem   After darkness I hope for light (Geneva).

Posui Deum Adiutorem Meum   I have made God my helper (England, Ireland, 1351–1603).

Praesidium et Decus   Protection and ornament (Bologna).

Prima Sedes Galliarum   First see of the Gauls (Lyon).

Primitiae Fodin Kuttenb ab Aerari Iterum Susceptarum   First results dug from the Kuttenberg mines in a renewed undertaking (Austria).

Princps Iuventutis   Prince of youth (Roman Empire).

Pro Defensione Urbis et Patriae   For the defence of city and country (France, Louis XIV).

Pro Deo et Patria   For God and the fatherland (Fulda).

Pro Deo et Populo   For God and the people (Bavaria).

Pro Ecclesia et Pro Patria   For the church and the fatherland (Constance).

Pro Fausio PP Reitur VS   For happy returns of the princes of the Two Sicilies (Naples and Sicily).

Pro Lege et Grege   For law and the flock (Fulda).

Pro maximo Dei Gloria et Bono Publico   For the greatest glory of God and the good of the people (Wurttemberg).

Pro Patria   For the fatherland (Wurzburg).

Propitio Deo Secura Ago   With God's favour I lead a secure life. (Saxe-Lauenburg).

Protector Literis Literae Nummis Corona et Salus   A protection to the letters (on the face of the coin), the letters (on the edge) are a garland and a safeguard to the coinage (Commonwealth, Cromwell broad).

Protege Virgo Pisas   Protect Pisa, O Virgin (Pisa).

Provide et Constanter   Wisely and firmly (Wurttem-berg).

Providentia et Pactis   Through foresight and pacts (Brandenburg-Ansbach).

Providentia Optimi Principis   With the foresight of the best prince (Naples and Sicily).

Proxima Fisica Finis   Nearest to natural end (Orciano).

Proxima Soli   Nearest to the sun (Modena).

Pulcra Virtutis Imago   The beautiful image of virtue (Genoa).

Pupillum et Viduam Suscipiat   May he support the orphan and the widow (Savoy).

Quae Deus Conjunxit Nemo Separet   What God hath joined let no man put asunder (England, James I).

Quem Quadragesies et Semel Patriae Natum Esse Gratulamur   Whom we congratulate for the forty-first time for being born for the fatherland (Lippe-Detmold).

Qui Dat Pauperi Non Indigebit   Who gives to the poor will never be in need (Munster).

Quid Non Cogit Necessitas To what does Necessity not drive. (Ypres).

Quin Matrimonii Lustrum Celebrant They celebrate their silver wedding (Austria, 1879).

Quocunque Gesseris (Jeceris) Stabit Whichever way you throw it it will stand (Isle of Man).

Quod Deus Vult Hoc Semper Fit What God wishes always occurs. (Saxe-Weimar).

Reconduntur non Retonduntur They are laid up in store, not thundered back (Savoy).

Recta Tueri Defend the right (Austria).

Recte Constanter et Fortiter Rightly, constantly and bravely (Bavaria).

Recte Faciendo Neminem Timeas May you fear no one in doing right. (Solms-Laubach).

Rector Orbis Ruler of the world (Rome, Didius Julianus).

Rectus et Immotus Right and immovable (Hesse).

Redde Cuique Quod Suum Est Render to each that which is his own (England, Henry VIII).

Redeunt antiqui Gaudia Moris There return the joys of ancient custom (Regensburg).

Reg Pr Pol et Lith Saxon Dux Royal prince of Poland and Lithuania and duke of Saxony (Trier).

Regia Boruss Societas Asiat Embdae Royal Prussian Asiatic Society of Emden (Prussia).

Regier Mich Her Nach Deinen Wort Govern me here according to Thy word (Palatinate).

Regnans Capitulum Ecclesiae Cathedralis Ratisbonensis Sede Vacante Administering the chapter of the cathedral church at Regensburg, the see being vacant (Regensburg).

Regni Utr Sic et Hier Of the kingdom of the Two Sicilies and of Jerusalem (Naples and Sicily).

Religio Protestantium Leges Angliae Libertas Parliamenti The religion of the Protestants, the laws of England and the freedom of Parliament (England, Royalists, 1642).

Relinquo Vos Liberos ab Utroque Homine I leave you as children of each man (San Marino).

Restauracao da Independencia Restoration of inde-pendence (Portugal, 1990).

Restitutor Exercitus Restorer of the army (Rome, Aurelian).

Restitutor Galliarum Restorer of the Gauls (Rome, Gallienus).

Restitutor Generis Humani Restorer of mankind (Rome, Valerian).

Restitutor Libertatis Restorer of freedom (Rome, Constantine).

Restitutor Orbis Restorer of the world (Rome, Valerian).

Restitutor Orientis Restorer of the east (Rome, Valerian).

Restitutor Saeculi Restorer of the century (Rome, Valerian).

Restitutor Urbis Restorer of the city (Rome, Severus).

Rosa Americana Utile Dulci The American rose, useful and sweet (American colonies).

Rosa Sine Spina A rose without a thorn (England, Tudor coins).

Rutilans Rosa Sine Spina A dazzling rose without a thorn (England, Tudor gold coins).

S Annae Fundgruben Ausb Tha in N Oe Mining thaler of the St Anne mine in Lower Austria (Austria).

S Ap S Leg Nat Germ Primas Legate of the Holy Apostolic See, born Primate of Germany (Salzburg).

S Carolus Magnus Fundator Charlemagne founder (Munster).

S. Gertrudis Virgo Prudens Niviella St Gertrude the wise virgin of Nivelles (Nivelles).

SI Aul Reg Her & P Ge H Post Mag General hereditary postmaster, supreme of the imperial court of the hereditary kingdom and provinces (Paar).

S. Ian Bapt F. Zachari St John the Baptist, son of Zachary (Florence).

S. Kilianus Cum Sociis Francorum Apostoli St Kilian and his companions, apostles to the Franks (Wurzburg).

S. Lambertus Patronus Leodiensis St Lambert, patron of Liege (Liege).

Sac Nupt Celeb Berol For the holy matrimony celebrated at Berlin (Brandenburg-Ansbach).

Sac Rom Imp Holy Roman Empire (German states).

Sac Rom Imp Provisor Iterum Administrator of the Holy Roman Empire for the second time (Saxony).

Salus Generis Humani Safety of mankind (Rome, Vindex).

Salus Patriae Safety of the fatherland (Italy).

Salus Populi The safety of the people (Spain).

Salus Provinciarum Safety of the provinces (Rome, Postumus).

Salus Publica Salus Mea Public safety is my safety (Sweden).

Salus Reipublicae The safety of the republic (Rome, Theodosius II).

Salus Reipublicae Suprema Lex The safety of the republic is the supreme law (Poland).

Salvam Fac Rempublicam Tuam Make your state safe (San Marino).

Sanctus Iohannes Innoce St John the harmless (Gandersheim).

Sans Changer Without changing (Isle of Man).

Sans Eclat Without pomp (Bouchain siege, 1711).

Sapiente Diffidentia Wise distrust (Teschen).

Scutum Fidei Proteget Eum / Eam The shield of faith shall protect him / her (England, Edward VI and Elizabeth I).

Secundum Voluntatem Tuam Domine Your favourable will o Lord (Hesse).

Securitati Publicae For the public safety (Brandenburg-Ansbach).

Sede Vacante The see being vacant (Papal states, Vatican and ecclesiastical coinage).

Sena Vetus Alpha et W Principum et Finis   Old Siena alpha and omega, the beginning and the end (Siena).

Senatus Populus QR   Senate and people of Rome (Rome, 1188).

Si Deus Nobiscum Quis Contra Nos   If God is with us who can oppose us (Hesse).

Si Deus Pro Nobis Quis Contra Nos   If God is for us who can oppose us (Roemhild).

Sieh Deine Seeligkeit Steht Fest Ins Vaters Liebe   Behold thy salvation stands surely in thy Father's love (Gotha).

Signis Receptis   When the standards had been recovered (Rome, Augustus).

Signum Crucis   The sign of the cross (Groningen).

Sincere et Constanter   Truthfully and steadfastly (Hesse-Darmstadt).

Sit Nomen Domini Benedictum   Blessed be the name of the Lord (Burgundy, Strasbourg).

St T X Adiuto Reg Iste Domba   Let it be to you, o Christ, the assistant to the king of Dombes (Dombes).

Sit Tibi Xpe Dat q'tu Regis Iste Ducat   May this duchy which Thou rulest be given to Thee, O Christ (Venice, ducat).

Sit Unio Haec Perennis   May this union last for ever (Hohenlohe-Langenberg).

Sola Bona Quae Honesta   The only good things are those which are honest (Brunswick).

Sola Facta Deum Sequor   Through deeds alone I strive to follow God (Milan).

Soli Deo Honor et Gloria   To God alone be honour and glory (Nassau).

Soli Reduci   To him, the only one restored (Naples and Sicily).

Solius Virtutis Flos Perpetuus   The flower of Virtue alone is perpetual (Strasbourg).

Spes Confisa Deo Nunquam Confusa Recedit   Hope entrusted in God never retreats in a disorderly fashion (Lippe).

Spes Nr Deus   God is our hope (Oudenarde siege, 1582).

Spes Rei Publicae   The hope of the republic (Rome, Valens).

Strena ex Argyrocopeo Vallis S Christoph   A New Year's gift from the silver-bearing valley of St Christopher (Wurttemberg, 1625).

Sub His Secura Spes Clupeus Omnibus in Te Sperantibus   Under these hope is safe, a shield for all who reside hope in Thee (Bavaria).

Sub Pondere   Under weight (Fulda).

Sub Protectione Caesarea   Under imperial protection (Soragna).

Sub Tuum Praesidium Confug   We flee to Thy protection (Salzburg).

Sub Umbra Alarum Tuarum   Under the shadow of Thy wings (Iever, Scotland, James V).

Subditorum Salus Felicitas Summa   The safety of the subjects is the highest happiness (Lubeck).

Sufficit Mihi Gratia Tua Domine   Sufficient to me is Thy grace, o Lord (Ploen).

Supra Firmam Petram   Upon a firm rock (Papacy).

Susceptor Noster Deus   God is our defence (Tuscany).

Sydera Favent Industriae   The stars favour industry (Furstenberg).

Sylvarum Culturae Praemium   Prize for the culture of the forest (Brandenburg-Ansbach).

Tali Dicata Signo Mens Fluctuari Nequit   Consecrated by such a sign the mind cannot waver (England, Henry VIII George noble).

Tandem Bona Caus Triumphat   A good cause eventually triumphs (Dillenburg).

Tandem Fortuna Obstetrice   With good luck ultimately as the midwife (Wittgenstein).

Te Stante Virebo   With you at my side I shall be strong (Moravia).

Tene Mensuram et Respice Finem   Hold the measure and look to the end (Burgundy).

Tert Ducat Secular   Tercentenary of the duchy (Wurttemberg).

Thu Recht Schev Niemand   Go with right and fear no one (Saxe-Lauenburg).

Tibi Laus et Gloria   To Thee be praise and glory (Venice).

Timor Domini Fons Vitae   The fear of the Lord is a fountain of life (England, Edward VI shillings).

Tout Avec Dieu   Everything with God (Brunswick, 1626).

Traiectum ad Mosam   The crossing of the Maas (Maastricht).

Transvolat Nubila Virtus   Marriageable virtue soon flies past (Grueyeres).

Travail, Famille, Patrie   Work, family, country (Vichy France).

Triumphator Gent Barb   Victor over the barbarian people (Byzantine Empire, Arcadius).

Tueatur Unita Deus   May God guard these united (Kingdoms) (England, James I; Britain, 1847).

Turck Blegert Wien   Vienna besieged by the Turks (Vienna, 1531).

Tut Mar Gab Pr Vid de Lobk Nat Pr Sab Car et Aug Pr de Lobk   Regency of Maria Gabriela, widow of the prince of Lobkowitz, born princess of Savoy-Carignan, and August prince of Lobkowitz (Lobkowitz).

Tutela Italiae   The guardianship of Italy (Rome, Nerva).

Ubi Vult Spirat   He breathes where he will (Papacy).

Ubique Pax   Peace everywhere (Rome, Gallienus).

Union et Force   Union and strength (France).

Urbe Obsessa   The city under siege (Maastricht).

Urbem Virgo Tuam Serva   Protects thy city o virgin (Mary) (Strasbourg).

USC & RAM Cons Int Gen C Mar & Nob Praet H Turmae Capit   Privy councillor of both their holy imperial and royal apostolic majesties, general field marshal and captain of the noble praetorian Hungarian squadrons (Eszterhazy).

Veni Luumen Cordium   Come light of hearts (Vatican).

Veni Sancte Spiritus   Come Holy Ghost (Vatican).

Verbum Domini Manet in Aeternum   The word of the Lord abides forever (Hesse-Darmstadt, Veldenz).

Veritas Lex Tua   The truth is your law (Salzburg).

Veritas Temporis Filia   Truth is the daughter of time (England and Ireland, Mary Tudor).

Veritate et Labore   By truth and work (Wittgenstein).

Veritate et Iustitia   By truth and justice (German states).

Victoria Principum   The victory of princes (Ostrogoths).

Videant Pauperes et Laetentur   Let the poor see and rejoice (Tuscany).

Virgo Maria Protege Civitatem Savonae   Virgin Mary Protect the city of Savona (Savona).

Viribus Unitis   With united strength (Austria).

Virtute et Fidelitate   By virtue and faithfulness (Hesse-Cassel).

Virtute et Prudentia   With virtue and prudence (Auersperg).

Virtute Viam Dimetiar   I shall mark the way with valour (Waldeck).

Virtutis Gloria Merces   Glory is the reward of valour (Holstein-Gottorp).

Vis Unita Concordia Fratrum Fortior   United power is the stronger harmony of brothers (Mansfeld).

Visitavit Nos Oriens ex Alto   He has visited us arising on high (Luneburg).

Vivit Post Funera   He lives after death (Bremen).

Vota Optata Romae Fel   Vows taken for the luck of Rome (Rome, Maxentius).

Vox de Throno   A voice from the throne (Papacy).

Was Got Beschert Bleibet Unerwert   What God hath endowed leave undisturbed

Wider macht und List Mein Fels Gott Ist   Against might and trickery God is my rock (Hesse-Cassel).

Xpc Vincit Xpc Regnat   Christ conquers, Christ reigns (Scotland, Spain).

Xpc Vivet Xpc Regnat Xpc Impat   Christ lives, Christ reigns, Christ commands (Cambrai).

Xpe Resurescit   Christ lives again (Venice).

Xpistiana Religio   Christian religion (Carolingian Empire).

Xps Ihs Elegit me Regem Populo   Jesus Christ chose me as king to the people (Norway).

Zelator Fidei Usque ad Montem   An upholder of the faith through and through (Portugal).

Zum Besten des Vaterlands   To the best of the fatherland (Bamberg).

Care
of coins

There is no point in going to a great deal of trouble and expense in selecting the best coins you can afford, only to let them deteriorate in value by neglect and mishandling. Unless you give some thought to the proper care of your coins, your collection is unlikely to make a profit for you if and when you come to sell it. Housing your coins is the biggest problem of all, so it is important to give a lot of attention to this.

Storage

The ideal, but admittedly the most expensive, method is the coin cabinet, constructed of air-dried mahogany, walnut or rosewood (*never* oak, cedar or any highly resinous timber likely to cause chemical tarnish). These cabinets have banks of shallow drawers containing trays made of the same wood, with half-drilled holes of various sizes to accommodate the different denominations of coins. Such cabinets are handsome pieces of furniture but, being largely handmade, tend to be rather expensive. Occasionally good specimens can be picked up in secondhand furniture shops, or at the dispersal of house contents by auction, but the best bet is still to purchase a new cabinet, tailored to your own requirements.

Peter Nichols of 3 Norman Road, St Leonards-on-Sea, East Sussex TN37 6NH (telephone 01424 436682) is a specialist manufacturer of display and storage systems who has also been producing coin and medal cabinets to suit every need for more than a quarter of a century. He can produce a cabinet to fit into a wall safe or some other form of security box. He can match existing work, and thus replicate cabinets which you may already be using, or even produce designs to suit your specific requirements. The only proviso is that the cabinets are made in only one timber—Brazilian mahogany, for reason of chemical balance. A nice touch is that all the products in the Nichols repertoire take their names from Elizabethan mint-marks.

Nichols produces a wide range of cabinets from the seven-tray Pheon all the way up to the massive 40-tray specials designed for the British Museum. All cabinets are fitted with double doors. Nichols also produces the glass-topped Crown display case and the Sceptre display case, fitted with a glazed lid and containing a single tray. The Orb range of display cases are intended for wall mounting and are ideal for a display of campaign medals and decorations.

Prices start at around £30 for a four-tray Martlet coin cabinet and go all the way to the Coronet thirty-tray version at about £350. They are not cheap, but you have the satisfaction of acquiring exquisite

The 4-tray Martlet— the smallest in an extensive range from Peter Nichols.

The Crozier—a cabinet for the connoisseur.

The Diplomat, Abafil's plush flagship of the portable Diplomat range.

examples of the cabinetmaker's craft which would be an elegant addition to any lounge or study.

Collectors Gallery of 24 The Parade, St Mary's Place, Shrewsbury, SY1 1DL (telephone: 01743 272140, www.collectors-gallery.co.uk) is the UK agent and distributor for the Abafil series manufactured in Milan. These cases are of stout wooden construction covered with simulated leather and lined with red plush. The trays to fit the cases are also manufactured in wood lined with plush although a less expensive lined plastic alternative is also available. The Diplomat range is designed primarily for secure transportation, but the Mini-diplomat makes a good static cabinet, and can take up to three trays holding a maximum of 241 coins, while the Custom case holds 14 de luxe or 20 standard trays and will house up to 1,500 coins. Even cheaper is the Mignon case holding up to 105 coins, ideally suited for carrying in a briefcase or travel bag.

An excellent compromise is provided by a number of firms who manufacture coin trays in durable, felt-lined materials with shallow compartments to suit the various sizes of coins. Most of these trays interlock so that they build up into a cabinet of the desired size, and there are also versions designed as carrying cases, which are ideal for transporting coins.

The popular and extensive Lighthouse range is distributed by The Duncannon Partnership, 4 Beaufort Road, Reigate, RH2 9DJ (telephone 01737 244222). This includes a wide variety of cases and albums for the general collector in basic or de luxe styles as required, as well as printed albums for the specialist. Their cases, including the popular aluminium range, are manufactured to the highest standards, lined with blue plush which displays any coin to its best advantage. The red-lined single trays come in deep or standard size and make an ideal cabinet when stacked together or housed in their attractive aluminium case, which is available separately. The trays themselves come with a variety

of compartments for every size of coin. As with most distributors nowadays their complete range can be viewed on-line at www.duncannon.co.uk.

Lindner Publications of 3A Hayle Industrial Park, Hayle, Cornwall TR27 5JR (telephone 01736 751914, www.prinz.co.uk) are well-known for their wide range of philatelic and numismatic accessories, but these include a full array of coin boxes, capsules, carrying cases and trays. The basic Lindner coin box is, in fact, a shallow tray available in a standard version or a smoked glass version. These trays have a crystal clear frame, red felt inserts and holes for various diameters of coins and medals. A novel feature of these trays is the rounded insert which facilitates the removal of coins from their spaces with the minimum of handling. These boxes are designed in such a manner that they interlock and can be built up into banks of trays, each fitted with a draw-handle and sliding in and out easily. Various types of chemically inert plastic capsules and envelopes have been designed for use in combination with plain shallow trays, without holes drilled. Lindner also manufacture a range of luxury cases lined in velvet and Atlas silk with padded covers and gold embossing on the spines, producing a most tasteful and elegant appearance.

Safe Albums of 16 Falcon Business Park, 38 Ivanhoe Road, Finchampstead, Berkshire RG40 4QQ (telephone 0118 932 8976, www.safealbums.co.uk) are the UK agents for the German Stapel-Element, a drawer-stacking system with clear plasticiser-free trays that fit into standard bookshelves. The sliding coin compartments, lined with blue velvet, can be angled for display to best advantage. Stackable drawers can be built up to any height desired. A wide range of drawer sizes is available, with compartments suitable for the smallest coins right up to four-compartment trays designed for very large artefacts such as card-cases or cigarette cases. The Mobel-Element cabinet is a superb specialised cabinet constructed of the finest timber with a steel

Adding on to the stacking Lindner range is easy.

Safe's cabinet combines elegance with security.

frame and steel grip bars which can be securely locked. It thus combines elegance with security and is the ideal medium for the most valuable coins and medals.

There are also various storage systems, such as Coindex, which operate on the principle of narrow drawers in which the coins are stored in envelopes of chemically-inert plastic. A strip across the top holds a little slip giving a brief description, catalogue number and the price of each coin.

Kwikseal of the USA produce cards with a plastic window: these cards are especially suitable for slabbing coins. The traditional method used by many collectors was to house coins in small, air-dried manila envelopes that could be stored upright in narrow wooden or stout card boxes—knife-boxes were highly regarded as being the right width and depth. The Sydney Museum in Australia, for example, keeps its coins in manila envelopes stored in plastic lunch-boxes which seemed to do the job pretty well!

Coin Albums

When coin collecting became a popular hobby in the 1960s, several firms marketed ranges of coin albums. They had clear plastic sleeves divided into tiny compartments of various sizes and had the merit of being cheap and taking up little room on a bookshelf.

They had several drawbacks, however, not the least being the tendency of the pages to sag with the weight of the coins, or even, in extreme cases, to pull away from the pegs or rings holding them on to the spine. They required very careful handling as the coins could easily fall out of the top row as the pages were turned. The more expensive albums had little flaps that folded over the top of the coin to overcome this problem.

Arguably the worst aspect of these albums was the use of polyvinyl chloride (PVC) in the construction of the sleeves. Collectors soon discovered to their horror that this reacted chemically with their coins, especially those made of silver, causing a rather disgusting yellow slime

to adhere to the coins' surface. I shudder to think how many fine collections were ruined as a result, or of the countless coins that required highly expert treatment in a bid to restore them to as near the original condition as possible.

Fortunately the lesson has been learned and the coin albums now on the market are quite safe. Lighthouse and Lindner offer a wide range of albums designed to house coins, medals or banknotes. The old problem about sagging pages is overcome by the use of a multi-ring binding

Albums are a convenient way to transport your coins.

welded to a very stout spine, while the sleeves contain neither Styrol nor PVC and will not affect any metals at all. In addition to pages with pockets of uniform size, the Karat range of albums operates on a slide principle which enables the user to insert vertical strips of different sizes on the same page, so that the coins of one country or series, or perhaps a thematic display of coins from different countries, can be displayed side by side.

Safe Albums offer a wide range of albums in the Coinholder System and Coin-Combi ranges. These, too, offer the choice of fixed pages with uniform-sized pockets, or interchangeable sliding inserts for different sizes side by side.

The Lighthouse range includes a wide selection of de luxe and printed albums.

Cleaning
Coins

This is like matrimony—it should not be embarked on lightly. Indeed, the advice given by the magazine *Punch* in regard to marriage is equally sound in this case—don't do it! It is far better to have a dirty coin than an irretrievably damaged one. Every dealer has horror stories of handling coins that previous owners have cleaned, to their detriment. The worst example I ever saw was a display of coins found by a metal detectorist who "improved" his finds by abrading them in the kind of rotary drum used by lapidarists to polish gemstones. If you really must remove the dirt and grease from coins, it is advisable to practise on coins of little value.

Warm water containing a mild household detergent or washing-up liquid will work wonders in removing surface dirt and grease from most coins, but silver is best washed in a weak solution of ammonia and warm water—one part ammonia to ten parts water. Gold coins can be cleaned with diluted citric acid, such as lemon juice. Copper or bronze coins present more of a problem, but patches of verdigris can usually be removed by careful washing in a 20 per cent solution of sodium sesquicarbonate. Wartime coins made of tin, zinc, iron or steel can be cleaned in a 5 per cent solution of caustic soda containing some aluminium or zinc foil or filings, but they must be rinsed afterwards in clean water and carefully dried. Cotton buds are ideal for gently prising dirt out of coin legends and crevices in the designs. Soft brushes (with animal bristles—*never* nylon or other artificial bristles) designed for cleaning silver are most suitable for gently cleaning coins.

Coins recovered from the soil or the sea bed present special problems, due to chemical reaction between the metals and the salts in the earth or sea water. In such cases, the best advice is to take them to the nearest museum and let the professional experts decide on what can or should be done.

Both Lindner and Safe Albums offer a range of coin-cleaning kits and materials suitable for gold, silver, copper and other base alloys respectively. Safe (living up to their name) also provide a stern warning that rubber gloves should be worn and care taken to avoid breathing fumes or getting splashes of liquid in your eyes or on your skin. Obviously, the whole business of cleaning is a matter that should not be entered into without the utmost care and forethought.

POLISHING: A WARNING

If cleaning should only be approached with the greatest trepidation, polishing is definitely *out!* Beginners sometimes fall into the appalling error of thinking that a smart rub with metal polish might improve the appearance of their coins. Short of actually punching a hole through it, there can hardly be a more destructive act. Polishing a coin may improve its superficial appearance for a few days, but such abrasive action will destroy the patina and reduce the fineness of the high points of the surface.

Even if a coin is only polished once, it will never be quite the same again, and an expert can tell this a mile off.

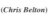

Celtic
coinage of Britain

Celtic coins were the first coins made in Britain. They were issued for a century and a half before the Roman invasion, and possibly a little later in some areas. They were issued by 11 tribal groups or administrative authorities situated southeast of a line from the Humber to the Severn. In this short article Celtic specialist CHRIS RUDD introduces this increasingly popular area.

The earliest coins were uninscribed and often abstract in design. Later ones carried the names of local leaders and tribal centres, and in the southeast became increasingly Roman in style, sometimes copying classical images quite closely.

Most Celtic coins were struck between two dies on flans of gold, silver, billion and bronze. Some were cast in strip moulds in tin-rich bronze alloy called "potin".

Because the Celts wrote no books and left no written records of their activities, little is known about the people and places behind their coins. Who made them? When? Where? And why? These are questions that are still largely unanswered, except in the very vaguest terms. Celtic cataloguers talk about gold quarters, silver units and silver minims. But the truth is we don't even know what the Celts themselves called their coins.

British Celtic coins are among the most fascinating ever fashioned and perhaps the least familiar to the average collector because of their rarity. Like the Celts themselves, Celtic coin designs are wild, free flowing, flamboyant and full of fun. Yes, Celtic moneyers had a great sense of humour!

Celtic coins bear a vast variety of gods and goddesses, armed warriors, chariot wheels, hidden faces, decapitated heads, suns, moons, stars, thunderbolts, floral motifs, magic signs and phallic symbols. Plus a menagerie of antelopes, bears, boars, bulls, cocks, crabs, cranes, dogs, dolphins, ducks, eagles, hares, all kinds of horses (some with wings, some with human heads, many with three tails, a few breathing fire), goats, lions, lizards, owls, rams, rats, ravens, snakes, stags, starfish, worms and wolves. Not to mention dragons, griffins, hippocamps, sphinxes and ram-horned serpents.

Ask any metal detectorist how many Celtic coins he or she has found and you will immediately realise they are rarer than Roman coins in this country—at least a thousand times rarer on average. This is because far fewer Celtic coins were minted, in smaller runs, over a much shorter time span. Though some may have been made as early as 80 BC, the majority of British Celtic coins were struck from 54 BC to AD 43; barely 100 years of production, and most of that seems to have been sporadic.

However, the greater rarity of Celtic coins doesn't mean they are necessarily more costly than other ancient coins: in fact, they are often cheaper. You see, in the coin market, demand determines price. The more collectors that want a coin, the higher its price.

A recent survey revealed "worldwide there may be no more than 150 regular private collectors of

Method that may have been used for striking Celtic coins (drawing by Simon Pressey).

Celtic coins, buying on average one or more coins per month". Whereas there are literally thousands of people collecting the other major series of ancient and medieval coins. That is why Celtic coins are still comparatively less costly than Greek, Anglo-Saxon and English hammered coins. The Celtic market is smaller, though expanding. For example a very fine Celtic gold stater typically costs half the price of a Greek gold stater or an English gold noble of comparable quality and rarity. The price differential

can be even more dramatic at major international auctions. But the disparity is diminishing as more and more collectors are beginning to appreciate the hitherto unrecognised beauty, scarcity and good value of British Celtic coins. So now could be a good time to start collecting Celtic coins, before their prices begin climbing more steeply.

Thirty years ago collecting British Celtic coins was a rich man's hobby and understanding them was the lonely pursuit of a few scholarly

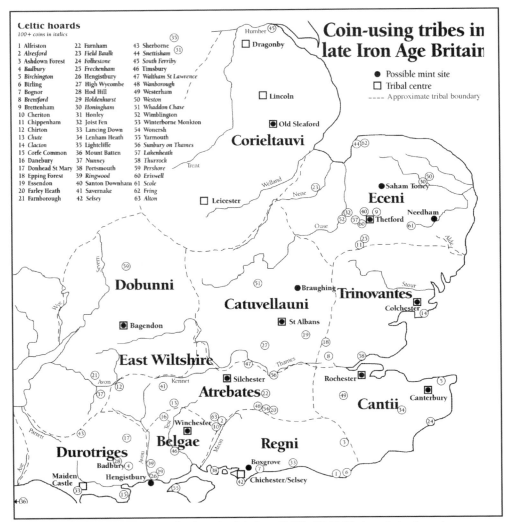

Celtic hoards
100+ coins in italics

1 Alfriston	22 Farnham	43 Sherborne
2 Alresford	23 Field Baulk	44 Snettisham
3 Ashdown Forest	24 Folkestone	45 South Ferriby
4 Badbury	25 Freckenham	46 Timsbury
5 Birchington	26 Hengistbury	47 Waltham St Lawrence
6 Birling	27 High Wycombe	48 Wanborough
7 Bognor	28 Hod Hill	49 Westerham
8 Brentford	29 Holdenhurst	50 Weston
9 Brettenham	30 Honingham	51 Whaddon Chase
10 Cheriton	31 Honley	52 Wimblington
11 Chippenham	32 Joist Fen	53 Winterborne Monkton
12 Chirton	33 Lancing Down	54 Wonersh
13 Chute	34 Lenham Heath	55 Yarmouth
14 Clacton	35 Lightcliffe	56 Sunbury on Thames
15 Corfe Common	36 Mount Batten	57 Lakenheath
16 Danebury	37 Nunney	58 Thurrock
17 Donhead St Mary	38 Portsmouth	59 Pershore
18 Epping Forest	39 Ringwood	60 Eriswell
19 Essendon	40 Santon Downham	61 Scole
20 Farley Heath	41 Savernake	62 Fring
21 Farnborough	42 Selsey	63 Alton

Coin-using tribes in late Iron Age Britain

● Possible mint site
□ Tribal centre
---- Approximate tribal boundary

Eleven tribal groups minted coins in late Iron Age Britain, c. 80 BC–AD 45. The boundaries shown here are guess-timates, not actual, and often follow rivers, many of which are still known by their Celtic names.

Silver unit attributed to King Esuprastus of the Eceni, whose death resulted in the revolt of Queen Boudica, AD 60 (drawn four times actual size by Susan White).

numismatists. Today, thanks to the popularity of metal detecting, Celtic coins are more plentiful and almost everyone can afford to collect them. Most ancient coin dealers sell Celtic coins, some for as little as £20 each, and you will always find a few trays of them at every coin fair.

British Celtic coins are also easier to study today, thanks to the publication of some excellent books on the subject. The Celtic collector's bible is *Celtic Coinage of Britain* by Robert D. Van Arsdell (Spink, 1989)—well researched, well written, well illustrated, always quoted in dealers' catalogues, often controversial when dates are discussed and hopefully to be republished soon in a revised edition. For the dedicated Celtic devotee *British Iron Age Coins in the British Museum* by Richard Hobbs (British Museum Press, 1996) is an invaluable companion volume to Van Arsdell—more cautious, less speculative.

By far the best introductory book is *Celtic Coinage in Britain* by Dr Philip de Jersey (Shire Archaeology, 1996) who manages the Celtic Coin Index, a photographic record of over 31,000 British coins at the Institute of Archaeology, Oxford. In plain language Dr Philip de Jersey explains how Celtic coins and the images they carry can reveal information on the political, economic and social life of the Celts. *Celtic Coinage in Britain* contains clear twice-size photos of over a hundred Celtic coins, some of them rarely seen before. It gives the names, addresses and phone numbers of the museums in England, Scotland and Wales with the best and most accessible collections of Celtic coins.

In short, if you want to know more about British Celtic coins, *Celtic Coinage in Britain* is where you start reading and keep reading. This is the best little book ever written about British Celtic coins and outstanding value for money at £4.99.

How should you start collecting British Celtic coins? First, get a few of the commoner uninscribed types from each of the 11 tribal areas, aiming for the highest grade you can comfortably afford. Then you may wish to get an inscribed coin of each of the main rulers. You would also be well advised to acquire some Gaulish coins at the same time, because many British coins were influenced by Gallic prototypes.

How much do British Celtic coins cost? Very little, considering how scarce they are. Types with legends usually cost more than those without and top quality bronze is frequently more pricey than top quality silver (which may surprise you) because silver is commoner and generally survives better after two-thousand years underground.

Chris Rudd is a well-known dealer who specialises in Celtic coins.

Collecting

Ancient coins

Ancient coins differ from most other series which are collected in Britain in that every piece has spent the major part of the last two thousand years in the ground. As JOHN CUMMINGS, dealer in ancient coins and antiquities explains here, the effect that burial has had on the surface of the coin determines more than anything else the value of a particular piece. With more modern coins, the only things which affect price are rarity and grade. There may be a premium for coins exhibiting particularly fine tone, or with outstanding pedigrees, but an 1887 crown in "extremely fine" condition has virtually the same value as every other piece with the same grade and of the same date. With ancient coins the story is very different.

A large number of different criteria affect the price of an ancient coin. Factors affecting prices can be broken down into several categories:

Condition

The most important factor by far in determining price. Ancient coins were struck by hand and can exhibit striking faults. Value suffers if the coin is struck with the designs off-centre, is weakly struck, or if the flan is irregular in shape. Many of the Celtic tribes issued coins of varying fineness and those made from low quality gold or silver are worth less than similar specimens where the metal quality is better. Conversely, coins on exceptional flans, particularly well struck, or with fine patinas command a premium.

Many ancient coins have suffered during their stay in the ground. It must be borne in mind that the prices given in the price guide are for uncorroded, undamaged examples. A Roman denarius should be graded using the same criteria as those used for grading modern coins. The surfaces must be good, and the coin intact. The fact that the coin is 2,000 years old is irrelevant as far as grading is concerned. Coins which are not perfectly preserved are not without value but the value for a given grade decreases with the degree of fault.

Rarity

As with all other series, rare coins usually command higher prices than common ones although this is not written in stone. A unique variety of a small fourth century Roman bronze coin, even in perfect condition, can be worth much less than a more worn and common piece from an earlier part of the empire. In the Celtic series, there is an almost infinite variety of minor types and a unique variety of an uninscribed type will rarely outbid an inscribed issue of a known king.

Historical and local significance

Types which have historical or local interest can command a price far above their scarcity value. Denarii of the emperor Tiberius are believed to have been referred to in the New Testament and command a far higher price than a less interesting piece of similar rarity. Similarly, pieces which have British reverse types such as the "VICT BRIT" reverse of the third century AD are more expensive than their scarcity would indicate. The 12 Caesars are ever popular especially in the American market and this affects prices throughout the world. In the Celtic series, coins of Cunobelin or Boudicca are far more popular than pieces which have no historical interest but which are far scarcer.

Reverse types

All Roman emperors who survived for a reasonable time issued coins with many different reverse types. The most common of these usually show various Roman gods. When a coin has an unusual reverse it always enhances the value.

Particularly popular are architectural scenes, animals, references to Judaism, and legionary types.

Artistic merit

The Roman coinage is blessed with a large number of bust varieties and these can have a startling effect on price. For example, a common coin with the bust facing left instead of right can be worth several times the price of a normal specimen. Like many of the emperors, the coinage of Hadrian has a large number of bust varieties, some of which are extremely artistic and these, too, can command a premium.

The coinage used in Britain from the time of the invasion in AD 43 was the same as that introduced throughout the Empire by the emperor Augustus around 20 BC. The simple divisions of 2 asses equal to one dupondius, 2 dupondii equal to 1 sestertius, 4 sestertii equal to one denarius and 25 denarii equal to one aureus continued in use until the reformation of the coinage by Caracalla in AD 214.

Aureus (gold)

Denarius (silver)

Sestertius (bronze)

Dupondius (copper)

As (copper)

Introducing
Hammered
coinage

The hammered currency of medieval Britain is among some of the most interesting coinage in the world. The turbulent history of these islands is reflected in the fascinating changes in size, design, fineness and workmanship, culminating in the many strange examples that emanated from the strife of the Civil War.

The Norman Conquest of England in 1066 and succeeding years had far-reaching effects on all aspects of life. Surprisingly, however, it had little impact on the coinage. William the Conqueror was anxious to emphasise the continuity of his reign, so far as the ordinary people were concerned, and therefore he retained the fabric, size and general design pattern of the silver penny. Almost 70 mints were in operation during this reign, but by the middle of the 12th century the number was reduced to 55 and under Henry II (1154–89) it fell to 30 and latterly to only eleven. By the early 14th century the production of coins had been centralised on London and Canterbury, together with the ecclesiastical mints at York and Canterbury. The silver penny was the principal denomination throughout the Norman period, pieces cut along the lines of the cross on the reverse continuing to serve as halfpence and farthings.

Eight types of penny were struck under William I and five under his son William Rufus, both profiles (left and right) and facing portraits being used in both reigns allied to crosses of various types. Fifteen types were minted under Henry I (1100–35), portraiture having now degenerated to crude caricature, the lines engraved on the coinage dies being built up by means of various punches. Halfpence modelled on the same pattern were also struck, but very sparingly and are very rare.

On Henry's death the succession was contested by his daughter Matilda and his nephew Stephen of Blois. Civil war broke out in 1138 and continued till 1153. Stephen controlled London and its mint, but Matilda and her supporters occupied the West Country and struck their own coins at Bristol. Several of the powerful barons struck their own coins, and there were distinct regional variants of the regal coinage. Of particular interest are the coins struck

Silver pennies of, from left to right, William I, William Rufus, Henry I and Stephen.

from obverse dies with Stephen's portrait erased or defaced, believed to date from 1148 when the usurper was under papal interdict.

Peace was restored in 1153 when it was agreed that Matilda's son Henry should succeed Stephen. On the latter's death the following year, Henry II ascended the throne. Coins of Stephen's last type continued to be minted till 1158, but Henry then took the opportunity to overhaul the coinage which had become irregular and sub-standard during the civil war. The new "Cross Crosslet" coins, usually known as the Tealby coinage (from the hoard of over 5,000 pennies found at Tealby, Lincolnshire in 1807), were produced at 30 mints, but when the recoinage was completed this number was reduced to a dozen. The design of Henry's coins remained virtually the same throughout more than two decades, apart from minor variants. Then, in 1180, a new type, known as the Short Cross coinage, was introduced. This was a vast improvement over the poorly struck Cross Crosslet coins and continued without alteration, not only to the end of the reign of Henry II in 1189, but throughout the reigns of his sons Richard (1189–99) and John (1199–1216) and the first half of the reign of his grandson Henry III (1216–46). Throughout that 66 year period, however, there were minor variations in portraits and lettering which enable numismatists to attribute the HENRICUS coins to specific reigns and periods.

"Tealby" type penny, left, and "Short Cross" penny of Henry II.

The style and workmanship of the Short Cross coinage deteriorated in the reign of Henry III. By the 1220s coin production was confined to the regal mints at London and Canterbury, the sole exception being the ecclesiastical mint maintained by the Abbot of Bury St Edmunds.

Halfpence and farthings were briefly struck in 1221–30, though halfpence are now extremely rare and so far only a solitary farthing has been discovered.

By the middle of this reign the coinage was in a deplorable state, being poorly struck, badly worn and often ruthlessly clipped. In 1247 Henry ordered a new coinage and in this the arms of the cross on the reverse were extended to the rim as a safeguard against clipping. This established a pattern of facing portrait and long cross on obverse and reverse respectively that was to continue till the beginning of the 16th century. Several provincial mints were re-activated to assist with the recoinage but they were all closed down again by 1250, only the regal mints at London and Canterbury and the ecclesiastical mints at Durham and Bury St Edmunds remaining active.

"Long Cross" pennies of Henry III, left, and Edward I.

In 1257 Henry tentatively introduced a gold penny (worth 20 silver pence and twice the weight of a silver penny). The coin was undervalued and soon disappeared from circulation.

The Long Cross coinage of Henry III continued under Edward I till 1279 when the king introduced a new coinage in his own name. The penny continued the style of its predecessors, though much better designed and executed; but new denominations were now added. Henceforward halfpence and farthings became a regular issue and, at the same time, a fourpenny coin known as the groat (from French *gros*) was briefly introduced (minting ceased in 1282 and was not revived till 1351). Due to the centralisation of coin production the name of the moneyer was now generally dropped, although it lingered on a few years at Bury St Edmunds. The provincial mints were again revived in 1299–1302 to recoin the lightweight foreign imitations of pennies which had flooded in from the Continent.

The coinage of Edward II (1307–27) differed only in minor respects from that of his father, and a similar pattern prevailed in the first years of Edward III. In 1335 halfpence and farthings below the sterling fineness were struck. More importantly, further attempts were made to introduce gold coins. In 1344 the florin or double

Pre-Treaty Noble of Edward III which contained reference to France in the legend.

leopard of six shillings was introduced, along with its half and quarter. This coinage was not successful and was soon replaced by a heavier series based on the noble of 80 pence (6s. 8d.), half a mark or one third of a pound. The noble originally weighed 138.5 grains but it was successively reduced to120 grains, at which weight it continued from 1351. During this reign the protracted conflict with France known as the Hundred Years' War erupted. Edward III, through his mother, claimed the French throne and inscribed this title on his coins. By the Treaty of Bretigny (1361) Edward temporarily gave up his claim and the reference to France

Noble of Edward IV, issued before he was forced to abandon the throne of England.

was dropped from the coins, but when war was renewed in 1369 the title was resumed, and remained on many English coins until the end of the 18th century. The silver coinage followed the pattern of the previous reign, but in 1351 the groat was re-introduced and with it came the twopence or half-groat. Another innovation was the use of mintmarks at the beginning of the inscriptions. Seven types of cross and one crown were employed from 1334 onwards and their sequence enables numismatists to date coins fairly accurately.

The full range of gold (noble, half-noble and quarter-noble) and silver (groat, half-groat, penny, halfpenny and farthing) continued under Richard II (1377–99). Little attempt was made to alter the facing portrait on the silver coins, by now little more than a stylised caricature anyway.

Noble of Henry IV which was reduced in weight due to the shortage of gold.

Under Henry IV (1399–1413) the pattern of previous reigns prevailed, but in 1412 the weights of the coinage were reduced due to a shortage of bullion. The noble was reduced to 108 grains and its sub-divisions lightened proportionately. The penny was reduced by 3 grains, and its multiples and sub-divisions correspondingly reduced. One interesting change was the reduction of the fleur de lis of France from four to three in the heraldic shield on the reverse of the noble; this change corresponded with the alteration in the arms used in France itself. The Calais mint, opened by Edward III in 1363, was closed in 1411. There was no change in the designs used for the coins of Henry V (1413–22) but greater use was now made of mintmarks to distinguish the various periods of production. Coins were by now produced mainly at London, although the episcopal mints at Durham and York were permitted to strike pennies.

The supply of gold dwindled early in the reign of Henry VI and few nobles were struck after 1426. The Calais mint was re-opened in 1424 and struck a large amount of gold before closing finally in 1440. A regal mint briefly operated at York in 1423–24. Mintmarks were now much more widely used and tended to correspond more closely to the annual trials of the Pyx. The series of civil upheavals known as the Wars of the Roses erupted in this period.

In 1461 Henry VI was deposed by the Yorkist Earl of March after he defeated the Lancastrians at Mortimer's Cross. The Yorkists advanced on London where the victor was crowned Edward IV. At first he continued the gold series of his predecessor, issuing nobles and quarter-nobles, but in 1464 the weight of the penny was reduced to 12 grains and the value of the noble was raised to 100 pence (8s. 4d.). The ryal or rose-

Groat of Richard III (1483–85).

noble of 120 grains, together with its half and quarter, was introduced in 1465 and tariffed at ten shillings or half a pound. The need for a coin worth a third of a pound, however, led to the issue of the angel of 80 grains, worth 6s. 8d., but this was initially unsuccessful and very few examples are now extant. The angel derived its name from the figure of the Archangel Michael on the obverse; a cross surmounting a shield appeared on the reverse.

In 1470 Edward was forced to flee to Holland and Henry VI was briefly restored. During this brief period (to April 1471) the ryal was discontinued but a substantial issue of angels and half-angels was made both at London and Bristol. Silver coins were struck at York as well as London and Bristol, the issues of the provincial mints being identified by the initials B or E (Eboracum, Latin for York). Edward defeated the Lancastrians at Tewkesbury and deposed the luckless Henry once more. In his second reign

Edward struck only angels and half-angels as well as silver from the groat to halfpenny. In addition to the three existing mints, silver coins were struck at Canterbury, Durham and the archiepiscopal mint at York. Mintmarks were now much more frequent and varied. Coins with a mark of a halved sun and rose are usually assigned to the reign of Edward IV, but they were probably also struck in the nominal reign of Edward V, the twelve-year-old prince held in the Tower of London under the protection of his uncle Richard, Duke of Gloucester. Coins with this mark on the reverse had an obverse mark of a boar's head, Richard's personal emblem. The brief reign of Richard III (1483–5) came to an end with his defeat at Bosworth and the relatively scarce coins of this period followed the pattern of the previous reigns, distinguished by the sequence of mint marks and the inscription RICAD or RICARD.

In the early years of Henry VII's reign the coinage likewise followed the previous patterns, but in 1489 the first of several radical changes was effected, with the introduction of the gold sovereign of 20 shillings showing a full-length portrait of the monarch seated on an elaborate throne. For reverse, this coin depicted a Tudor rose surmounted by a heraldic shield. A similar reverse appeared on the ryal of 10 shillings, but the angel and angelet retained previous motifs. The silver coins at first adhered to the medieval pattern, with the stylised facing portrait and long cross, but at the beginning of the 16th century a large silver coin, the testoon or shilling of 12 pence, was introduced and adopted a realistic profile of the king, allied to a reverse showing a cross surmounted by the royal arms. The same design was also used for the later issue of groat and half groat.

First coinage Angel of Henry VIII which retained the traditional 23.5 carat fineness.

This established a pattern which was to continue till the reign of Charles I. In the reign of Henry VIII, however, the coinage was subject to considerable debasement. This led to the eventual introduction of 22 carat (.916 fine) gold for the crown while the traditional 23 1/2 carat gold was retained for the angel and ryal. This dual system continued until the angel was discontinued at the outset of the Civil War in 1642; latterly it had been associated with the ceremony of touching for "King's Evil" or scrofula, a ritual used by the early Stuart monarchs to bolster their belief in the divine right of kings.

Under the Tudors and Stuarts the range and complexity of the gold coinage increased, but it was not until the reign of Edward VI that the silver series was expanded. In 1551 he introduced the silver crown of five shillings, the first English coin to bear a clear date on the obverse. Under Mary dates were extended to the shilling and sixpence.

The mixture of dated and undated coins continued under Elizabeth I, a reign remarkable for the range of denominations—nine gold and eight silver. The latter included the sixpence, threepence, threehalfpence and threefarthings, distinguished by the rose which appeared behind the Queen's head.

The coinage of James I was even more complex, reflecting the king's attempts to unite his dominions. The first issue bore the legend ANG:SCO (England and Scotland), but from 1604 this was altered to MAG: BRIT (Great Britain). This period witnessed new denominations, such as the rose-ryal and spur-ryal, the unite, the Britain crown and the thistle crown, and finally the laurel of 20 shillings and its sub-divisions.

In the reign of Elizabeth experiments began with milled coinage under Eloi Mestrell. These continued sporadically in the 17th century, culminating in the beautiful coins struck by Nicholas Briot (1631–39). A branch mint was established at Aberystwyth in 1637 to refine and coin silver from the Welsh mines. Relations between King and Parliament deteriorated in the reign of Charles I and led to the Civil War (1642). Parliament controlled London but continued to strike coins in the King's name. The Royalists struck coins, both in pre-war and new types, at Shrewsbury, Oxford, Bristol, Worcester, Exeter, Chester, Hereford and other Royalist strongholds, while curious siege pieces were pressed into service at Newark, Pontefract and Scarborough.

After the execution of Charles I in 1649 the Commonwealth was proclaimed and gold and silver coins were now inscribed in English instead of Latin. Patterns portraying Cromwell and a crowned shield restored Latin in 1656. Plans for milled coinage were already being considered before the Restoration of the monarchy in 1660. Hammered coinage appeared initially, resuming the style of coins under Charles I, but in 1662 the hand-hammering of coins was abandoned in favour of coins struck on the mill and screw press. The hammered coins of 1660–62 were undated and bore a crown mintmark, the last vestiges of medievalism in British coinage.

The magnificent Rose-Ryal of James I.

For The Roman Connoisseur

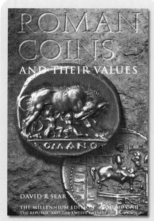

Roman Coins and their Values Vol I

An excellent reference for anyone interested in the fascinating Roman coinage. This first volume deals with the coins of the Republic and the 12 Caesars 280 BC - AD.96.

Price £45.00
(+£4.00p&p)

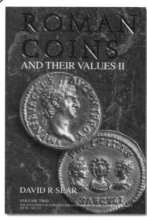

Roman Coins and their Values Vol II

The second volume in this excellent series covers the Coinage of the Empire from the Accession of Nerva in AD96 to the overthrow of the Severan Dynasty in AD. 235.

Price £65.00
(+£4.00p&p)

Roman Coins and their Values Vol III

This, the most recent volume of David R. Sear's magnificent work on Roman Coinage, takes us from the Accession of Maximinus I in AD. 235 up to the Death of Carinus 50 years later.

Price £45.00
(+£4.00p&p)

ORDER ALL 3 AND RECEIVE POST FREE!

Schema of average percentage increments of retail values of selected commoner types of Late Iron Age coins monitored 1993-2005 with annual fluctuations flattened out. Source: EC Retail Review 8/05.

A SIMPLIFIED PRICE GUIDE
TO
ANCIENT COINS USED IN BRITAIN

PART I
CELTIC

The prices given in this section are those that you would expect to pay from a reputable dealer and not the prices at which you could expect to sell coins.

The list below, which has been generously provided by Celtic coin dealer Chris Rudd, contains most of the commonly available types: a full comprehensive guide is beyond the scope of this book. Prices are for coins with good surfaces which are not weakly struck or struck from worn dies. Examples which are struck from worn or damaged dies can be worth considerably less. Particularly attractive examples of bronze Celtic coins command a very high premium. Where a price is given for an issue of which there are many varieties, the price is for the most common type.

	F	VF	EF

UNINSCRIBED COINAGE

GOLD STATERS

	F	VF	EF
Gallo-Belgic A	£650	£1500	£5500
Gallo-Belgic E (Ambiani)	£150	£250	£450
Chute type	£150	£275	£450
Cheriton type			
normally rather "brassy" metal	£200	£400	£850
Corieltauvi (various types)	£150	£350	£550
Norfolk "wolf" type			
fine gold	£200	£400	£750
brassy gold	£125	£250	£450
very debased	£85	£175	£375
Whaddon Chase types	£200	£400	£850
Wonersh type	£200	£400	£850
Eceni (various types)	£250	£450	£850
Remic type	£200	£350	£575
Dobunni	£250	£450	£850

Cheriton Smiler gold stater

GOLD QUARTER STATERS

	F	VF	EF
North Thames types	£155	£250	£450
North Kent types	£155	£250	£450
Eceni	£145	£200	£375
Sussex types	£100	£175	£325
Dobunni	£150	£250	£500

SILVER COINAGE

	F	VF	EF
North Thames types	£85	£155	£300
South Thames types	£85	£155	£300
Durotriges full stater			
fine silver	£65	£155	£275
base silver	£20	£50	£125
Durotriges small silver	£10	£30	£60
Dobunni	£50	£100	£250

(Note—Most examples are for base coins as better quality items are appreciably higher)

Cranborne Chase silver stater

	F	VF	EF
Corieltavi	£45	£100	£200
Eceni ("crescent" types)	£30	£75	£150
Eceni ("Norfolk god" types)	£50	£100	£250
Armorican Billon staters	£75	£150	£400

POTIN COINAGE

Kent	£20	£50	£100

BRONZE COINAGE

Durotriges debased stater	£25	£55	£100
Durotriges cast bronzes	£60	£120	£200
North Thames types. Various issues from:	£40	£100	£400

Hengistbury cast bronze

INSCRIBED CELTIC COINAGE

ATTREBATES & REGNI

Commios
stater	£550	£1500	£2850
silver unit	£75	£150	£300
silver minim	£60	£120	£250

Tincomarus
stater	£420	£850	£2000
quarter stater	£145	£250	£450
silver unit	£75	£140	£275
silver minim	£60	£120	£175

Eppillus
quarter stater	£145	£235	£425
silver unit	£75	£145	£300
bronze			Rare

Verica
stater	£255	£550	£1000
quarter stater	£155	£275	£425
silver unit	£55	£150	£250
silver minim	£50	£120	£225

Epaticcus
stater	£1000	£2000	£4000
silver unit	£50	£100	£265
silver minim	£55	£110	£275

Caratacos
silver unit	£165	£320	£465
silver minim	£110	£220	£325

CANTIACI

Dubnovellaunos
stater	£280	£565	£900
silver unit	£130	£210	£500
bronze unit	£55	£150	£350

Vosenos
stater	£1000	£2500	£5000
quarter stater	£275	£585	£1200
silver unit	£135	£285	£650

Sam
silver unit	£175	£350	£750
bronze unit	£100	£250	£500

Eppillus
stater	£1000	£2000	£4250
quarter stater	£145	£255	£500
silver unit	£65	£145	£350
bronze unit	£55	£125	£450
bronze minim	£85	£150	£275

Amminus
silver unit	£155	£320	£650
silver minim	£110	£215	£450
bronze unit	£80	£155	£500

Solidu
silver unit	£500	£1000	£2250
silver minim	£500	£1000	£1500

Tincomarus gold stater

Verica gold stater

Vosenos gold quarter stater

	F	VF	EF

DUROTRIGES
Crab
| silver | £155 | £320 | £650 |
| silver minim | £100 | £250 | £400 |

TRINOVANTES
Addedomaros
stater	£265	£500	£800
quarter stater	£155	£320	£550
bronze	£30	£65	£150
Dubnovellaunos
stater	£255	£455	£775
quarter stater	£155	£310	£550
bronze unit	£55	£130	£450

Addedomaros gold stater

CATUVELLAUNI
Tasciovanos
*stater	£225	£425	£1000
quarter stater	£130	£235	£450
silver unit	£80	£165	£375
bronze unit	£55	£135	£350
bronze half unit	£55	£135	£275
Sego
stater	£1000	£3000	£4000
quarter stater	£600	£1750	£3000
silver unit	£250	£500	£1000
bronze unit	£80	£200	£400
Dias
silver unit	£100	£200	£400
bronze unit	£50	£150	£400
Rues
bronze unit	£50	£150	£400
Andoco
stater	£510	£1250	£2750
quarter stater	£210	£420	£755
silver unit	£155	£400	£750
bronze	£85	£215	£355
Cunobelin
stater	£200	£455	£1000
quarter stater	£145	£265	£420
silver unit	£85	£165	£360
bronze unit	£65	£145	£320
AGR
quarter stater	£600	£1500	£3000
silver unit	£500	£1000	£2000

Tasciovanos gold stater

DOBUNNI
Anted
| stater | £325 | £650 | £1350 |
| silver unit | £55 | £120 | £300 |
Eisu
| stater | £450 | £750 | £1500 |
| silver unit | £55 | £125 | £325 |
Catti
| stater | £255 | £525 | £1250 |
Comux
| stater | £800 | £1650 | £3250 |
Corio
| stater | £265 | £525 | £1000 |
| quarter stater | £200 | £355 | £625 |
Boduoc
| stater | £1000 | £2250 | £3000 |
| silver unit | £200 | £500 | £850 |

Cunobelinus gold stater

Catti gold stater

ECENI	F	VF	EF
Duro Cam			
silver unit..	£110	£265	£550
Anted			
stater...	£425	£1000	£2500
silver unit..	£35	£65	£185
silver half unit...................................	£45	£95	£200
Ecen			
silver unit..	£40	£75	£185
silver half unit...................................	£45	£95	£200
Saenu			
silver unit..	£65	£125	£285
Aesu			
silver unit..	£65	£125	£285
Esuprastus			
silver unit..	£420	£1,000	£1850
Ale Scavo			
silver unit..	£355	£765	£1550

Ale Scavo silver unit

CORIELTAUVI			
Cat			
silver unit..	£400	£1000	£2000
Vep			
stater...	£400	£1000	£2500
silver unit..	£75	£150	£300
Aunt Cost			
stater...	£255	£565	£1000
silver unit..	£85	£185	£315
silver half unit...................................	£85	£160	£300
Esuprasu			
stater...	£330	£675	£1250
silver unit..	£155	£310	£550
Vep Corf			
stater...	£410	£1000	£2150
silver unit..	£80	£185	£300
silver half unit...................................	£100	£215	£450
Dumno Tigir Seno			
stater...	£755	£1850	£3150
silver unit..	£100	£185	£500
Volisios Dumnocoveros			
stater...	£310	£725	£1550
silver unit..	£100	£185	£475
silver half unit...................................	£100	£185	£450
Volisios Dumnovellaunos			
stater...	£300	£675	£1250
silver half unit...................................	£150	£335	£655
Volisios Cartivellaunos			
stater	£1000	£2000	£4000
silver half unit...................................	£300	£620	£1150
Latios Ison			
stater...	£1000	£2000	£4000
silver unit..	£155	£420	£1150

Vep CorF gold stater

Dumno Tigir Seno gold stater

Illustrations by courtesy of Chris Rudd

A SIMPLIFIED PRICE GUIDE
TO
ANCIENT COINS USED IN BRITAIN

PART II
ROMAN BRITAIN

The list below has been generously provided by coin dealer Mike Vosper. These prices are for the most common types unless otherwise noted. In most cases, especially with large bronze coins, the price for coins in extremely fine condition will be _much_ higher than the price for the same coin in very fine condition as early bronze coins are seldom found in hoards and perfect, undamaged examples are rarely available.

The illustrations provided are a representative guide to assist with identification only.

REPUBLICAN COINAGE 280–41 BC

	FROM F	VF	EF
Republican			
Quadrigatus (Janus/Quadriga)..........	£70	£200	£595
Victoriatus (Jupiter/Victory)	£20	£50	£160
Denarius (Roma/Biga)	£20	£50	£160
Denarius (other types)	£22	£55	£175
Denarius (Gallic warrior, L. Hostilius			
Saserna)..	£270	£675	£2000
Quinarius	from £22	£50	£160
Cast Aes Grave, As	£175	£500	—
Struck As/Semis	£50	£155	—
Struck Triens/Quadrands.................	£42	£110	—

Gnaeus Pompey Junior

IMPERIAL COINAGE 49–27 BC

	FROM F	VF	EF
Pompey the Great			
Denarius (Hd. of Pompilius/Prow).....	£95	£260	£750
Scipio			
Denarius (Jupiter/Elephant)	£45	£125	£350
Cato Uticensis			
Quinarius (Bacchus/Victory)	£25	£80	£250
Gnaeus Pompey Junior			
Denarius (Roma/Hispania)	£70	£210	£525
Sextus Pompey			
Denarius (his bust)	£185	£610	£1600
Denarius (other types)	£110	£350	£975
As	£100	£310	—
Julius Caesar			
Aureus	£400	£1000	£2200
Denarius ("elephant" type)	£70	£195	£475
Denarius (Caesar portrait)	£220	£650	£1800
Denarius (heads of godesses)	£60	£140	£420

Julius Caesar

	FROM F	VF	EF
Brutus			
Denarius (his portrait/EID MAR)	£7000	£22500	£60500
Denarius (others)	£115	£350	£975
Cassius			
Denarius...	£90	£255	£720
Ahenobarbus			
Denarius	£250	£700	£2250
Mark Antony			
Denarius ("Galley" type)	£45	£120	£330
Denarius (with portrait)	£95	£285	£725
Denarius (other types)	£70	£185	£495
AR quinarius	£40	£110	£275
Mark Antony & Lepidus			
AR quinarius	£35	£110	£295
Mark Antony & Octavian			
AR denarius	£135	£380	£910
Mark Antony & Lucius Antony			
AR denarius	£225	£675	£1600
Mark Antony & Octavia			
AR Cistophorus	£140	£475	£1200
Cleopatra VII & Mark Antony			
AR denarius	£650	£2500	£8000
Fulvia			
AR quinarius	£65	£185	£555
Octavian (later known as Augustus)			
Gold Aureus	£880	£2310	£5575
Denarius	£80	£230	£655
Quinarius (ASIA RECEPTA)	£35	£95	£265
AE Sestertius	£110	£410	—
Octavian & Mark Antony			
AR denarius	£85	£285	£710
Quinarius	£32	£85	£255

Brutus

Mark Antony & Octavian

IMPERIAL COINAGE—Julio-Claudian Dynasty 27BC–69 AD

Augustus			
Gold Aureus (Caius & Lucius Caesar)	£485	£1280	£2850
AR Cistophorus..................................	£110	£310	£815
Denarius (Caius & Lucius Caesar)	£45	£130	£385
Denarius (other types)	£65	£185	£485
AR quinarius	£45	£120	£295
Sestertius (large SC)	£70	£210	£800
Dupondius or as (large SC)...............	£40	£110	£335
Quadrans	£12	£35	£100
Divus Augustus (struck under Tiberius)			
As	£55	£155	£430
Augustus & Agrippa			
Dupondius (Crocodile rev)	£45	£155	£510
Livia			
Sestertius	£130	£455	£1850
Dupondius	£130	£450	£1800
Gaius Caesar			
AR denarius	£285	£875	£2315
Tiberius			
Aureus (Tribute penny)	£410	£1200	£2760
Denarius (Tribute penny)	£65	£180	£450
Sestertius	£135	£445	£1850
Dupondius	£155	£485	£1460
As	£55	£145	£485
Drusus			
Sestertius...	£200	£610	£2560
As	£65	£185	£525

Augustus

Tiberius

	FROM F	VF	EF
Caligula			
Denarius (rev. portrait)	£365	£1200	£2820
Sestertius	£265	£785	£32 0
As	£75	£250	£775
Agrippa (struck under Caligula)			
As	£55	£160	£555
Germanicus (struck under Caligula or Claudius)			
As	£65	£185	£475
Agrippina Senior (struck under Caligula)			
Sestertius	£395	£1175	£4950
Nero & Drusus (struck under Caligula)			
Dupondius	£175	£500	£1,600
Claudius			
Aureus ("DE BRITANN" type)	£850	£2250	£5400
Denarius as above	£285	£800	£2250
Didrachm as above	£265	£775	£1950
Denarius other types	£250	£655	£1750
Sestertius	£140	£380	£1650
Dupondius	£55	£170	£575
As	£50	£135	£400
Quadrans	£15	£40	£115
Irregular British Sestertius	£25	£75	£275
Irregular British As	£19	£55	£180
Claudius & Agrippina Junior or Nero			
Denarius	£340	£1,000	£2,500
Nero Cludius Drusus (struck under Claudius)			
Sestertius	£175	£485	£1950
Antonia (struck under Claudius)			
Dupondius	£100	£300	£975
Britannicus			
Sestertius	£10000	£30000	—
Nero			
Aureus	£450	£1200	£2700
Denarius	£90	£260	£685
Sestertius	£150	£485	£1950
Sestertius (Port of Ostia)	£1000	£3500	£20000
Dupondius	£80	£230	£685
As	£45	£140	£425
Semis	£38	£110	£335
Quadrans	£19	£54	£140
Civil War			
Denarius	£165	£475	£1350
Galba			
Denarius	£95	£335	£955
Sestertius	£215	£655	£2800
Dupondius	£100	£310	£1000
As	£78	£235	£800
Otho			
Denarius	£195	£555	£1650
Vitellius			
Denarius	£98	£278	£825
Sestertius	£700	£2100	£7500
Dupondius	£225	£625	£2100
As	£120	£358	£1020

IMPERIAL COINAGE—Flavian Dynasty 69–96 AD

Vespasian			
Aureus	£455	£1150	£2855
Denarius	£25	£68	£210
Denarious (IVDAEA)	£65	£195	£600
Sestertius	£95	£285	£900
Dupondius	£42	£120	£405
As	£40	£112	£378

Caligula

Agrippina Senior

Claudius

Nero

Galba

	FROM F	VF	EF
Titus			
Aureus..	£450	£1200	£3950
Denarius as Caesar	£35	£100	£300
Denarius as Augustus	£40	£120	£350
Sestertius	£130	£375	£1200
Dupondius	£50	£150	£490
As	£45	£140	£460
As (IVDAEA CAPTA)	£150	£450	£1400
Julia Titi			
Denarius	£180	£560	£1635
Domitian			
Aureus	£425	£1150	£2950
Cistophorus	£110	£310	£910
Denarius as Caesar	£28	£75	£225
Denarius as Augustus	£22	£55	£178
Sestertius	£90	£278	£910
Dupondius	£38	£115	£335
As	£38	£100	£295
Ae Semis	£32	£82	£255
Ae Quadrans	£18	£52	£152
Domitia			
Cistophorus	£228	£678	£1790

Titus

Domitian

IMPERIAL COINAGE — Adoptive Emperors 96–138 AD

Nerva			
Aureus	£860	£2720	£7300
Denarius	£42	£110	£375
Sestertius	£148	£428	£1850
Sestertius (Palm-tree)	£425	£1300	£6000
Dupondius	£68	£200	£670
As	£52	£160	£560
Trajan			
Aureus	£400	£1000	£2900
Denarius	£20	£50	£160
Denarius (Trajan's Column)	£35	£100	£300
Sestertius	£62	£200	£675
Sestertius (Dacian rev.)	£65	£230	£775
Dupondius or as	£32	£90	£320
Ae Quadrands	£20	£50	£145
Plotina or Marciana			
Denarius	£400	£1250	£4000
Hadrian			
Aureus	£475	£1160	£3200
Cistophourus	£98	£300	£900
Denarius (provinces)	£38	£110	£285
Denarius other types	£22	£62	£180
Sestertius	£75	£225	£720
Sertertius (RETITVTORI province types)	£125	£395	£1460
Sestertius (Britannia std)	£2350	£7600	—
Dupondius or As	£33	£110	£360
As (Britannia std).............................	£160	£475	—
Ae Semiis or Quadrands...................	£25	£78	£200
Eygpt. Alexandrian Billon Tetradrachm	£28	£78	£310
Sabina			
Denarius	£28	£80	£235
Sestertius	£110	£325	£1150
As or Dupondius	£60	£175	£545
Aelius Ceasar			
Denarius	£68	£210	£555
Sestertius	£138	£410	£1300
As or Dupondius	£58	£165	£610

Nerva

Trajan

Hadrian

IMPERIAL COINAGE—The Antonines 138–193 AD

Antoninus Pius

	F	VF	EF
Antoninus Pius			
Aureus	£325	£800	£2500
Denarius	£15	£35	£145
Sestertius Britannia seated	£450	£1350	£5700
Sestertius other types	£42	£140	£480
As – Britannia rev.	£62	£185	£650
Dupondius or As other types	£25	£65	£275
Antoninus Pius & Marcus Aurelius			
Denarius (bust each side)	£28	£78	£250
Diva Faustina Senior			
Denarius	£15	£40	£135
Sestertius	£35	£135	£460
As or Dupondius	£20	£60	£230
Marcus Aurelius			
Aureus	£375	£850	£2550
Denarius as Caesar	£15	£42	£145
*Denarius as Augustus	£14	£35	£130
Sestertius	£40	£135	£450
As or Dupondius	£22	£68	£245
Faustina Junior			
Denarius	£15	£40	£142
Sestertius	£38	£130	£425
As or Dupondius	£18	£55	£215
Lucius Verus			
Denarius	£18	£50	£175
Sestertius	£50	£170	£600
As or Dupondius	£25	£80	£280
Lucilla			
Denarius	£18	£50	£180
Sestertius	£50	£165	£575
As or Dupondius	£27	£80	£280
Commodus			
Aureus	£425	£1150	£3600
Denarius as Caesar	£25	£55	£165
Denarius as Augustus	£16	£42	£135
Denarius as DIVVS	£20	£55	£155
Sestertius	£40	£125	£475
Sestertius (VICT BRIT)	£90	£275	£900
As or Dupondius	£22	£65	£225
Crispina			
Denarius	£20	£58	£195
Sestertius	£65	£195	£645
As or Dupondius	£30	£90	£275

Marcus Aurelius

Faustina Junior

IMPERIAL COINAGE—The Severan Dynasty 193–235 AD

	F	VF	EF
Pertinax			
Denarius	£185	£525	£1300
Sestertius	£350	£975	£3400
Didius Julianus			
Denarius	£325	£850	£1850
Sestertius or Dupondius	£240	£660	£2150
Manlia Scantilla or Didia Clara			
Denarius	£325	£860	£2600
Pescennius Niger			
Denarius	£200	£625	£1700
Clodius Albinus			
Denarius as Caesar	£38	£110	£310
Denarius as Augustus	£70	£210	£575
Sestertius	£150	£500	£2000
As	£75	£228	£775

Lucius Verus

Commodus

	FROM F	VF	EF
Septimius Severus			
Aureus	£495	£1250	£3800
Aureus (VICT BRIT)	£950	£3000	£7000
Denarius	£12	£38	£110
Denarius (VICT BRIT)	£20	£65	£200
Sestertius other types	£65	£195	£625
Sestertius (VICT BRIT)	£28	£70	£210
Sestertius other types....................	£65	£195	£625
Sestertius (VICT BRIT)	£280	£825	£2900
Dupondius or as	£48	£128	£395
Dupondius or As (VICT BRIT)	£100	£295	£955
Julia Domna			
Denarius	£12	£32	£110
Sestertius	£65	£195	£595
As or Dupondius	£45	£125	£398
Caracalla			
Aureus (VICT BRIT)	£1000	£3100	£7900
Denarius as Caesar..........................	£12	£38	£115
Denarius as Augustus	£12	£30	£110
Denarius (VICT BRIT)	£27	£75	£210
Antoninianus	£28	£70	£178
Sestertius	£75	£230	£800
Sestertius (VICT BRIT)	£240	£700	£2350
Dupondius or As	£40	£125	£395
Dupondius or As (VICT BRIT)	£95	£255	£778
Plautilla			
Denarius	£20	£48	£160
Geta			
Denarius as Caesar	£14	£35	£110
Denarius as Augustus	£18	£50	£165
Denarius (VICT BRIT)	£28	£82	£240
Sestertius......................................	£110	£300	£925
Sestertius (VICT BRIT)	£240	£660	£2300
Dupondius or as	£65	£195	£600
As (VICT BRIT)	£98	£275	£875
Macrinus			
Antoninianus	£85	£250	£525
Denarius	£28	£80	£250
Sestertius	£195	£575	£2300
Diadumenian			
Denarius	£50	£160	£450
Dupondius or As............................	£120	£340	£1100
Elagabalus			
Aureus	£650	£1850	£5100
Antoninianus	£18	£50	£155
Denarius	£12	£28	£95
Sestertius	£85	£250	£825
Dupondius or As	£55	£142	£540
Julia Paula			
Denarius	£28	£80	£265
Aquilla Severa			
Denarius	£50	£145	£435
Julia Soaemias			
Denarius	£25	£60	£175
Dupondius or As	£60	£185	£600
Julia Maesa			
Denarius	£15	£42	£125
Sestertius	£82	£230	£795
Severus Alexander			
Aureus	£350	£900	£2750
Denarius as Caesar..........................	£60	£160	£400
Denarius as Augustus.....................	£10	£29	£95
Denarius	£10	£30	£90
Sestertius	£32	£85	£300
Dupondius or As	£22	£70	£238

Septimus Severus

Julia Domna

Geta

Macrinus

Elagabalus

Julia Maesa

	FROM F	VF	EF
Orbiana			
Denarius	£55	£155	£395
As	£88	£240	£775
Julia Mamaea			
Denarius	£12	£30	£100
Sestertius	£32	£90	£310

Orbiana

IMPERIAL COINAGE—Military Anarchy 235–270 AD

	FROM F	VF	EF
Maximinus I			
Denarius	£13	£35	£110
Sestertius, Dupondius or As	£35	£95	£300
Diva Paula			
Denarius	£110	£310	£875
Maximus Caesar			
Denarius	£52	£155	£475
Sestertius	£52	£155	£465
Gordian I & II, Africanus			
Denarius	£225	£800	£2200
Balbinus & Pupienus			
Antoninianus	£65	£185	£480
Denarius	£55	£168	£450
Gordian III			
Antoninianus	£5	£15	£55
Denarius	£9	£25	£90
Sestertius or As	£22	£75	£220
Tranquillina			
Common Colonial	£30	£100	£350
Philip I			
Antoninianus "Animal"			
Lion, stag, antelope, wolf & twins	£14	£42	£135
Other Antoninianus	£6	£17	£55
Sestertius, Dupondius or As	£25	£75	£225
Otacilla Severa			
Antoniniaus	£8	£18	£65
Antoninianus "Hipo"	£16	£55	£150
Sestertius	£25	£82	£250
Philip II			
Antoninianus	£7	£18	£65
Antoninianus "Goat"	£16	£50	£150
Sestertius, Dupondius or As	£28	£85	£250
Pacatian			
Antoninianus	£1250	£3750	—
Trajan Decius			
Antoninianus	£6	£16	£65
Antoninianus (DIVI series Augustus, Trajan etc)	£32	£80	£200
Double Sestertius	£170	£550	£2000
Sestertius, Dupondius or As	£27	£85	£250
Herennius Etruscilla			
Antoniniaus	£7	£18	£65
Sestertius, Dupondius or As	£32	£95	£310
Herennius Etruscus			
Antoninianus	£17	£45	£150
Sestertius, Dupondius or As	£58	£175	£525
Hostilian			
Antoninianus as Caesar	£28	£82	£275
Antoninianus as Augustus	£65	£215	£600
Trebonianus Gallus			
Antoninianus	£8	£18	£65
Sestertius or As	£25	£82	£275
Volusian			
Antoninianus	£10	£25	£85
Sestertius	£28	£85	£275

Julia Mamaea

Diva Paula

Gordian III

Trajan Decius

Hostilian

	FROM F	VF	EF
Aemilian			
Antoninianus	£48	£135	£350
Valerian I			
Antoninianus	£6	£18	£62
Sestertius & As	£45	£145	£475
Diva Mariniana			
Antoninianus	£35	£110	£310
Gallienus			
Silver Antoninianus	£8	£22	£60
Ae Antoninianus	£5	£14	£48
Ae Antoninianus (Military bust)	£8	£24	£75
AE Antoninianus (Legionary)	£50	£175	—
Ae Sestertius	£40	£130	£412
Ae Denarius	£45	£125	£365
Saloninus			
Ae Antoninianus	£6	£16	£52
Valerian II			
Billon Antoninianus	£10	£30	£95
Saloninus			
Antoninianus	£12	£35	£100
Macrianus & Quietus			
Billon Antoninianus	£40	£100	£280
Regalianus or Dryantilla			
Billon Antoninianus	£1500	£5000	—
Postumus			
Silver Antoninianus	£8	£25	£65
Ae Antoninianus	£5	£17	£45
Radiated sestertius	£45	£155	£575
Laelianus			
Ae Antoninianus	£98	£275	£750
Marius			
Ae Antoninianus	£35	£100	£275
Victorinus			
Ae Antoninianus	£5	£17	£45
Tetricus I & II			
Ae Antoninianus	£6	£17	£45
Claudius II Gothicus			
Ae Antoninianus	£4	£15	£40
Egypt, Alexandrian Billon tetradrachm	£5	£15	£45
DIVO Ae Antoninianus	£5	£20	£55
Quintillus			
Ae Antoninianus	£13	£38	£90

Postumus

Aurelian

Severina

IMPERIAL COINAGE—The Illyrian Emperors—270–285 AD

	FROM F	VF	EF
Aurelian			
Ae Antoninianus	£8	£22	£60
Ae Denarius	£18	£55	£150
Vabalathus & Aurelian			
Ae Antoninianus (bust both sides) ...	£25	£60	£175
Vabalathus			
Ae Antoninianus	£200	£500	—
Severina			
Ae Antoninianus	£15	£42	£100
Ae As..	£35	£100	£275
Zenobia			
Eygpt, Alexandrian Billon Tetradrachm	£500	£1750	—
Tacitus			
Ae Antoninianus	£12	£30	£90
Florian			
Ae Antoninianus	£27	£75	£200

Tacitus

Florian

	FROM F	VF	EF
Probus			
Gold Aureus	£1000	£2500	£5500
Ae Antoninianus	£7	£19	£65
Antoninianus (military or imp. busts)	£10	£30	£95
Antoninianus (VICTOR GERM rev.) ..	£12	£37	£120
Egypt, Alexandrian Billon tetradrachm	£2	£8	£35
Carus			
Ae Antoninianus	£13	£38	£100
Numerian			
Ae Antoninianus	£12	£38	£95
Carinus			
Ae Antoninianus	£12	£30	£80
Magna Urbica			
Ae Antoninianus	£55	£170	£425
Julian of Pannonia			
Ae Antoninianus	£210	£600	£1800

Diocletian

IMPERIAL COINAGE — The Tetrarchy 285–307 AD

Diocletian			
Gold Aureus	£595	£1755	£4400
AR Argenteus	£85	£250	£645
Ae Antoninianus & Radiates	£7	£25	£65
Ae Follis (London Mint)	£12	£40	£110
As above with LON mint mark	£100	£285	£760
Ae Follis (other mints)	£9	£27	£82
Ae Follis (Imperial bust)....................	£23	£75	£225
Maximianus			
AR Argenteus	£85	£250	£625
Ae Follis (London mint)	£12	£40	£110
Ae Follis (other mints)	£10	£27	£82
Ae Follis (MONETA rev.)	£10	£35	£95
Carausius			
Aureus	£5000	£15000	—
Denarius	£250	£750	£2260
Ae Antoninianus (PAX)......................	£25	£65	£295
As above but full silvering	£30	£95	£425
Legionary Antoninianus	£70	£195	£775
Expectate Veni Antoninianus	£90	£275	—
In the name of Diocletian or Maximian	£30	£95	£425
Allectus			
Aureus..	£6500	£20000	—
Ae Antoninianus	£25	£80	£345
As above but full silvering	£40	£120	£500
Quinarius	£25	£85	£310
Constantius I			
AR Argenteus	£90	£275	£695
Ae Follis (London Mint)	£14	£40	£110
Ae Follis (other mints)	£9	£27	£80
Ae Follis (SALVS rev.)......................	£11	£35	£110
Ae 4 (Lion or Eagle)	£9	£28	£85
Galerius			
Ae Follis (London mint)	£12	£30	£95
Ae Follis (other mints)	£8	£25	£65
Galeria Valeria			
Ae Follis	£28	£75	£225
Severus II			
Ae Follis (London mint)	£35	£95	£275
Ae Follis (other mints)	£27	£75	£220
Ae Radiate	£15	£45	£135
Ae Denarius	£28	£85	£225
Maximinus II			
Ae Follis (London mint)	£12	£35	£110
Ae Follis (other mints)	£6	£18	£55
Ae Radiate	£8	£26	£75

Maximianus

Carausius

Severus II

Maximinus II

	FROM F	VF	EF
Maxentius			
Ae Follis	£8	£27	£85
Romulus			
Ae Follis	£40	£125	£425
Licinius I			
Billon Argenteus	£60	£190	£575
Ae Follis (London mint)	£7	£20	£60
Ae Follis (other mints)	£6	£16	£55
AE3	£6	£15	£45
Licinius II			
AE3	£7	£20	£65
Alexander or Martinian			
AE	£1250	£4000	—

Licinius II

IMPERIAL COINAGE—Family of Constantine 307–350 AD

Constantine I			
Billon Argenteus	£50	£150	£450
Ae Follis (London mint)	£8	£23	£65
As above—helmeted bust	£13	£42	£120
Ae Follis (other mints) as Caesar ...	£12	£45	£150
Ae Follis (other mints) as Augustus	£4	£13	£45
AE3	£4	£13	£42
AE3 (London mint)	£7	£20	£60
AE3 (SARMATIA rev)	£10	£30	£95
Urbs Roma / Wolf & twins AE3/4....	£4	£14	£45
Constantinopolis AE3/4	£3	£12	£40
Fausta & Helena			
AE3 (London mint)	£50	£145	£395
AE3 (other mints)	£14	£40	£125
Theodora			
AE4	£7	£25	£65
Crispus			
AE3 (London mint)	£8	£25	£75
AE3	£7	£18	£58
Delmatius			
AE3/4	£12	£40	£95
Hanniballianus Rex			
AE4	£82	£225	£650
Constantine II			
AE3 (London mint)	£8	£23	£65
AE3	£5	£16	£50
AE3/4	£2	£8	£30
Constans			
AE2 (centenionalis)	£9	£25	£75
AE3 (half centenionalis)	£5	£20	£50
AE4	£4	£8	£35
Constantius II			
Gold Solidus	£185	£450	£,200
Siliqua	£23	£65	£165
AE2 (or centenionalis)	£7	£22	£60
AE3 (or half centenionalis)	£6	£16	£42
AE3 (London mint)..........................	£20	£60	£180
AE3...	£2	£6	£28

Constantine I

Constantine II

Magnentius

IMPERIAL COINAGE—Late period to the collapse of the Empire 350 AD to end

Magnentius			
Gold Solidus....................................	£525	£1600	£4000
Silver Siliqua	£200	£750	£2000
Double centenionalis	£45	£155	£500
Centenionalis	£15	£45	£160
Decentius			
Double centenionalis.......................	£65	£225	£7755
Centenionalis	£17	£55	£175
Vetranio			
AE2 (centenionalis)	£35	£115	£300
AE3 (half centenionalis)	£29	£95	£245

Vetranio

	FROM F	VF	EF
Nepotian			
AE2 (centenionalis)	£1750	£5500	—
Constantius Gallus			
AE2 (centenionalis)	£11	£35	£95
AE3 (half centenionalis)	£5	£17	£50
Julian II			
Siliqua	£23	£60	£155
AE1	£40	£125	£360
AE3 (helmeted bust)	£8	£25	£75
Anonymous, Serapis + Jupiter AE3	£175	£500	—
Jovian			
AE1	£65	£210	£580
AE3	£12	£38	£95
Valentinian I			
Sold Solidus	£120	£280	£625
Silver Milliarense	£165	£500	£1200
Siliqua	£25	£75	£155
AE3	£5	£18	£50
Valens			
Gold Solidus	£120	£280	£625
Silver Milliarense	£190	£575	£1375
Siliqua	£22	£65	£160
AE3	£5	£18	£55
Procopius			
AE3	£45	£138	£425
Gratian			
Silver Milliarense	£165	£500	£1200
Siliqua	£24	£65	£165
AE3	£4	£15	£55
AE4	£4	£12	£38
Valentinian II			
Solidus	£160	£395	£850
Siliqua	£25	£75	£190
AE2	£12	£28	£80
AE4	£4	£12	£35
Theodosius I			
Solidus	£160	£395	£850
Siliqua	£28	£85	£210
AE2	£10	£30	£85
AE3	£8	£25	£75
Aelia Flaccilla			
AE2	£28	£85	£250
AE4	£18	£48	£125
Magnus Maximus			
Solidus (AVGOB)	£4500	£11000	—
Solidus	£700	£1800	£4500
Siliqua	£30	£90	£225
Siliqua (AVGPS)	£700	£1,800	—
AE2	£18	£55	£160
Flavius Victor			
Silver Sliqua	£100	£300	£725
AE4	£35	£85	£250
Eugenius			
Silver Siliqua	£110	£335	£800
Arcadius			
Gold Solidus...................................	£100	£260	£550
Silver Siliqua..................................	£25	£75	£195
Silver Half-siliqua	£90	£265	£675
AE2	£12	£27	£75
AE4	£4	£10	£25
Eudoxia			
AE3	£25	£65	£185

Julian II

Jovian

Valentinian I

Valens

Theodosius I

Arcadius

Honorius

Gold Solidus	£110	£260	£550
Silver Siliqua	£30	£85	£210
AE4	£6	£18	£48

Constantine III

Silver Siliqua	£100	£310	£725

Theodosius II

Gold Solidus	£110	£265	£520

Johannes

AE4	£110	£425	—

Valentinian III

Gold Soldius....................................	£110	£265	£500
AE4	£28	£75	£250

Ae = bronze; AE 1, 2, 3, 4 = bronze coins in descending order of size.

Honorius

Theodosius II

Illustrations by courtesy of Classical Numismatic Group/Seaby Coins.

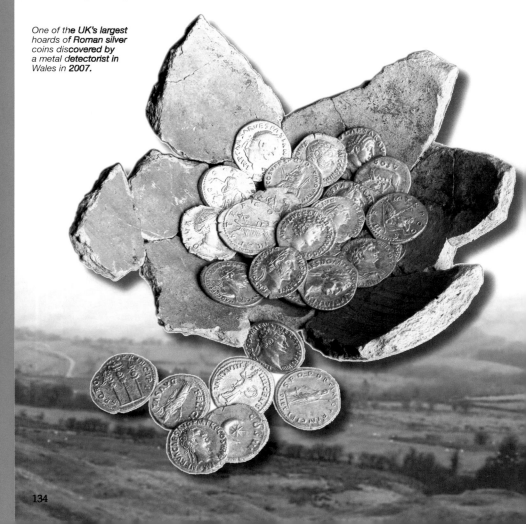

One of the UK's largest hoards of Roman silver coins discovered by a metal detectorist in Wales in 2007.

A SIMPLIFIED PRICE GUIDE
TO
ENGLISH HAMMERED COINS

PART I
959–1485

INTRODUCTION

We have taken our starting point for hammered coin prices back to the Anglo-Saxon reign of Edgar; who could reasonably claim to be the first king of All England. Also it is from this time onwards that we start to get regular "portraits" as well as moneyers and mints on most issues. This gives a total of eight rulers to the list of kings prior to the Norman Conquest and most of these have coin issues that can be purchased quite reasonably. It is also worth pointing out here that of course coins had previously been struck in England for approximately 1000 years prior to our listings by Celtic, Roman and earlier Saxon rulers, details of which can be found in more specific publications.

PRICING

The prices given in the following pages are intended to be used as a "Pocket book guide" to the values of the *most common* coins within any denomination of any one reign. The price quoted is what a collector may expect to pay for such a piece in the condition indicated. For more detailed information we recommend the reader to one of the many specialist publications.

GRADING

The prices quoted are for three different grades of condition: Fine (F), Very Fine (VF) and Extremely Fine (EF). A "Fine" coin is assumed to be a fairly worn, circulated, piece but with all or most of the main features and lettering still clear. "Very Fine" is a middle grade with a small amount of wear and most details fairly clear. For this edition we have included the prices for coins in Extremely Fine condition where appropriate, although very few hammered coins actually turn up in this grade (i.e. nearly mint state with hardly any wear). In some instances the prices quoted are theoretically based and are only included to provide a guide. It is important to note that on all hammered coins the very nature of striking, i.e. individually, by hand, means hammered coinage is rarely a straight grade and when listed by a dealer the overall condition will often be qualified by terms such as: *weak in parts, struck off-centre, cracked or chipped flan, double struck,* etc. When applicable the price should be adjusted accordingly.

HISTORY

Below the heading for each monarch we have given a few historical notes as and when they apply to significant changes in the coinage.

EDGAR
(959–975)

	F	VF	EF
Edgar Penny, non portrait (2 line inscription)	£200	—	—

EDWARD THE MARTYR
(975–978)

	F	VF	EF
Edward, Penny, Portrait	£900	£2400	—

AETHELRED II
(978–1016)

	F	VF	EF
Aethelred II, Penny, last small cross type (First hand type illustrated)	£110	£225	—

CNUT
(1016–1035)

	F	VF	EF
Cnut, Penny (short cross type) (*Helmet type illustrated*)	£85	£150	£325

HAROLD I
(1035–40)

	F	VF	EF
Harold I, Penny	£250	£550	—

HARTHACANUTE
(1035–42)

	F	VF	EF
Harthacanute, Penny, English Mint (in his own name)	£875	£2000	—
Harthacanute, Penny, Danish type	£250	£560	—

Danish type

EDWARD THE CONFESSOR
(1042–66)

	F	VF	EF
Edward the Confessor, Penny	£100	£185	—

HAROLD II
(1066)

	F	VF	EF
Harold II, Penny	£600	£1300	—

WILLIAM I
(1066–87)

The Norman Conquest had very little immediate effect on the coinage of England. The Anglo-Saxon standard of minting silver pennies was very high and the practice of the moneyer putting his name and mint town on the reverse continued as before, except with William's portrait of course. It is worth noting here that non-realistic, stylised portraits were used until the reign of Henry VII.
There are eight major types of pennies of which the last, the PAXS type, is by far the commonest.

	F	VF	EF
William I, Penny	£225	£420	£850

WILLIAM II
(1087–1100)

Very little change from his father's reign except that five new types were issued, most of which were much more crudely designed than previous, all are scarce.

	F	VF	EF
William II, Penny	£575	£1300	—

HENRY I
(1100–35)

There are fifteen different types of penny for this reign of which the last two are the most common. Most issues are of a very poor standard both in workmanship and metal, the prices reflect a poor quality of issue.

	F	VF	EF
Henry I, Penny	£175	£400	—

STEPHEN
(1135–54)

This is historically a very complicated time for the coinage, mainly due to civil war and a consequential lack of central control in the country which resulted in very poor quality and deliberately damaged pieces. Coins were struck not only in the name of Stephen and his main rival claimant Matilda but also by their supporters. The commonest issue is the "Watford" type; so named, as are many issues, after the area in which a hoard was found.

	F	VF	EF
Stephen, Penny	£220	£600	—

HENRY II
(1154–89)

There were two distinct issues struck during this reign. The first, Cross and Crosslets or "Tealby" coinage (named after Tealby in Lincolnshire), continued to be very poorly made and lasted 20 years. However, in 1180 the new and superior "Short Cross" issue commenced, being issued from only twelve major

	F	VF	EF
Henry II, Penny, Tealby	£85	£220	—

| Henry II, Penny, Short Cross | £50 | £135 | — |

RICHARD I
(1189–1199)

There were no major changes during this reign, in fact pennies continued to be struck with his father Henry's name throughout the reign. The coins struck under Richard tend to be rather crude in style.

	F	VF	EF
Richard I, Penny	£70	£175	—

JOHN
(1199–1216)

As with his brother before him, there were no major changes during the reign of King John, and pennies with his father's name were struck throughout the reign, although they tended to be somewhat neater in style than those struck during the reign of Richard I.

	F	VF	EF
John, Penny..	£45	£125	£250

HENRY III
(1216–72)

The coinage during Henry III's reign continued as before with the short cross issue. However, in 1247 a new long cross design was introduced to prevent clipping. This design was to last in one form or another for many centuries.

	F	VF	EF
Henry III, Penny, Short Cross	£30	£60	£140

	F	VF	EF
Henry III, Penny, Long Cross...................	£20	£50	£125

EDWARD I
(1272–1307)

After a few years of issuing similar pieces to his father, in 1279 Edward I ordered a major re-coinage. This consisted of well-made pennies, halfpennies and farthings in relatively large quantities, and for a brief period a groat (four pence) was produced. The pennies are amongst the most common of all hammered coins.

	F	VF	EF
Edward I (and Edward II)			
Groat (often damaged).....................	£1800	£6000	—
Penny...	£20	£50	£120
Halfpenny....................................	£20	£70	£180
Farthing......................................	£15	£60	£170

Edward I penny

EDWARD II
(1307–1327)

The coinage of Edward II differs in only a very few minor details from that of Edward I and are of similar value.

EDWARD III
(1327–77)

This was a long reign which saw major changes in the coinage, the most significant being the introduction of a gold coinage (based on the Noble, valued at 6s 8d, and its fractions) and a regular issue of a large silver groat (and half groat). The mints were limited to a few episcopal cities but coins of English type were also struck in the newly-acquired Calais.

	F	VF	EF
Gold			
Noble	£525	£1200	£2650
Half Noble	£325	£850	£1750
Quarter Noble	£225	£500	£850
Silver			
Groat	£50	£160	£600
Half Groat	£30	£90	£300
Penny	£20	£60	£175
Half Penny	£18	£50	£140
Farthing	£35	£75	£175

Gold Noble

RICHARD II
(1377–1399)

The denominations continued during this reign much as before. However, coins are quite rare mainly due to the lack of bullion gold and silver going into the mints, mainly because of an inbalance with European weights and fineness.

	F	VF	EF
Gold			
Noble	£700	£1650	£3250
Half Noble	£750	£1900	—
Quarter Noble	£360	£825	£1350
Silver			
Groat	£400	£1150	—
Half Groat	£200	£580	—
Penny	£60	£175	—
Half Penny	£40	£125	—
Farthing	£125	£275	—

Gold Noble

HENRY IV
(1399–1413)

Because of the continuing problems with the scarcity of gold and silver the coinage was reduced in weight in 1412, towards the end of the reign. All coins of this reign are quite scarce.

Noble

	F	VF
Gold		
Noble	£1500	£3500
Half Noble	£2000	£5250
Quarter Noble	£500	£1200
Silver		
Groat	£1825	£5550
Half Groat	£500	£1250
Penny	£280	£750
Half Penny	£250	£500
Farthing	£600	£1400

HENRY V
(1413–22)

Monetary reform introduced towards the end of his father's reign in 1412 improved the supply of bullion and hence coins of Henry V are far more common. All of the main denominations continued as before.

Penny

	F	VF	EF
Gold			
Noble	£700	£1500	£3000
Half Noble	£600	£1360	—
Quarter Noble	£280	£675	£1100
Silver			
Groat	£150	£425	—
Half Groat	£100	£300	—
Penny	£35	£135	—
Half Penny	£25	£75	—
Farthing	£150	£475	—

HENRY VI
(1422–61 and again 1470–71)

Although there were no new denominations during these reigns (see Edward IV below), Henry's first reign saw eleven different issues, each for a few years and distinguished by privy marks, i.e. crosses, pellets, annulets, etc.

HENRY VI *continued*

	F	VF	EF
Gold			
First reign—			
Noble	£550	£1300	£2500
Half Noble	£375	£1000	£1750
Quarter Noble	£225	£495	£900
2nd reign—			
Angel	£1350	£3250	—
Half Angel	£1600	£4500	—
Silver			
Groat	£50	£120	£240
Half Groat	£35	£85	£180
Penny	£30	£80	£200
Half Penny	£15	£50	£125
Farthing	£100	£250	—

Groat

EDWARD IV
(1461–70 and again 1471–83)

The significant changes during these reigns were the replacement of the noble by the rose ryal (and revalued at 10 shillings) and the introduction of the angel at the old noble value. We also start to see mint-marks or initial marks appearing, usually at the top of the coin, they were used to denote the period of issue for dating purposes and often lasted for two to three years.

	F	VF	EF
Gold			
Ryal	£600	£1350	£2350
Half Ryal	£500	£1200	£1000
Quarter Ryal	£325	£800	£1200
Angel	£500	£1100	£2150
Half Angel	£475	£1100	£2000
Silver			
Groat	£50	£140	£350
Half Groat	£45	£115	£275
Penny	£35	£90	£225
Half Penny	£25	£85	—
Farthing	£230	£600	—

Gold Ryal

RICHARD III
(1483–85)

The close of the Yorkist Plantagenet and the beginning of the Medieval period come together at this time. There are no new significant numismatic changes but most coins of Richard whilst not really rare, continue to be very popular and priced quite high.

	F	VF	EF
Gold			
Angel	£1750	£4800	—
Half Angel	£3250	£8500	—
Silver			
Groat	£575	£1400	—
Half Groat	£600	£1650	—
Penny	£240	£625	—
Half Penny	£180	£450	—
Farthing	£775	£2000	—

Gold Angel

PART II: 1485–1663

Among the more significant features of the post-Renaissance period as it affected coinage is the introduction of realistic portraiture during the reign of Henry VII. We also have a much wider and varied number of new and revised denominations, for example eleven different gold denominations of Henry VIII and the same number of silver for Elizabeth I. Here we only mention the introduction or changes in the main denominations, giving a value for all of them, once again listing the commonest type.

HENRY VII
(1485–1509)

The gold sovereign of 20 shillings makes its first appearance in 1489 as does the testoon (later shilling) in about 1500. The silver penny was re-designed to a rather crude likeness of the sovereign.

Profile Groat

	F	VF	EF
Gold			
Sovereign	£11,000	£30,000	—
Ryal	£12,500	£35,000	—
Angel	£500	£1100	—
Half Angel	£475	£1050	—
Silver			
Testoon 1/-	£8500	£18,500	—
Groat	£60	£165	£450
Half Groat	£30	£90	£250
Penny	£35	£95	£200
Half Penny	£20	£75	—
Farthing	£175	£600	—

HENRY VIII
(1509–47)

After a long initial period of very little change in the coinage, in 1526 there were many, with an attempt to bring the gold/silver ratio in line with the continental currencies. Some gold coins only lasted a short time and are very rare. The crown (in gold) makes its first appearance. Towards the end of the reign we see large issues of debased silver coins (with a high copper content) bearing the well-known facing portrait of the ageing King. These tend to turn up in poor condition.

Gold			
Sovereign	£3000	£9000	—
Half Sovereign	£550	£1500	—
Angel	£500	£1100	£2000
Half Angel	£425	£1000	£1750
Quarter Angel	£450	£1100	—
George Noble	£5000	£14,000	—
Half George Noble	Rare	Rare	—
Crown of the rose	Rare	Rare	—
Crown of the double rose	£475	£1000	£1850
Half Crown of the double rose	£400	£875	—
Silver			
Testoon 1/-	£650	£2650	—
Groat	£85	£275	£550
Half Groat	£45	£130	£375
Penny	£35	£120	£225
Half Penny	£25	£80	—
Farthing	£220	£600	—

Gold Sovereign

EDWARD VI
(1547–53)

Some of the coins struck in the first few years of this short reign could really be called Henry VIII posthumous issues as there is continuity in both name and style from his father's last issue. However, overlapping this period are portrait issues of the boy King, particularly shillings (usually poor quality coins). This period also sees the first dated English coin (shown in Roman numerals). In 1551 however, a new coinage was introduced with a restored silver quality from the Crown (dated 1551) down to the new sixpence and threepence.

	F	VF	EF
Gold			
Sovereign (30s)	£3500	£9000	—
Half Sovereign	£1150	£2750	—
Crown	£1200	£3300	—
Half Crown	£1050	£3000	—
Angel	£5500	£15000	—
Half Angel	—	—	—
Sovereign (20s)	£2500	£6500	—
Silver			
Crown	£700	£1900	—
Half Crown	£600	£1350	—
Shilling	£90	£375	£1000
Sixpence	£100	£450	—
Groat	£750	£2000	—
Threepence	£175	£650	—
Half Groat	£300	£825	—
Penny	£50	£200	—
Half Penny	£150	£500	—
Farthing	£750	£2400	—

Crowned bust half sovereign

MARY
(1553–54)

The early coins of Mary's sole reign are limited and continue to use the same denominations as Edward, except that the gold ryal was reintroduced.

	F	VF
Gold		
Sovereign (30s)	£3000	£8000
Ryal	£10000	—
Angel	£1250	£3150
Half Angel	£2250	£6500
Silver		
Groat	£135	£420
Half Groat	£675	£2000
Penny	£500	£1700

Groat

PHILIP & MARY
(1554–58)

After a very short reign alone, Mary married Philip of Spain and they technically ruled jointly (although not for very long in practise) until her death. After her marriage we see both her and Philip on the shillings and sixpences.

	F	VF
Gold		
Angel	£2600	£6750
Half Angel	£4500	—
Silver		
Shilling	£325	£1200
Sixpence	£350	£1275
Groat	£135	£440
Half Groat	£375	£950
Penny	£80	£235

Shilling

ELIZABETH I
(1558–1603)

As might be expected with a long reign there are a number of significant changes in the coinage which include several new denominations—so many in silver that every value from the shilling downwards was marked and dated to distinguish them. Early on we have old base Edward VI shillings countermarked to a new reduced value (not priced here). Also due to a lack of small change and the expense of making a miniscule farthing we have a new threehalfpence and threefarthings. Finally we see the beginnings of a milled (machine produced) coinage for a brief period from 1561–71.

	F	VF	EF
Gold			
Sovereign (30s)	£3250	£8000	—
Ryal (15s)	£7000	£20,000	—
Angel	£675	£1600	—
Half Angel	£650	£1450	—
Quarter Angel	£550	£1300	—
Pound (20s)	£1650	£4000	—
Half Pound	£850	£2500	—
Crown	£700	£1800	—
Half Crown	£700	£1700	—
Silver			
Crown	£1150	£2850	—
Half Crown	£778	£2000	—
Shilling	£90	£320	£900
Sixpence	£50	£150	£450
Groat	£50	£175	£400
Threepence	£35	£130	£300
Half Groat	£30	£75	—
Threehalfpence	£35	£125	—
Penny	£25	£75	£150
Threefarthings	£60	£200	—
Half Penny	£30	£85	£125

Shilling

JAMES I
(1603–25)

Although the size of the gold coinage remains much the same as Elizabeth's reign, the name and weight or value of the denominations have several changes, i.e. Pound = Sovereign = Unite = Laurel. A new four shilling gold coin (thistle crown) was introduced. A number of the silver coins now have their value in Roman numerals on the coin. Relatively few angels were made from this period onwards and they are usually found pierced.

	F	VF	EF
Gold			
Sovereign (20s)	£1200	£3500	—
Unite	£420	£1000	£2150
Double crown/half unite	£325	£800	£1650
Crown	£200	£475	£1000
Thistle Crown	£225	£625	£1050
Half Crown	£175	£425	—
Rose Ryal (30s)	£1650	£4350	—
Spur Ryal (15s)	£2800	£8250	—
Angel (pierced)	£500	£1000	—
Half Angel (Unpierced)	£1400	£4250	—
Laurel	£400	£950	1750
Half Laurel	£385	£775	1500
Quarter Laurel	£200	£450	£900
Silver			
Crown	£675	£1650	—
Half Crown	£265	£800	—
Shilling	£70	£240	—
Sixpence	£60	£190	—
Half Groat	£20	£50	£100
Penny	£20	£40	£90
Half Penny	£15	£30	£50

Halfcrown

CHARLES I
(1625–49)

This reign is probably the most difficult to simplify as there are so many different issues and whole books have been produced on this period alone. From the beginning of the King's reign and throughout the Civil War, a number of mints operated for varying lengths of time, producing both regular and irregular issues. The Tower mint was taken over by Parliament in 1642 but before this a small quantity of milled coinage was produced alongside the regular hammered issues. The Court then moved to Oxford from where, for the next three years, large quantities of gold and silver were struck (including rare triple unites and large silver pounds). The most prolific of the provincial mints were those situated at Aberystwyth, York, Oxford, Shrewsbury, Bristol, Exeter, Truro, Chester and Worcester as well as some smaller mints mainly situated in the West Country. Among the more interesting coins of the period are the pieces struck on unusually-shaped flans at Newark and Pontefract whilst those towns were under siege. As many of the coins struck during the Civil War were crudely struck on hastily gathered bullion and plate, they provide a fascinating area of study. The prices indicated below are the minimum for the commonest examples of each denomination irrespective of town of origin.

	F	VF	EF
Gold			
Triple Unite (£3)	£6000	£15,000	—
Unite	£450	£1050	—
Double crown/Half unite	£350	£850	—
Crown	£200	£450	—
Angel (pierced)	£550	£1250	—
Angel (unpierced)	£1350	£4500	—
Silver			
Pound (20 shillings)	£1800	£4250	—
Half Pound	£925	£2250	—
Crown	£350	£900	—
Half Crown	£70	£175	—
Shilling	£50	£170	£550
Sixpence	£55	£185	£500
Groat	£60	£160	£325
Threepence	£50	£150	£300
Half Groat	£20	£55	£125
Penny	£20	£50	£115
Half Penny	£15	£35	£55

Triple unite

Above: Newark siege shilling.

Oxford Halfcrown

THE COMMONWEALTH
(1649–60)

After the execution of Charles I, Parliament changed the design of the coinage. They are simple non- portrait pieces with an English legend.

	F	VF	EF
Gold			
Unite	£1000	£2500	£5250
Double crown/Half unite	£650	£1650	—
Crown	£675	£1500	—
Silver			
Crown	£675	£1400	£3000
Half Crown	£225	£550	£1600
Shilling	£140	£350	£1350
Sixpence	£125	£325	£1100
Half Groat	£30	£85	£225
Penny	£30	£80	£200
Halfpenny	£25	£70	£150

Crown

CHARLES II
(1660–85)

Although milled coins had been produced for Oliver Cromwell in 1656–58, after the Restoration of the monarchy hammered coins continued to be produced until 1663, when the machinery was ready to manufacture large quantities of good milled pieces.

	F	VF	EF
Gold			
Unite	£1050	£2650	—
Double crown/Half unite	£775	£2100	—
Crown	£800	£2300	—
Silver			
Half Crown	£170	£575	—
Shilling	£150	£450	—
Sixpence	£125	£350	—
Fourpence	£30	£95	£175
Threepence	£30	£90	£165
Twopence	£20	£50	£100
Penny	£25	£60	£130

Unite

A COMPREHENSIVE PRICE GUIDE
TO THE COINS OF

THE
UNITED KINGDOM
1656–2007

including

ENGLAND
SCOTLAND
ISLE OF MAN
GUERNSEY, JERSEY, ALDERNEY

also
IRELAND

When referring to this price guide one must bear a number of important points in mind. The points listed here have been taken into consideration during the preparation of this guide and we hope that the prices given will provide a true reflection of the market at the time of going to press. Nevertheless, the publishers can accept no liability for the accuracy of the prices quoted.

1. "As struck" examples with flaws will be worth less than the indicated price.
2. Any coin which is particularly outstanding, with an attractive natural toning or in superb state will command a much *higher* price than that shown.
3. These prices refer strictly to the British market, and do not reflect outside opinions.
4. Some prices given for coins not seen in recent years are estimates based on a knowledge of the market.
5. In the case of coins of high rarity, prices are not generally given.
6. In the listing, "—" indicates, where applicable, one of the following:
    a. Metal or bullion value only
    b. Not usually found in this grade
    c. Not collected in this condition
7. Proof coins are listed in FDC under the UNC column.
8. All prices are quoted in £ sterling, exclusive of VAT (where applicable).

FIVE GUINEAS

	F	VF	EF
CHARLES II (1660–85)			
1668 First bust	£1250	£3800	£8500
1668 — Elephant	£1250	£3800	£9000
1669 —	£1500	£3800	—
1669 — Elephant	£1800	£4250	—
1670 —	£1600	£4000	£9000
1671 —	£1600	£4000	£9000
1672 —	£1600	£4000	£9000
1673 —	£1600	£4000	£9500
1674 —	£1800	£4200	£9000
1675 —	£1600	£4000	£9250
1675 — Elephant	£1600	£4100	—
1675 — Elephant & Castle		Extremely rare	
1676 —	£1700	£4200	£9500
1676 — Elephant & Castle	£1350	£4000	£8000
1677 —	£1350	£3750	£8000
1677/5 — Elephant		Extremely rare	
1677 — Elephant & Castle	£1500	£4000	£9000
1678 —	£1600	£4000	£9000
1678 — Elephant & Castle	£1750	£4500	£9500
1678/7 —	£1400	£3800	£8000
1678/7 — Elephant & Castle	£1500	£4200	£9000
1678/7 Second Bust	£1600	£4000	£8500
1679 —	£1800	£4000	£8500
1680 —	£1800	£4000	£8500
1680 — Elephant & Castle		Extremely rare	
1681 —	£1800	£4000	£8500
1681 — Elephant & Castle	£1700	£4500	£10000
1682 —	£1500	£3800	£8000
1682 — Elephant & Castle	£1500	£3800	£8500
1683 —	£1600	£3800	£8000
1683 — Elephant & Castle	£1800	£4800	£10000
1684 —	£1500	£4000	£8500
1684 — Elephant & Castle	£1550	£4200	£8500

	F	VF	EF
JAMES II (1685–88)			
1686	£1650	£6000	£13000
1687	£1350	£5000	£11000
1687 Elephant & Castle	£1650	£5000	£11000
1688	£1650	£4750	£11000
1688 Elephant & Castle	£1650	£5000	£12000

	F	VF	EF
WILLIAM AND MARY (1688–94)			
1691	£1350	£4000	£9000
1691 Elephant & Castle	£1600	£4000	£10000
1692	£1350	£4000	£9000
1692 Elephant & Castle	£1550	£4500	£11000
1693	£1350	£4000	£8500
1693 Elephant & Castle	£1800	£4500	£12000
1694	£1500	£5250	£11000
1694 Elephant & Castle	£1600	£4500	£12000

	F	VF	EF
WILLIAM III (1694–1702)			
1699 First bust	£1400	£5000	£10000
1699 — Elephant & Castle	£1600	£5000	£12000
1700 —	£1450	£5000	£11000
1701 Second bust "fine work"	£1400	£4700	£12000

	F	VF	EF

ANNE (1702–14)

Pre-Union with Scotland

	F	VF	EF
1703 VIGO below bust	£18000	£50000	£120000
1705..	£1600	£4400	£11000
1706..	£1400	£4000	£11000

Post-Union (different shields)

1706..	£1800	£4000	£10000
1709 Narrow shields............................	£1600	£4000	£10000
1711 Broader shields	£1600	£4000	£10000
1713 —	£1600	£4500	£10000
1714 —	£1600	£4500	£11500
1714/3	£1750	£4600	£12000

GEORGE I (1714–27)

1716..	£1800	£4400	£11000
1717..	£2000	£6000	£15000
1720..	£2350	£6500	£18000
1726..	£1750	£5000	£12000

GEORGE II (1727–60)

1729 Young head	£1600	£4500	£10000
1729 — E.I.C. below head.....................	£1600	£4500	£9000
1731 —	£1500	£3750	£10000
1735 —	£1500	£4600	£12500
1738 —	£2000	£5000	£10000
1741 —	£1400	£4000	£9000
1746 Old head, LIMA	£1300	£4000	£9000
1748 —	£1300	£4000	£9000
1753 —	£1500	£4000	£10000

GEORGE III (1760–1820)

1770 Patterns	—	—	£90000
1773..	—	—	£80000
1777..	—	—	£70000

TWO GUINEAS

	F	VF	EF

CHARLES II (1660–85)

	F	VF	EF
1664 First bust	£900	£2500	£5500
1664 — Elephant	£800	£2200	£4750
1665 —		Extremely rare	
1669 —		Extremely rare	
1671 —	£900	£4000	£11000
1675 Second bust	£1000	£3250	—
1676 —	£900	£3000	—
1676 — Elephant & Castle	£900	£3500	£7000
1677 —	£900	£3500	£6500
1677 — Elephant & Castle		Extremely rare	
1678/7 —	£800	£2800	£5500
1678 — Elephant		Extremely rare	
1678 — Elephant & Castle	£800	£2700	£6000
1679 —	£1000	£3500	—
1680 —	£1000	£3500	£6500
1681 —	£800	£2700	£5000
1682 — Elephant & Castle	£900	£3500	£7000
1683 —	£900	£3000	£6000
1683 — Elephant & Castle	£900	£3250	£6000
1684 —	£900	£3500	£6000
1684 — Elephant & Castle	£1000	£3500	£7000

JAMES II (1685–88)

	F	VF	EF
1687	£900	£3000	£5800
1688/7	£1100	£3500	£7000

WILLIAM AND MARY (1688–94)

	F	VF	EF
1691 Elephant & Castle		Extremely rare	
1693	£900	£2500	£5750
1693 Elephant & Castle	£900	£2600	£5500
1694	£800	£2400	£5500
1694 Elephant & Castle	£900	£2700	£6000

WILLIAM III (1694–1702)

	F	VF	EF
1701 "fine work"	£1250	£3800	£5700

ANNE (1702–14)

	F	VF	EF
1709	£700	£2200	£5000
1711	£700	£2000	£4500
1713	£700	£2000	£4500
1714	£750	£2100	£5500

GEORGE I (1714–27)

	F	VF	EF
1717	£700	£1800	£4500
1720	£700	£1800	£4750
1726	£600	£1700	£4200

	F	VF	EF
### GEORGE II (1727–60)			
1734 Young head 4 over 3	£1600	£3400	—
1735 —	£500	£1400	£3300
1738 —	£425	£800	£2000
1739 —	£400	£750	£1900
1739 Intermediate head	£450	£850	£2000
1740 —	£450	£850	£2000
1748 Old head	£450	£1100	£3000
1753 —	£550	£1400	£3750

### GEORGE III (1760–1820)		
1768 Patterns only	—	Extremely Rare
1773 Patterns only	—	Extremely Rare
1777 Patterns only	—	Extremely Rare

GUINEAS

	F	VF	EF
### CHARLES II (1660–85)			
1663 First bust	£750	£2500	—
1663 — Elephant below	£700	£2500	—
1664 Second bust	£600	£2500	—
1664 — Elephant		Extremely Rare	
1664 Third bust	£600	£2000	£5000
1664 — Elephant	£600	£2200	£5000
1665 —	£650	£2200	£5000
1665 — Elephant	£650	£2500	£6000
1666 —	£550	£2200	£5000
1667 —	£500	£2000	£5000
1668 —	£550	£2200	£5000
1668 — Elephant		Extremely rare	
1669 —	£550	£2500	—
1670 —	£500	£2500	£5000
1671 —	£500	£2200	£5000
1672 —	£550	£2500	—
1672 Fourth bust	£400	£2000	£4500
1673 Third bust	£600	£2700	—
1673 Fourth bust	£450	£2000	£5000
1674 —	£450	£2000	—
1674 — Elephant & Castle		Extremely rare	
1675 —	£425	£2000	£5000
1675 — CRAOLVS Error		Extremely rare	
1675 — Elephant & Castle	£500	£2000	—
1676 —	£400	£1200	£4000
1676 — Elephant & Castle	£450	£1600	£4000
1677 —	£450	£1500	£3500
1677/5 — Elephant 7 over 5		Extremely rare	
1677 — Elephant & Castle	£250	£1800	£4500
1678 —	£350	£1400	£3500
1678 — Elephant		Extremely rare	
1678 — Elephant & Castle	£500	£2000	—

Charles II, third bust

Charles II, fourth bust, elephant & castle below

James II, first bust, elephant & castle below

	F	VF	EF
1679 —	£375	£1250	£3500
1679 — Elephant & Castle	£500	£1800	£5000
1680 —	£500	£1800	£5000
1680 — Elephant & Castle	£600	£2250	—
1681 —	£425	£2000	£4500
1681 — Elephant & Castle	£500	£1900	—
1682 —	£400	£1600	£3750
1682 — Elephant & Castle	£450	£1800	£4500
1683 —	£350	£1300	£3500
1683 — Elephant & Castle	£600	£2500	£5500
1684 —	£400	£1600	£4250
1684 — Elephant & Castle	£450	£1800	£4500

JAMES II (1685–1688)

	F	VF	EF
1685 First bust	£400	£1800	£5000
1685 — Elephant & Castle	£500	£2200	£4500
1686 —	£450	£2000	£4000
1686 — Elephant & Castle		Extremely rare	
1686 Second bust	£325	£1500	£3500
1686 — Elephant & Castle	£500	£2500	£5500
1687 —	£300	£1700	£3500
1687 —Elephant & Castle	£375	£1700	£4500
1688 —	£350	£1600	£5000
1688 — Elephant & Castle	£375	£2000	£5000

James II, second bust

WILLIAM AND MARY (1688–94)

	F	VF	EF
1689..	£375	£1800	£4500
1689 Elephant & Castle	£375	£1800	£4500
1690..	£375	£1800	£4500
1690 Elephant & Castle	£550	£2000	£5500
1691..	£375	£1800	£4500
1691 Elephant & Castle	£375	£1800	£4500
1692..	£375	£1800	£4500
1692 Elephant	£600	£2400	£5500
1692 Elephant & Castle	£450	£2400	£4500
1693..	£375	£2000	£4500
1693 Elephant		Extremely rare	
1693 Elephant & Castle		Extremely rare	
1694..	£375	£2000	£4500
1694 Elephant & Castle	£400	£2200	£4500

WILLIAM III (1694–1702)

	F	VF	EF
1695 First bust	£300	£1700	£3750
1695 — Elephant & Castle	£400	£1900	£4500
1696 —	£325	£1800	£4000
1696 — Elephant & Castle		Extremely rare	
1697 —	£325	£1800	£4300
1697 Second bust	£300	£1700	£4300
1697 — Elephant & Castle	£800	£4000	—
1698 —	£275	£1600	£3250
1698 — Elephant & Castle	£400	£1800	£4500
1699 —	£350	£1600	£4500
1699 — Elephant & Castle		Extremely rare	
1700 —	£250	£1400	£3500
1700 — Elephant & Castle	£900	£3750	—
1701 —	£250	£1400	£3250
1701 — Elephant & Castle		Extremely rare	
1701 Third bust "fine work"...........................	£500	£2000	£5000

	F	VF	EF

ANNE (1702–1714)

	F	VF	EF
1702 (Pre-Union) First bust	£400	£1700	£4250
1703 — VIGO below	£5000	£12500	—
1705 —	£5000	£1650	£4250
1706 —	£5000	£1650	£4250
1707 —	£500	£2000	£4700
1707 — (Post-Union)	£300	£2000	£3000
1707 — Elephant & Castle	£750	£1750	—
1707 Second bust		Extremely rare	
1708 First bust		Extremely rare	
1708 Second bust	£325	£1100	£3750
1708 — Elephant & Castle	£800	£1850	£4000
1709 —	£325	£1100	£3200
1709 — Elephant & Castle	£800	£1700	£4250
1710 Third bust	£325	£1100	£2650
1711 —	£325	£1000	£2500
1712 —	£325	£1000	£2500
1713 —	£325	£1000	£2200
1714 —	£325	£1000	£2200
1714 GRΛTIΛ	£700	£1400	£3500

GEORGE I (1714–27)

	F	VF	EF
1714 First bust (Prince Elector)	£1000	£2750	£5000
1715 Second bust	£400	£1500	£3300
1715 Third bust	£400	£1500	£3300
1716 —	£400	£1500	£3300
1716 Fourth bust	£300	£1200	£3000
1717 —	£300	£1100	£3000
1718 —		Extremely rare	
1719 —	£275	£1300	£2500
1720 —	£300	£1300	£3000
1721 —	£300	£1300	£3000
1721 — Elephant & Castle		Extremely rare	
1722 —	£300	£1300	£3000
1722 — Elephant & Castle		Extremely rare	
1723 —	£300	£1300	£3000
1723 Fifth bust	£300	£1100	£3000
1724 —	£300	£1100	£2850
1725 —	£300	£1100	£2850
1726 —	£280	£1050	£2700
1726 — Elephant & Castle	£1200	£3750	£9000
1727 —	£350	£1800	£4500

GEORGE II (1727–60)

	F	VF	EF
1727 First young head, early large shield	£750	£2000	£4000
1727 — Larger lettering, early small shield	£375	£1200	£3000
1728 — —	£400	£1200	£3000
1729 2nd young head E.I.C. below	£500	£1500	£4000
1729 — Proof		Very Rare	
1730 —	£375	£1400	£3500
1731 —	£325	£1100	£3200
1731 — E.I.C. below	£475	£1400	£3500
1732 —	£350	£1200	£2750
1732 — E.I.C. below	£425	£1200	£3500
1732 — Larger lettering obverse	£325	£1200	£3000
1732 — — E.I.C. below	£400	£1600	£3500
1733 — —	£300	£1100	£2500
1734 — —	£300	£1100	£2500
1735 — —	£300	£1100	£2500
1736 — —	£300	£1200	£2700
1737 — —	£350	£1250	£3000

	F	VF	EF
1738 — —	£300	£1250	£3000
1739 Intermediate head	£300	£1000	£2400
1739 — E.I.C. below	£425	£1400	£3500
1740 —	£300	£1100	£3000
1741/39 —		Extremely rare	
1743 —		Extremely rare	
1745 — Larger lettering obv. Older bust	£325	£1100	£3400
1745 — LIMA below	£900	£2250	£5000
1746 — (GEORGIVS) Larger lettering obv.	£300	£800	£2700
1747 Old head, large lettering	£275	£600	£1650
1748 —	£275	£600	£1800
1749 —	£275	£600	£1800
1750 —	£275	£600	£1800
1751 — small lettering	£275	£600	£1800
1753 —	£275	£600	£1800
1755 —	£275	£600	£1800
1756 —	£275	£600	£1800
1758 —	£275	£600	£1800
1759 —	£275	£600	£1800
1760 —	£275	£600	£1800

George III first head

GEORGE III (1760–1820)

	F	VF	EF
1761 First head	£900	£2500	£5000
1763 Second head	£800	£1500	£4500
1764 —	£700	£1600	£3250
1765 Third head	£225	£450	£900
1766 —	£225	£450	£900
1767 —	£225	£450	£900
1768 —	£225	£450	£900
1769 —	£225	£450	£900
1770 —	£225	£450	£900
1771 —	£225	£450	£900
1772 —	£225	£450	£900
1773 —	£225	£450	£900
1774 Fourth head	£130	£325	£550
1775 —	£130	£325	£550
1776 —	£130	£325	£550
1777 —	£130	£325	£550
1778 —	£140	£375	£650
1779 —	£130	£355	£550
1781 —	£130	£350	£550
1782 —	£130	£350	£550
1783 —	£130	£350	£550
1784 —	£130	£350	£550
1785 —	£130	£350	£550
1786 —	£130	£350	£550
1787 Fifth head, "Spade" reverse	£125	£300	£525
1788 —	£125	£295	£525
1789 —	£125	£295	£525
1790 —	£125	£295	£525
1791 —	£125	£295	£525
1792 —	£125	£295	£525
1793 —	£125	£295	£525
1794 —	£125	£295	£525
1795 —	£125	£220	£525
1796 —	£150	£260	£575
1797 —	£130	£300	£575
1798 —	£120	£250	£425
1799 —	£170	£350	£675
1813 Sixth head, "Military" reverse	£500	£1250	£2200

(Beware of counterfeits of this series—many dangerous copies exist)

Fourth head

Fifth head, Spade reverse

Sixth head

HALF GUINEAS

	F	VF	EF
CHARLES II (1660–85)			
1669 First bust	£325	£1000	£3750
1670 —	£300	£1000	£3000
1671 —	£350	£1000	£3750
1672 —	£350	£1000	£3750
1672 Second bust	£325	£900	£3000
1673 —	£450	£1300	£3750
1674 —	£500	£1600	—
1675 —		Extremely rare	
1676 —	£325	£1000	£2800
1676 — Elephant & Castle	£600	£2200	—
1677 —	£325	£1000	£2800
1677 — Elephant & Castle	£500	£1500	—
1678 —	£375	£1100	£3300
1678 — Elephant & Castle	£350	£1100	£3750
1679 —	£325	£1000	£3000
1680 —	£400	£1400	—
1680 — Elephant & Castle		Extremely rare	
1681 —	£400	£1400	—
1682 —	£400	£1300	£3500
1682 — Elephant & Castle	£450	£1500	—
1683 —	£325	£900	£2800
1683 — Elephant & Castle		Extremely rare	
1684 —	£325	£850	£2800
1684 — Elephant & Castle	£350	£1100	£3400

	F	VF	EF
JAMES II (1685–88)			
1686	£300	£1100	£3250
1686 Elephant & Castle	£700	£3750	£7000
1687	£400	£1300	£3800
1688	£325	£1300	£3800

	F	VF	EF
WILLIAM AND MARY (1688–94)			
1689 First busts	£400	£1800	£4000
1690 Second busts	£400	£1850	£4200
1691 —	£425	£1800	£4000
1691 — Elephant & Castle	£325	£1700	£3800
1692 —	£350	£1400	£3200
1692 — Elephant		Extremely rare	
1692 — Elephant & Castle	£325	£1600	£3800
1693 —		Extremely rare	
1694 —	£325	£1600	£3500

	F	VF	EF
WILLIAM III (1694–1702)			
1695	£275	£750	£2800
1695 Elephant & Castle	£425	£1100	£3200
1696 —	£250	£950	£2800
1697 Larger Harp rev.	£300	£1000	£3000
1698	£250	£700	£2700
1698 Elephant & Castle	£350	£800	£3000
1699		Extremely rare	
1700	£200	£650	£2500
1701	£200	£650	£2500

	F	VF	EF

ANNE (1702–14)

	F	VF	EF
1702 (Pre-Union)	£450	£1800	£4250
1703 VIGO below bust	£4000	£10000	£20000
1705	£500	£1700	£4500
1707 (Post-Union)	£300	£900	£2500
1708	£325	£900	£2500
1709	£300	£900	£2300
1710	£275	£750	£2000
1711	£275	£750	£2000
1712	£275	£750	£2000
1713	£275	£750	£2000
1714	£275	£750	£2000

GEORGE I (1714–27)

	F	VF	EF
1715 First bust	£350	£800	£2200
1717 —	£270	£600	£1600
1718 —	£270	£600	£1600
1719 —	£270	£600	£1600
1720 —	£300	£650	£1600
1721 —		Extremely rare	
1721 — Elephant & Castle		Extremely rare	
1722 —	£250	£600	£2000
1723 —		Extremely rare	
1724 —	£300	£700	£2000
1725 Second bust	£250	£500	£1200
1726 —	£250	£500	£1400
1727 —	£250	£475	£1500

GEORGE II (1727–60)

	F	VF	EF
1728 Young head	£275	£700	£2350
1729 —	£300	£700	£2350
1729 — E.I.C.	£325	£1000	£3000
1730 —	£550	£2000	—
1730 — E.I.C.	£600	£2000	—
1731 —	£300	£950	£3000
1731 — E.I.C.		Extremely rare	
1732 —	£300	£900	£2800
1732 — E.I.C.		Extremely rare	
1733 —		Unknown	
1734 —	£300	£800	£2500
1735 —		Extremely rare	
1736 —	£300	£700	£3000
1737 —		Extremely rare	
1738 —	£300	£750	£2500
1739 —	£300	£750	£2500
1739 — E.I.C.		Extremely rare	
1740 Intermediate head	£375	£1000	£3000
1743 —		Extremely rare	
1745 —	£300	£900	£2850
1745 — LIMA	£800	£2750	—
1746 —	£275	£700	£2200
1747 Old head	£300	£700	£2200
1748 —	£220	£600	£1400
1749 —	£200	£600	£1750
1750 —	£225	£600	£1500
1751 —	£225	£600	£1500
1752 —	£225	£600	£1500
1753 —	£225	£600	£1500
1755 —	£225	£600	£1500

George II, young head

George II, old head

		F	VF	EF
1756	—	£225	£600	£1400
1758	—	£250	£650	£1650
1759	—	£225	£500	£1450
1760	—	£225	£500	£1400

GEORGE III (1760–1820)

		F	VF	EF
1762	First head	£420	£1250	£3000
1763	—	£500	£1500	£3500
1764	Second head	£140	£375	£850
1765	—	£400	£900	£2400
1766	—	£175	£400	£1000
1768	—	£200	£450	£1000
1769	—	£200	£455	£1000
1772	—		Extremely rare	
1773	—	£200	£400	£900
1774	—	£250	£550	£1600
1774	Third head		Extremely rare	
1775	—	£750	£1800	£4000
1775	Fourth head	£120	£275	£500
1775	— Proof		Extremely rare	
1776	—	£110	£250	£500
1777	—	£110	£250	£500
1778	—	£110	£225	£550
1779	—	£130	£300	£700
1781	—	£110	£300	£700
1783	—	£425	£1250	—
1784	—	£120	£300	£600
1785	—	£120	£300	£600
1786	—	£120	£300	£600
1787	Fifth head, "Spade" rev.	£110	£225	£500
1788	—	£110	£225	£500
1789	—	£110	£240	£600
1790	—	£110	£240	£500
1791	—	£110	£240	£500
1792	—	£500	£1600	—
1793	—	£110	£220	£450
1794	—	£110	£220	£450
1795	—	£150	£300	£600
1796	—	£110	£275	£550
1797	—	£110	£275	£550
1798	—	£110	£275	£550
1800	—	£225	£700	£1400
1801	Sixth head, Shield in Garter rev.	£70	£150	£320
1802	—	£75	£150	£350
1803	—	£75	£150	£350
1804	Seventh head	£75	£150	£350
1805			Extremely rare	
1806	—	£100	£150	£360
1808	—	£100	£150	£360
1899	—	£100	£150	£360
1810	—	£80	£150	£360
1811	—	£140	£275	£700
1813	—	£140	£260	£700

George III, second head

George III, fifth head, "spade" reverse

THIRD GUINEAS

DATE		F	VF	EF

GEORGE III (1760–1820)

	F	VF	EF
1797 First head,date in legend	£60	£100	£225
1798 — —	£60	£100	£225
1799 — —	£70	£110	£250
1800 — —	£55	£100	£225
1801 Date under crown	£55	£100	£225
1802 —	£55	£100	£225
1803 —	£55	£100	£225
1804 Second head	£60	£100	£225
1806 —	£60	£100	£225
1808 —	£60	£100	£225
1809 —	£60	£100	£225
1810 —	£60	£100	£225
1811 —	£175	£400	£900
1813 —	£125	£200	£475

George III, date in legend

George III, date under crown

QUARTER GUINEAS

GEORGE I (1714–27)

	F	VF	EF
1718	£90	£175	£325

GEORGE III (1760–1820)

	F	VF	EF
1762	£65	£150	£300

FIVE POUNDS

DATE	Mintage	F	VF	EF	UNC

GEORGE III (1760–1820)

	Mintage	F	VF	EF	UNC
1820 (pattern only)		—		Extremely rare	

GEORGE IV (1820–30)

	Mintage	F	VF	EF	UNC
1826 proof only		—	—	—	£6,000 £10,000

VICTORIA (1837–1901)

	Mintage	F	VF	EF	UNC
1839 Proof Only Many Varieties		—	—	£25,000 upwards	
1887	53,844	£350	£525	£700	£900
1887 Proof	797	—	—	—	£3,000
1887 S on ground on rev. (Sydney Mint)				Excessively rare	
1893	20,405	£458	£750	£1100	£1800
1893 Proof	773	—	—	—	£3000

EDWARD VII (1902–10)

	Mintage	F	VF	EF	UNC
1902	34,910	—	£400	£575	£825
1902 Matt proof	8,066	—	—	—	£800

DATE	MINTAGE	F	VF	EF	UNC

GEORGE V (1911–36)

1911 Proof only .... 2,812 — — — £1,500

GEORGE VI (1937–52)

1937 Proof only .... 5,501 — — — £675

Later issues are listed in the Decimal section.

TWO POUNDS

GEORGE III (1760–1820)

1820 (pattern only) .... — — — Extremely rare

GEORGE IV (1820–30)

1823 St George reverse .... — £275 £500 £1000 £1850
1826 Proof only, shield reverse — — — £2750 £4500

WILLIAM IV (1830–37)

1831 Proof only .... 225 — — £3000 £5250

VICTORIA (1837–1901)

1887................................... 91,345 £170 £250 £400 £525
1887 Proof......................... 797 — — — £900
1887 S on ground of rev. (Sydney Mint) Excessively rare
1893................................... 52,212 £240 £400 £600 £705
1893 Proof......................... 773 — — — £1100

EDWARD VII (1902–10)

1902................................... 45,807 £150 £200 £300 £400
1902 Matt proof................. 8,066 — — — £400

GEORGE V (1911–36)

1911 Proof only .... 2,812 — — — £700

GEORGE VI (1937–52)

1937 Proof only .... 5,501 — — — £375

Later issues are listed in the Decimal section.

SOVEREIGNS

DATE	MINTAGE	F	VF	EF	UNC

GEORGE III (1760–1820)

DATE	MINTAGE	F	VF	EF	UNC
1817	3,235,239	£160	£350	£800	£1400
1818	2,347,230	£160	£350	£800	£1400
1819	3,574			Exceedingly rare	
1820	931,994	£160	£350	£800	£1400

GEORGE IV (1820–30)

DATE	MINTAGE	F	VF	EF	UNC
1821 First bust, St George reverse	9,405,114	£175	£300	£800	£1700
1821 — Proof	incl. above	—	—	—	£3500
1822 —	5,356,787	£170	£300	£700	£16s00
1823 —	616,770	£400	£1500	£4000	—
1824 —	3,767,904	£170	£400	£1000	£1800
1825 —	4,200,343	£325	£1000	£2800	£3000
1825 Second bust, shield reverse	incl. above	£200	£500	£800	£1650
1826 —	5,724,046	£200	£500	£800	£1650
1826 — Proof	—	—	—	—	£2750
1827 —	2,266,629	£200	£400	£900	£1800
1828 —	386,182	—	£3500	£1100	—
1829 —	2,444,652	£275	£500	£900	£1800
1830 —	2,387,881	£275	£500	£900	£1800

WILLIAM IV (1830–37)

DATE	MINTAGE	F	VF	EF	UNC
1831	598,547	£220	£450	£1000	£1850
1831 Proof	—	—	—	—	£3000
1832	3,737,065	£240	£450	£1000	£1750
1833	1,225,269	£240	£450	£1000	£1750
1835	723,441	£240	£450	£1000	£1750
1836	1,714,349	£240	£450	£1000	£1750
1837	1,172,984	£240	£450	£1000	£1750

VICTORIA (1837–1901)

Many of the gold coins struck at the colonial mints found their way into circulation in Britain, for the sake of completeness these coins are listed here. These can easily be identified by a tiny initial letter for the appropriate mint which can be found below the base of the reverse shield or, in the case of the St George reverse, below the bust on the obverse of the Young Head issues, or on the "ground" below the horse's hoof on the later issues.

YOUNG HEAD ISSUES

Shield reverse
(Note—Shield back sovereigns in Fine/VF condition, common dates, are normally traded as bullion + a percentage)

DATE	MINTAGE	F	VF	EF	UNC
1838	2,718,694	£125	£300	£1000	£3000
1839	503,695	£275	£800	£1600	£3500
1839 Proof, plain edge	—	—	—	—	£5000
1841	124,054	£1200	£2500	£6500	—
1842	4,865,375	—	£90	£200	£450
1843	5,981,968	—	£90	£200	£450
1843 "Narrow shield" variety	incl. above				Rare
1844	3,000,445	£90	£100	£300	£550
1845	3,800,845	£90	£100	£300	£550
1846	3,802,947	£90	£100	£300	£550
1847	4,667,126	£90	£100	£300	£550

PAUL DAVIES

DATE	MINTAGE	F	VF	EF	UNC
1848	2,246,701	£90	£100	£250	£500
1849	1,755,399	£90	£100	£250	£500
1850	1,402,039	£90	£100	£250	£500
1851	4,013,624	£90	£100	£250	£500
1852	8,053,435	£90	£100	£250	£500
1853	10,597,993	£90	£100	£250	£500
1853 Proof	—	—	—	—	£7000
1854	3,589,611	£125	£275	£750	£1650
1855	8,448,482	£100	£150	£300	£500
1856	4,806,160	£90	£100	£250	£425
1857	4,495,748	£90	£100	£250	£425
1858	803,234	£90	£100	£250	£425
1859	1,547,603	£90	£100	£250	£425
1859 "Ansell" (additional line on lower part of hair ribbon)	—	£300	£800	£3500	—
1860	2,555,958	£90	£100	£200	£375
1861	7,624,736	£90	£100	£200	£340
1862	7,836,413	—	£100	£200	£340
1863	5,921,669	—	£100	£200	£340
1863 Die No 827 on Truncation				Extremely rare	
1863 with Die number below shield	incl. above	£90	£100	£200	£375
1864 —	8,656,352	£90	£100	£200	£375
1865 —	1,450,238	£90	£100	£200	£375
1866 —	4,047,288	£90	£100	£200	£375
1868 —	1,653,384	£90	£100	£200	£375
1869 —	6,441,322	£90	£100	£200	£375
1870 —	2,189,960	£90	£100	£200	£375
1871 —	8,767,250	£90	£100	£200	£375
1872 —	8,767,250	£90	£100	£200	£375
1872 no Die number	incl. above	£90	£100	£200	£375
1873 with Die number	2,368,215	£90	£100	£200	£375
1874	520,713	£800	—	—	—

M below (Melbourne Mint)

	MINTAGE	F	VF	EF	UNC
1872	748,180	£90	£90	£200	£600
1873	—			Extremely rare	
1874	1,373,298	£90	£90	£200	£600
1879				Extremely rare	
1880	3,053,454	£300	£650	£2500	£1500
1881	2,325,303	£90	£100	£300	£1100
1882	2,465,781	£90	£125	£225	£550
1883	2,050,450	£100	£200	£600	—
1884	2,942,630	£90	£100	£220	£600
1885	2,967,143	£90	£100	£220	£600
1886	2,902,131	£500	£2000	£4000	£5000
1887	1,916,424	£350	£750	£2400	£5000

"S" below the shield indicates that the coin was struck at the Sydney Mint

S below (Sydney Mint)

	MINTAGE	F	VF	EF	UNC
1871	2,814,000	£90	£100	£240	£500
1872	1,815,000	£90	£100	£240	£500
1873	1,478,000	£90	£100	£240	£500
1875	2,122,000	£90	£100	£240	£500
1877	1,590,000	£90	£100	£240	£500
1878	1,259,000	£90	£100	£240	£500
1879	1,366,000	£90	£100	£240	£500
1880	1,459,000	£90	£100	£240	£500
1881	1,360,000	£90	£100	£240	£500
1882	1,298,000	£90	£100	£240	£500
1883	1,108,000	£90	£100	£240	£500
1884	1,595,000	£90	£100	£240	£500
1885	1,486,000	£90	£100	£240	£500
1886	1,667,000	£90	£100	£240	£500
1887	1,000,000	£90	£100	£240	£500

DATE	MINTAGE	F	VF	EF	UNC
St George & Dragon reverse					
1871	incl. above	—	£90	£90	£200
1872	incl. above	—	£90	£90	£200
1873	incl. above	—	£90	£90	£200
1874	incl. above	—	£90	£90	£200
1876	3,318,866	—	£90	£90	£200
1878	1,091,275	—	£90	£90	£200
1879	20,013	£125	£400	£1000	—
1880	3,650,080	—	£90	£90	£180
1884	1,769,635	—	£90	£90	£200
1885	717,723	—	£90	£90	£180
M below (Melbourne Mint)					
1872	incl. above	—	£90	£100	£225
1873	752,199	—	£90	£100	£225
1874	incl. above	—	£90	£100	£225
1875	incl. above	—	£90	£100	£225
1876	2,124,445	—	£90	£100	£225
1877	1,487,316	—	£90	£100	£225
1878	2,171,457	—	£90	£100	£225
1879	2,740,594	—	£90	£100	£225
1880	incl. above	—	£90	£100	£225
1881	incl. above	—	£90	£100	£225
1882	incl. above	—	£90	£100	£225
1883	incl. above	—	£90	£100	£225
1884	incl. above	—	£90	£100	£225
1885	incl. above	—	£90	£100	£225
1886	incl. above	—	£90	£100	£225
1887	incl. above	—	£90	£100	£225
S below (Sydney Mint)					
1871	2,814,000	—	£90	£110	£225
1872	incl. above	—	£90	£110	£225
1873	incl. above	—	£90	£110	£225
1874	1,899,000	—	£90	£100	£225
1875	inc above	—	£90	£100	£225
1876	1,613,000	—	£90	£100	£225
1877	—		Extremely rare		
1879	incl. above	—	£75	£100	£225
1880	incl. above	—	£75	£100	£225
1881	incl. above	—	£75	£100	£225
1882	incl. above	—	£75	£100	£225
1883	incl. above	—	£75	£100	£225
1884	incl. above	—	£75	£100	£225
1885	incl. above	—	£75	£100	£225
1886	incl. above	—	£75	£100	£225
1887	incl. above	—	£75	£100	£225
JUBILEE HEAD ISSUES					
1887	1,111,280	—	—	£90	£110
1887 Proof	797	—	—	—	£700
1888	2,717,424	—	—	£90	£110
1889	7,257,455	—	—	£90	£110
1890	6,529.887	—	—	£90	£110
1891	6,329,476	—	—	£90	£110
1892	7,104,720	—	—	£90	£110
M below (Melbourne Mint)					
1887	940,000	£90	£90	£140	£200
1888	2,830,612	£90	£90	£110	£120
1889	2,732,590	£90	£90	£110	£120
1890	2,473,537	£90	£90	£110	£120
1891	2,749,592	£90	£90	£110	£120
1892	3,488,750	£90	£90	£110	£120
1893	1,649,352	£90	£90	£110	£120

"M" below the horse's hoof above the date indicates that the coin was struck at the Melbourne Mint

Jubilee head type

DATE	MINTAGE	F	VF	EF	UNC
S below (Sydney Mint)					
1887	1,002,000	£100	£125	£270	£550
1888	2,187,000	—	£90	£100	£140
1889	3,262,000	—	£90	£100	£140
1890	2,808,000	—	£90	£100	£140
1891	2,596,000	—	£90	£100	£140
1892	2,837,000	—	£90	£100	£140
1893	1,498,000	—	£90	£100	£140
OLD HEAD ISSUES					
1893	6,898,260	—	—	£90	£100
1893 Proof	773	—	—	—	£900
1894	3,782,611	—	—	£90	£100
1895	2,285,317	—	—	£90	£100
1896	3,334,065	—	—	£90	£100
1898	4,361,347	—	—	£90	£100
1899	7,515,978	—	—	£90	£100
1900	10,846,741	—	—	£90	£100
1901	1,578,948	—	—	£90	£100
M below (Melbourne Mint)					
1893	1,914,000	—	—	£90	£110
1894	4,166,874	—	—	£90	£110
1895	4,165,869	—	—	£90	£110
1896	4,456,932	—	—	£90	£110
1897	5,130,565	—	—	£90	£110
1898	5,509,138	—	—	£90	£110
1899	5,579,157	—	—	£90	£110
1900	4,305,904	—	—	£90	£110
1901	3,987,701	—	—	£90	£110
P below (Perth Mint)					
1899	690,992	£75	£120	£300	£1200
1900	1,886,089	—	—	£90	£150
1901	2,889,333	—	—	£90	£150
S below (Sydney Mint)					
1893	1,346,000	—	—	£90	£100
1894	3,067,000	—	—	£90	£100
1895	2,758,000	—	—	£90	£100
1896	2,544,000	—	—	£100	£160
1897	2,532,000	—	—	£90	£100
1898	2,548,000	—	—	£90	£100
1899	3,259,000	—	—	£90	£100
1900	3,586,000	—	—	£90	£100
1901	3,012,000	—	—	£90	£100

Old head type

EDWARD VII (1902–10)

1902	4,737,796	—	—	£90	£90
1902 Matt proof	15,123	—	—	—	£140
1903	8,888,627	—	—	£90	£90
1904	10,041,369	—	—	£90	£90
1905	5,910,403	—	—	£90	£90
1906	10,466,981	—	—	£90	£90
1907	18,458,663	—	—	£90	£90
1908	11,729,006	—	—	£90	£90
1909	12,157,099	—	—	£90	£90
1910	22,379,624	—	—	£90	£90
C below (Ottawa Mint)					
1908 Satin finish Proof only	633		Extremely rare		
1909	16,300	—	£90	£220	—
1910	28,020	—	£90	£220	—

DATE	MINTAGE	F	VF	EF	UNC
M below (Melbourne Mint)					
1902	4,267,157	—	—	£90	£110
1903	3,521,780	—	—	£90	£110
1904	3,743,897	—	—	£90	£110
1905	3,633,838	—	—	£90	£110
1906	3,657,853	—	—	£90	£110
1907	3,332,691	—	—	£90	£110
1908	3,080,148	—	—	£90	£110
1909	3,029,538	—	—	£90	£110
1910	3,054,547	—	—	£90	£110
P below (Perth Mint)					
1902	3,289,122	—	—	£90	£110
1903	4,674,783	—	—	£90	£110
1904	4,506,756	—	—	£90	£110
1905	4,876,193	—	—	£90	£110
1906	4,829,817	—	—	£90	£110
1907	4,972,289	—	—	£90	£110
1908	4,875,617	—	—	£90	£110
1909	4,524,241	—	—	£90	£110
1910	4,690,625	—	—	£90	£110
S below (Sydney Mint)					
1902	2,813,000	—	—	£90	£110
1902 Proof	incl. above			Extremely rare	
1903	2,806,000	—	—	£90	£110
1904	2,986,000	—	—	£90	£110
1905	2,778,000	—	—	£90	£110
1906	2,792,000	—	—	£90	£110
1907	2,539,000	—	—	£90	£110
1908	2,017,000	—	—	£90	£110
1909	2,057,000	—	—	£90	£110
1910	2,135,000	—	—	£90	£110

GEORGE V (1911–36)

(Extra care should be exercised when purchasing as good quality forgeries exist of virtually all dates and mintmarks)

DATE	MINTAGE	F	VF	EF	UNC
1911	30,044,105	—	—	£90	£100
1911 Proof	3,764	—	—	—	£325
1912	30,317,921	—	—	£90	£100
1913	24,539,672	—	—	£90	£100
1914	11,501,117	—	—	£90	£100
1915	20,295,280	—	—	£90	£100
1916	1,554,120	—	—	£90	£100
1917	1,014,714	£1500	£2000	£4500	—
1925	4,406,431	—	—	£90	£100
C below (Ottawa Mint)					
1911	256,946	—	£90	£90	£140
1913	3,715	£100	£120	£500	—
1914	14,891	£100	£180	£350	—
1916	6,111			Extremely rare	
1917	58,845	—	£90	£110	£140
1918	106,516	—	£90	£110	£140
1919	135,889	—	£90	£110	£140
I below (Bombay Mint)					
1918	1,295,372	—	—	£90	—
M below (Melbourne Mint)					
1911	2,851,451	—	—	£90	£100
1912	2,469,257	—	—	£90	£100
1913	2,323,180	—	—	£90	£100
1914	2,012,029	—	—	£90	£100
1915	1,637,839	—	—	£90	£100

DATE	MINTAGE	F	VF	EF	UNC
1916	1,273,643	—	—	£90	£100
1917	934,469	—	—	£90	£100
1918	4,969,493	—	—	£75	£100
1919	514,257	—	—	£90	£140
1920	530,266	—	£1500	£2500	—
1921	240,121	—	—	£5500	—
1922	608,306	—	£2500	£4500	—
1923	510,870	—	—	£90	£110
1924	278,140	—	—	£90	£125
1925	3,311,622	—	—	£90	£100
1926	211,107	—	—	£90	£100
1928	413,208	—	£550	£1250	£2000
1929	436,719	—	£500	£1500	£2000
1930	77,547	—	£75	£150	£200
1931	57,779	—	£140	£300	£375

P below (Perth Mint)

1911	4,373,165	—	—	£90	£100
1912	4,278,144	—	—	£90	£100
1913	4,635,287	—	—	£90	£100
1914	4,815,996	—	—	£90	£100
1915	4,373,596	—	—	£90	£100
1916	4,096,771	—	—	£90	£100
1917	4,110,286	—	—	£90	£100
1918	3,812,884	—	—	£90	£100
1919	2,995,216	—	—	£90	£100
1920	2,421,196	—	—	£90	£100
1921	2,134,360	—	—	£90	£100
1922	2,298,884	—	—	£90	£100
1923	2,124,154	—	—	£90	£100
1924	1,464,416	—	—	£90	£140
1925	1,837,901	—	—	£120	£275
1926	1,313,578	£300	£600	£1500	£1800
1927	1,383,544	—	£175	£300	£450
1928	1,333,417	—	—	£100	£175
1929	1,606,625	—	—	£90	£100
1930	1,915,352	—	—	£90	£100
1931	1,173,568	—	—	£90	£100

S below (Sydney Mint)

1911	2,519,000	—	—	£90	£90
1912	2,227,000	—	—	£90	£90
1913	2,249,000	—	—	£90	£90
1914	1,774,000	—	—	£90	£90
1915	1,346,000	—	—	£90	£90
1916	1,242,000	—	—	£90	£90
1917	1,666,000	—	—	£90	£90
1918	3,716,000	—	—	£90	£90
1919	1,835,000	—	—	£90	£90
1920	—		Excessively rare		
1921	839,000	—	£600	£1500	—
1922	578,000		Extremely rare		
1923	416,000		Extremely rare		
1924	394,000	—	£500	£800	£1250
1925	5,632,000	—	—	£90	£100
1926	1,031,050		Extremely rare		

SA below (Pretoria Mint)

1923	719	—	—	—	£4000
1923 Proof	655		Extremely rare		
1924	3,184	£1500	—	£3250	—
1925	6,086,264	—	£90	£90	£110
1926	11,107,611	—	£90	£90	£110
1927	16,379,704	—	£90	£90	£110
1928	18,235,057	—	£90	£90	£110

DATE	MINTAGE	F	VF	EF	UNC
1929	12,024,107	—	—	£90	£95
1930	10,027,756	—	—	£90	£95
1931	8,511,792	—	—	£90	£95
1932	1,066,680	—	—	£90	£110

GEORGE VI (1937–52)

1937 Proof only	5,501	—	—	£725	£1200

ELIZABETH II (1952–)

Pre Decimal Issues

1957	2,072,000	—	—	—	£100
1958	8,700,140	—	—	—	£90
1959	1,358,228	—	—	—	£100
1962	3,000,000	—	—	—	£100
1963	7,400,000	—	—	—	£100
1964	3,000,000	—	—	—	£100
1965	3,800,000	—	—	—	£100
1966	7,050,000	—	—	—	£100
1967	5,000,000	—	—	—	£100
1968	4,203,000	—	—	—	£100

Later issues are included in the Decimal section.

HALF SOVEREIGNS

GEORGE III (1760–1820)

1817	2,080,197	£70	£120	£275	£500
1818	1,030,286	£70	£120	£275	£500
1820	35,043	£70	£120	£275	£500

GEORGE IV (1820–30)

1821 First bust, ornate shield reverse	231,288	£200	£600	£1500	£2750
1821 — Proof	unrecorded	—	—	£2000	£3000
1823 First bust, Plain shield rev.	224,280	£70	£150	£400	£700
1824 —	591,538	£70	£150	£425	£700
1825 —	761,150	£70	£150	£425	£700
1826 bare head, shield with full legend reverse	344,830	£70	£130	£400	£700
1826 — Proof	unrecorded	—	—	£750	£1100
1827 —	492,014	£75	£150	£400	£750
1828 —	1,224,754	£70	£135	£400	£775

WILLIAM IV (1830–37)

1831 Proof only	unrecorded	—	—	£750	£1600
1834	133,899	£100	£200	£500	£900
1835	772,554	£100	£300	£425	£800
1836	146,865	£90	£200	£500	£900
1836 obverse from 6d die	incl. above	£600	£1200	£2500	—
1837	160,207	£100	£200	£475	£825

VICTORIA (1837–1901)

YOUNG HEAD ISSUES

Shield reverse

DATE	MINTAGE	F	VF	EF	UNC
1838	273,341	£60	£90	£225	£600
1839 Proof only	1,230	—	—	—	£2000
1841	508,835	£65	£90	£260	£700
1842	2,223,352	—	£65	£200	£450
1843	1,251,762	£65	£90	£260	£650
1844	1,127,007	£60	£70	£240	£450
1845	887,526	£100	£300	£700	£1400
1846	1,063,928	£60	£80	£220	£450
1847	982,636	£60	£80	£220	£450
1848	410,595	£60	£80	£220	£450
1849	845,112	—	£75	£180	£400
1850	179,595	£100	£200	£500	£1100
1851	773,573	—	£75	£200	£450
1852	1,377,671	—	£80	£200	£450
1853	2,708,796	—	£70	£180	£400
1853 Proof	unrecorded	—	—	—	£3750
1854	1,125,144		Extremely rare		
1855	1,120,362	—	£75	£180	£400
1856	2,391,909	—	£75	£180	£400
1857	728,223	—	£80	£190	£425
1858	855,578	—	£80	£190	£425
1859	2,203,813	—	£70	£180	£400
1860	1,131,500	—	£70	£180	£400
1861	1,130,867	—	£70	£180	£400
1862	unrecorded	£275	£800	£3000	—
1863	1,571,574	—	£70	£180	£400
1863 with Die number	incl. above	—	£65	£180	£400
1864 —	1,758,490	—	£70	£180	£400
1865 —	1,834,750	—	£70	£180	£400
1866 —	2,058,776	—	£70	£180	£400
1867 —	992,795	—	£70	£180	£400
1869 —	1,861,764	—	£65	£180	£400
1870 —	1,159,544	—	£65	£175	£325
1871 —	2,062,970	—	£60	£150	£325
1872 —	3,248,627	—	£65	£150	£325
1873 —	1,927,050	—	£60	£150	£325
1874 —	1,884,432	—	£60	£150	£325
1875 —	516,240	—	£60	£150	£325
1876 —	2,785,187	—	£60	£150	£325
1877 —	2,197,482	—	£60	£130	£325
1878 —	2,081,941	—	£60	£130	£325
1879 —	35,201	—	£60	£140	£325
1880 —	1,009,049	—	£60	£140	£325
1880 no Die number	incl. above	—	£60	£140	£325
1883 —	2,870,457	—	£60	£135	£270
1884 —	1,113,756	—	£60	£125	£270
1885 —	4,468,871	—	£60	£125	£270

M below (Melbourne Mint)

1873	165,034	£50	£120	£500	—
1877	80,016	£50	£120	£450	—
1881	42,009	£60	£175	£550	—
1882	107,522	£60	£100	£500	—
1884	48,009	£60	£100	£500	—
1885	11,003	£70	£200	£1200	—
1886	38,008	£60	£110	£1200	—
1887	64,013	£100	£300	£1200	£4000

S below (Sydney Mint)

1871	180,000 (?)	£60	£125	£600	—
1872	356,000	£65	£125	£600	—
1875	unrecorded	£55	£125	£600	—

Date	Mintage	F	VF	EF	UNC
1879	94,000	£55	£100	£750	—
1880	80,000	£55	£900	£750	—
1881	62,000	£55	£100	£750	—
1882	52,000	£100	£500	£2500	—
1883	220,000	£55	£80	£500	—
1886	82,000	£55	£80	£450	—
1887	134,000	£55	£100	£650	£2000

JUBILEE HEAD ISSUES

1887	871,770	—	£50	£70	£95
1887 Proof	797	—	—	—	£400
1890	2.266,023	—	£50	£70	£125
1891	1,079,286	—	£50	£70	£125
1892	13,680,486	—	—	£60	£125
1893	4,426,625	—	—	£65	£125

M below (Melbourne Mint)

1887	incl. above	£50	£100	£275	£450
1893	110,024	£60	£125	£375	—

S below (Sydney Mint)

1887	incl. above	£50	£90	£250	£400
1889	64,000	£60	£100	£250	—
1891	154,000	£60	£120	£275	—

OLD HEAD ISSUES

1893	incl. above	—	£40	£60	£110
1893 Proof	773	—	—	—	£500
1894	3,794,591	—	£40	£70	£110
1895	2,869,183	—	£40	£70	£110
1896	2,946,605	—	£40	£70	£110
1897	3,568,156	—	£40	£70	£110
1898	2,868,527	—	£40	£70	£110
1899	3,361,881	—	£40	£70	£110
1900	4,307,372	—	£40	£70	£110
1901	2,037,664	—	£40	£70	£110

M below (Melbourne Mint)

1893	unrecorded		Extremely rare		
1896	218,946	£50	£100	£400	—
1899	97,221	£50	£100	£400	—
1900	112,920	£50	£100	£400	—

P below (Perth Mint)

1899			Proof Unique		
1900	119,376	£125	£300	£500	—

S below (Sydney Mint)

1893	250,000	£60	£100	£275	—
1897	unrecorded	£50	£90	£275	—
1900	260,00	£50	£80	£275	—

EDWARD VII (1902–10)

1902	4,244,457	—	—	£45	£55
1902 Matt proof	15,123	—	—	—	£120
1903	2,522,057	—	—	£45	£55
1904	1,717,440	—	—	£45	£55
1905	3,023,993	—	—	£45	£55
1906	4,245,437	—	—	£45	£55
1907	4,233,421	—	—	£45	£55
1908	3,996,992	—	—	£45	£55
1909	4,010,715	—	—	£45	£55
1910	5,023,881	—	—	£45	£55

DATE		F	VF	EF	UNC
M below (Melbourne Mint)					
1906	82,042	—	£40	£100	£300
1907	405,034	—	£40	£80	£250
1908	incl. above	—	£40	£80	£300
1909	186,094	—	£40	£80	£250
P below (Perth Mint)					
1904	60,030	£100	£150	£550	—
1908	24,668	£100	£150	£550	—
1909	44,022	£70	£130	£450	—
S below (Sydney Mint)					
1902	84,000	—	£45	£100	£300
1902 Proof				Extremely rare	
1903	231,000	—	£45	£100	£250
1906	308,00	—	£45	£100	£275
1908	538,000	—	£45	£100	£275
1910	474,000	—	£45	£100	£275

GEORGE V (1911–36)

		F	VF	EF	UNC
1911	6,104,106	—	£40	£50	£75
1911 Proof	3,764	—	—	—	£175
1912	6,224,316	—	£40	£50	£75
1913	6,094,290	—	£40	£50	£75
1914	7,251,124	—	£40	£50	£75
1915	2,042,747	—	£40	£50	£75
M below (Melbourne Mint)					
1915	125,664	—	—	£100	£200
P below (Perth Mint)					
1911	130,373	—	—	£100	£200
1915	136,219	—	—	£100	£200
1918	unrecorded	£120	£275	£600	—
S below (Sydney Mint)					
1911	252,000	—	—	£70	£110
1912	278,000	—	—	£70	£110
1914	322,000	—	—	£70	£110
1915	892,000	—	—	£70	£110
1916	448,000	—	—	£70	£110
SA below (Pretoria Mint)					
1923 Proof only	655	—	—	—	£350
1925	946,615	—	—	£40	£80
1926	806,540	—	—	£40	£80

GEORGE VI (1937–52)

		F	VF	EF	UNC
1937 Proof only	5,501	—	—	—	£300

Later issues are included in the Decimal section.

Leading the way

in Numismatics

St James's Auctions

Regular auctions held in
Central London

Negotiable commission rates

0% Commission* for special collections

No hidden costs

Photography and insurance
free of charge

For enquiries and to consign contact:
St James's Auctions (Knightsbridge Coins-Stephen Fenton)
43 Duke Street, St James's, London SW1Y 6DD
Tel: 020 7930 7597 / 7888 / 8215   Fax: 020 7930 8214

* This applies to individual lots over £1,000

CROWNS

DATE	F	VF	EF	UNC

OLIVER CROMWELL

	F	VF	EF	UNC
1658 8 over 7 (always)................................	£1800	£3200	£5000	—
1658 Dutch Copy			Extremely rare	
1658 Patterns. In Various Metals................			Extremely rare	

CHARLES II (1660–85)

	F	VF	EF	UNC
1662 First bust, rose (2 varieties)	£140	£700	£3500	—
1662 — no rose (2 varieties).......................	£140	£700	£3500	—
1663 —	£150	£700	£3600	—
1664 Second bust	£120	£600	£3400	—
1665 —	£750	—	—	—
1666 —	£175	£900	£4000	—
1666 — error RE.X for REX			Extremely rare	
1666 — Elephant below bust	£325	£1400	£5000	—
1667 —	£120	£500	£3000	—
1668/7 — 8 over 7......................................	£110	£500	—	—
1668 —	£100	£500	£3000	—
1669/8 — 9 over 8......................................	£350	£800	—	—
1669 —	£300	£900	£4000	—
1670/69 — 70 over 69................................	£150	£800	—	—
1670 —	£120	£600	£3250	—
1671..	£110	£600	£3000	—
1671 Third bust	£110	£500	£2950	—
1672 —	£110	£500	£2950	—
1673 —	£110	£500	£2950	—
1674 —			Extremely rare	
1675 —	£1200	—	—	—
1675/3 —	£700	£2200	—	—
1676 —	£100	£550	£3000	—
1677 —	£110	£550	£3000	—
1677/6 — 7 over 6......................................	£150	£900	—	—
1678/7 —	£150	£900	—	—
1678/7 — 8 over 7......................................	£175	—	—	—
1679 —	£100	£600	£3000	—
1679 Fourth bust	£100	£600	£3000	—
1680 Third bust	£120	£700	£3500	—
1680/79 — 80 over 79................................	£140	£800	—	—
1680 Fourth bust	£100	£600	£3500	—
1680/79 — 80 over 79................................	£150	£1000	—	—
1681 —	£100	£600	£3000	—
1681 — Elephant & Castle below bust.......	£3000	£6000	—	—
1682/1 —	£110	£600	£3000	—
1682 — edge error QVRRTO for QVARTO .	£400	—	—	—
1683 —	£400	£1000	£4000	—
1684 —	£350	£1200	—	—

JAMES II (1685–88)

	F	VF	EF	UNC
1686 First bust	£210	£800	£3700	—
1686 — No stops on obv	£325	£1100	—	—
1687 Second bust	£190	£600	£3000	—
1688/7 — 8 over 7......................................	£210	£800	—	—
1688 —	£200	£800	£2900	—

WILLIAM AND MARY (1688–94)

	F	VF	EF	UNC
1691	£300	£950	£3850	—
1692	£300	£950	£3850	—
1692 2 over upside down 2	£300	£950	£3850	—

DATE	F	VF	EF	UNC

WILLIAM III (1694–1702)

	F	VF	EF	UNC
1695 First bust	£75	£250	£1400	—
1696 —	£70	£240	£1150	—
1696 — no stops on obv.	£225	—	—	—
1996 — no stops obv./rev.	£250	—	—	—
1696 — GEI for DEI	£300	£1200	—	—
1696 Second bust				Unique
1696 Third bust	£75	£250	£1200	—
1697 —	£800	£2000	£3500	—
1700 Third bust variety edge year DUODECIMO	£80	£350	£1200	—
1700 — edge year DUODECIMO TERTIO..	£80	£350	£1200	—

ANNE (1702–14)

	F	VF	EF	UNC
1703 First bust, VIGO	£260	£900	£3500	—
1705 — Plumes in angles on rev.	£500	£1500	£5000	—
1706 — Roses & Plumes in angles on rev...	£140	£600	£1900	—
1707 — —	£140	£600	£1900	—
1707 Second bust, E below	£125	£500	£1400	—
1707 — Plain	£125	£500	£1400	—
1708 — E below	£125	£500	£1400	—
1708/7 — 8 over 7	£160	£800	—	—
1708 — Plain	£120	£600	£1400	—
1708 — — error BR for BRI.......................		Extremely rare		
1708 — Plumes in angles on rev.	£170	£650	£1850	—
1713 Third bust, Roses & Plumes in				
angles on rev..	£175	£650	£1700	—

GEORGE I (1714–27)

	F	VF	EF	UNC
1716..	£350	£1000	£4000	—
1718 8 over 6..	£350	£1000	£4000	—
1720 20 over 18..	£350	£1000	£4000	—
1723 SSC in angles on rev. (South Sea Co.)	£370	£900	£3500	—
1726	£400	£1000	£4250	—

GEORGE II (1727–60)

	F	VF	EF	UNC
1732 Young head, Plain, Proof	—	—	£5000	
1732 — Roses & Plumes in angles on rev ..	£160	£700	£2000	—
1734 — —	£160	£700	£2000	—
1735 — —	£160	£700	£2000	—
1736 — —	£175	£700	£2000	—
1739 — Roses in angles on rev..................	£160	£600	£1900	—
1741 — —	£160	£600	£1900	—
1743 Old head, Roses in angles on rev.......	£150	£600	£1700	—
1746 — — LIMA below bust	£160	£600	£1700	—
1746 — Plain, Proof	—	£800	£3800	—
1750 — —	£250	£800	£2500	—
1751 — —	£350	£950	£2500	—

GEORGE III (1760–1820)

	F	VF	EF	UNC
Dollar with oval counterstamp....................	£125	£400	£750	—
Dollar with octagonal counterstamp	£175	£500	£800	—
1804 Bank of England Dollar, Britannia rev.	£100	£225	£500	—
1818 LVIII..	£25	£70	£250	£700
1818 LIX	£25	£70	£250	£700
1819 LIX	£25	£70	£250	£700
1819 LIX 9 over 8	£30	£125	£400	—
1819 LIX no stops on edge	£50	£120	£300	£900
1819 LX	£30	£70	£325	£800
1820 LX	£25	£70	£300	£700
1820 LX 20 over 19	£55	£200	£500	—

DATE	MINTAGE	F	VF	EF	UNC

GEORGE IV (1820–30)

1821 First bust, St George rev.					
SECUNDO on edge	437,976	£30	£150	£500	£1000
1821 — — Proof	Incl. above	–	–	–	£4000
1821 — — Proof TERTIO (error edge)	Incl above	–	–	–	£4000
1822 — — SECUNDO	124,929	£30	£150	£500	£1000
1822 — — TERTIO	Incl above	£30	£150	£500	£1000
1823 — — Proof only				Extremely rare	
1826 Second bust, shield rev, SEPTIMO					
Proof only		–	–	£1950	£4200

WILLIAM IV (1830–37)

					UNC
1831 Proof only W.W. on truncation		–	–		£10000
1831 Proof only W. WYON on truncation		–	–		£12000
1834 Proof only		–	–		–£18000

VICTORIA (1837–1901)

YOUNG HEAD ISSUES

1839 Proof only	–	–	–	–	£4000
1844 Star stops on edge	94,248	£35	£150	£900	£2500
1844 Cinquefoil stops on edge	incl. above	£30	£150	£900	£2500
1845 Star stops on edge	159,192	£32	£150	£900	£2500
1845 Cinquefoil stops on edge	incl. above	£30	£150	£900	£2500
1847	140,976	£40	£175	£1000	£2750

GOTHIC HEAD ISSUES (Proof only)

1847 mdcccxlvii UNDECIMO on edge	8,000	£400	£700	£1600	£2750
1847 — Plain edge	–	–	–	–	£3250
1853 mdcccliii SEPTIMO on edge	460	–	–	–	£6000
1853 — Plain edge	–	–	–	–	£8000

JUBILEE HEAD ISSUES

1887	173,581	£12	£24	£55	£120
1887 Proof	1,084	–	–	–	£425
1888 Narrow date	131,899	£15	£30	£85	£200
1888 Wide date	incl above	£25	£60	£300	–
1889	1,807,224	£10	£20	£50	£110
1890	997,862	£12	£25	£60	£170
1891	556,394	£12	£25	£60	£170
1892	451,334	£12	£25	£70	£200

OLD HEAD ISSUES (Regnal date on edge in Roman numerals)

1893 LVI	497,845	£12	£30	£130	£350
1893 LVII	incl. above	£15	£40	£200	£425
1893 Proof	1,312	–	–	–	£500
1894 LVII	144,906	£14	£45	£150	£375
1894 LVIII	incl. above	£14	£45	£150	£375
1895 LVIII	252,862	£12	£35	£130	£375
1895 LIX	incl. above	£12	£35	£130	£375
1896 LIX	317,599	£14	£35	£140	£400
1896 LX	incl. above	£12	£35	£130	£350
1897 LX	262,118	£12	£35	£130	£350
1897 LXI	incl. above	£12	£35	£130	£400
1898 LXI	166,150	£15	£40	£130	£500
1898 LXII	incl. above	£12	£35	£130	£350
1899 LXII	166,300	£12	£35	£130	£350
1899 LXIII	incl. above	£12	£35	£130	£350
1900 LXIII	353,356	£12	£35	£130	£350
1900 LXIV	incl. above	£12	£52	£130	£350

Victoria, Jubilee head

DATE	MINTAGE	F	VF	EF	UNC

EDWARD VII (1901–10)

DATE	MINTAGE	F	VF	EF	UNC
1902	256,020	£25	£55	£105	£160
1902 "Matt Proof"	15,123	—	—	—	£160

GEORGE V (1910–36)

DATE	MINTAGE	F	VF	EF	UNC
1927 Proof only	15,030	—	£80	£120	£200
1928	9,034	£60	£100	£200	£400
1929	4,994	£60	£100	£200	£410
1930	4,847	£60	£100	£200	£425
1931	4,056	£60	£100	£200	£400
1932	2,395	£110	£250	£600	£900
1933	7,132	£60	£100	£600	£400
1934	932	£450	£1000	£1800	£3000
1935 Jubilee issue. Incuse edge inscription	714,769	£8	£12	£16	£25
1935 — — error edge inscription	incl. above	—	—	—	£1500
1935 — Specimen in box	incl. above	—	—	—	£45
1935 — Proof	incl. above	—	—	—	£150
1935 — Proof. Raised edge inscription	2,500	—	—	£175	£300
1935 — — fine lettering	incl. above	—	—	—	£1000
1935 — — error edge inscription	incl. above	—	—	—	£1500
1935 — Gold proof	30	—	—Extremely rare		
1936	2,473	£100	£250	£370	£875

GEORGE VI (1936–52)

DATE	MINTAGE	F	VF	EF	UNC
1937 Coronation	418,699	£9	£15	£25	£35
1937 Proof	26,402	—	—	—	£40
1951 Festival of Britain, Proof-like	1,983,540	—	—	£3	£6

ELIZABETH II (1952–   )

Pre-Decimal issues (Five Shillings)

DATE	MINTAGE	F	VF	EF	UNC
1953	5,962,621	—	—	£3	£6
1953 Proof	40,000	—	—	—	£20
1960	1,024,038	—	—	£3	£6
1960 Polished dies	70,000	—	—	—	£8
1965 Churchill	19,640,000	—	—	—	£1

Later issues are listed in the Decimal section.

DOUBLE FLORINS

VICTORIA (1837–1901)

DATE	MINTAGE	F	VF	EF	UNC
1887 Roman I	483,347	£10	£18	£40	£80
1887 Roman I Proof	incl. above	—	—	—	£300
1887 Arabic 1	incl. above	£10	£18	£40	£80
1887 Arabic 1 Proof	incl. above	—	—	—	£300
1888	243,340	£12	£30	£80	£120
1888 Second I in VICTORIA an inverted 1	incl. above	£20	£35	£80	£250
1889	1,185,111	£15	£23	£40	£100
1889 inverted 1	incl. above	£20	£35	£80	£300
1890	782,146	£12	£33	£55	£110

Patterns were also produced in 1911, 1914 and 1950 and are all extremely rare.

HALFCROWNS

DATE	MINTAGE	F	VF	EF	UNC

OLIVER CROMWELL

DATE	F	VF	EF	UNC
1656			Extremely rare	
1658	£850	£1700	£3250	—
1658 Proof in Gold			Extremely rare	

CHARLES II (1660–1685)

DATE	F	VF	EF	UNC
1663 First bust	£100	£400	£2000	—
1663 — no stops on obv.	£130	£600	—	—
1664 Second bust	£130	£500	£2200	—
1666 Third bust	£900	—	—	—
1666 — Elephant	£700	£1800	—	—
1667/4 — 7 over 4			Extremely rare	
1668/4 — 8 over 4	£200	—	—	—
1669 —	£400	£1600	—	—
1669/4 — 9 over 4	£200	£750	—	—
1670 —	£80	£400	£2000	—
1670 — MRG for MAG	£300	£1000	—	—
1671 —	£80	£300	£2200	—
1671/0 — 1 over 0	£90	£500	£2400	—
1672 —	£90	£500	£2200	—
1672 Fourth bust	£95	£500	£2200	—
1673 —	£80	£300	£2000	—
1673 — Plumes both sides			Extremely rare	
1673 — Plume below bust	£2000	—	—	—
1674 —	£90	£500	—	—
1675 —	£95	£325	£1800	—
1676 —	£90	£300	£1500	—
1676 — inverted 1 in date	£100	£350	£1000	—
1677 —	£90	£350	£1000	—
1678 —	£200	£800	—	—
1679 — GRATTA error			Extremely rare	
1679 —	£90	£350	£1800	—
1680 —	£150	£700	—	—
1681/0 — 1 over 0	£160	—	—	—
1681 —	£110	£400	£200	—
1681 — Elephant & Castle	£2000	—	—	—
1682 —	£110	£400	£2500	—
1683 —	£110	£375	£2200	—
1683 — Plume below bust			Extremely rare	
1684/3 — 4 over 3	£200	£700	£3250	—

JAMES II (1685–1688)

DATE	F	VF	EF	UNC
1685 First bust	£140	£550	£2250	—
1686 —	£140	£550	£2250	—
1686/5 — 6 over 5	£175	£650	—	—
1686 — V over S	£220	£600	—	—
1687 —	£150	£600	£1800	—
1687/6 — 7 over 6	£200	£700	—	—
1687 Second bust	£150	£500	£1800	—
1688 —	£150	£500	£1800	—

WILLIAM AND MARY (1688–1694)

DATE	F	VF	EF	UNC
1689 First busts; first shield	£70	£300	£1250	—
1689 — — no pearls in crown	£70	£300	£1250	—
1689 — FRA for FR.	£120	£400	£1500	—
1689 — — No stop on obv	£70	£300	£1250	—
1689 — Second shield	£70	£300	£1250	—
1689 — — no pearls in crown	£70	£325	£1250	—

DATE	MINTAGE	F	VF	EF	UNC
1690 — —		£125	£650	£2500	—
1690 — — error GRETIA for GRATIA		£275	£1500	£3750	—
1691 Second busts		£110	£420	£1900	—
1692 —		£110	£420	£1900	—
1693 —		£110	£420	£1900	—
1693 — 3 over inverted 3		£120	£475	£2000	—

WILLIAM III (1694–1702)

DATE	MINTAGE	F	VF	EF	UNC
1696 First bust, large shields, early harp		£60	£220	£800	—
1696 — — — B (Bristol) below bust		£60	£240	£1000	—
1696 — — — C (Chester)		£70	£300	£1000	—
1696 — — — E (Exeter)		£100	£400	£1250	—
1696 — — — N (Norwich)		£80	£400	£1100	—
1696 — — — y (York)		£80	£350	£1100	—
1696 — — — — Scottish arms at date				Extremely rare	
1696 — — ordinary harp		£65	£250	—	—
1696 — — — C		£90	£400	—	—
1696 — — — E		£90	£400	—	—
1696 — — — N		£125	£550	£2000	—
1696 — Small shields, ordinary harp		£55	£225	£700	—
1696 — — — B		£70	£300	£1000	—
1696 — — — C		£70	£300	£1050	—
1696 — — — E		£90	£350	—	—
1696 — — — N		£80	£350	£1250	—
1696 — — — y		£80	£350	£1250	—
1696 Second bust				Only one known	
1697 First bust, large shields, ordinary harp		£60	£250	£700	—
1697 — — — GRR for GRA				Extremely rare	
1697 — — — B		£60	£300	£1000	—
1697 — — — C		£60	£350	£1100	—
1697 — — — E		£75	£350	£1100	—
1697 — — — N		£75	£350	£1100	—
1697 — — — y		£75	£350	£1100	—
1698 — —		£80	£300	£950	—
1698/7 — — 8 over 7				Extremely rare	
1699 — —		£90	£300	£1000	—
1699 — — Scottish arms at date				Extremely rare	
1700 — —		£70	£300	£850	—
1701 — —		£80	£300	£900	—
1701 — — No stops on rev		£90	£300	—	—
1701 — — Elephant & Castle below				Fair	£1150
1701 — — Plumes in angles on rev.		£160	£550	£1500	—

ANNE (1702–1714)

DATE	MINTAGE	F	VF	EF	UNC
1703 Plain (pre-Union)		£500	£2200	—	—
1703 VIGO below bust		£100	£300	£1000	—
1704 Plumes in angles on rev.		£150	£500	£1600	—
1705 —		£100	£450	£1400	—
1706 Roses & Plumes in angles on rev.		£75	£300	£1000	—
1707 —		£75	£300	£900	—
1707 Plain (post-Union)		£70	£200	£650	—
1707 E below bust		£70	£200	£650	—
1707 — SEPTIMO edge				Extremely rare	
1708 Plain		£70	£250	£800	—
1708 E below bust		£70	£250	£800	—
1708 Plumes in angles on rev.		£70	£250	£900	—
1709 Plain		£65	£250	£700	—
1709 E below bust		£220	£800	—	—
1710 Roses & Plumes in angles on rev.		£70	£275	£850	—
1712 —		£70	£275	£850	—
1713 Plain		£70	£275	£850	—
1713 Roses & Plumes in angles on rev.		£70	£275	£850	—
1714 —		£70	£275	£850	—
1714/3 4 over 3		£100	£400	—	—

DATE   MINTAGE   F   VF   EF   UNC

GEORGE I (1714–1727)

DATE	MINTAGE	F	VF	EF	UNC
1715 Roses & Plumes in angles on rev.		£250	£650	£2100	—
1715 Plain edge				Extremely rare	
1717 —		£250	£650	£2000	—
1720 —		£250	£650	£2000	—
1720/17 20 over 17		£260	£700	—	—
1723 SSC in angles on rev.		£250	£700	£2000	—
1726 Small Roses & Plumes in angles on rev.		£3250	£17500	—	—

GEORGE II (1727–1760)

DATE	MINTAGE	F	VF	EF	UNC
1731 Young head, Plain, proof only	—	—	£4500	—
1731 — Roses & Plumes in angles on rev.	£85	£400	£1000	—
1732 — —	£85	£400	£1000	—
1734 — —	£85	£400	£1000	—
1735 — —	£85	£400	£1000	—
1736 — —	£80	£400	£1000	—
1739 — Roses in angles on rev.	£80	£350	£900	—
1741/39 — — 41 over 30	£125	£400	—	—
1741 — —	£80	£325	£900	—
1743 Old head, Roses in angles on rev.	£65	£160	£650	—
1745 — —	£65	£160	£650	—
1745 — LIMA below bust	£65	£150	£625	—
1746 — —	£65	£150	£625	—
1746/5 — — 6 over 5	£75	£180	£700	—
1746 — Plain, Proof	—	—	£1600	—
1750 — —	£100	£425	£1200	—
1751 — —	£120	£500	£1400	—

GEORGE III (1760–1820)

DATE	MINTAGE	F	VF	EF	UNC
1816 "Bull head"	—	£15	£60	£175	£400
1817 —	8,092,656	£15	£60	£175	£400
1817 "Small head"	incl. above	£15	£60	£175	£400
1818 —	2,905,056	£15	£60	£175	£400
1819/8 — 9 over 8	incl. above			Extremely rare	
1819 —	4,790,016	£15	£60	£175	£400
1820 —	2,396,592	£25	£100	£300	£750

GEORGE IV (1820–30)

DATE	MINTAGE	F	VF	EF	UNC
1820 First bust, first reverse	incl. above	£20	£50	£200	£450
1821 — —	1,435,104	£20	£50	£200	£450
1821 — — Proof	incl. above	—	—	—	£1200
1823 — —	2,003,760	£800	£2500	—	—
1823 — Second reverse	incl. above	£20	£50	£180	£450
1824 — —	465,696	£25	£65	£200	£550
1824 Second bust, third reverse	incl. above			Extremely rare	
1825 — —	2,258,784	£20	£50	£150	£350
1826 — —	2,189,088	£18	£50	£150	£350
1826 — — Proof	incl. above	—	—	—	£1200
1828 — —	49,890	£45	£110	£325	£800
1829 — —	508,464	£50	£110	£325	£700

WILLIAM IV (1830–37)

DATE	MINTAGE	F	VF	EF	UNC
1831	—			Extremely rare	
1831 Proof (W.W. in script & block)	—	—	—	—	£850
1834 W.W. in block	993,168	£20	£60	£200	£475
1834 W.W. in script	incl. above	£20	£60	£200	£475
1835	281,952	£25	£70	£220	£500
1836	1,588,752	£20	£50	£200	£500
1836/5 6 over 5	incl. above	£40	£100	£400	—
1837	150,526	£30	£100	£375	£850

DATE	MINTAGE	F	VF	EF	UNC

VICTORIA (1837–1901)

YOUNG HEAD ISSUES

DATE	MINTAGE	F	VF	EF	UNC
1839 (two varieties)	—	£500	£1300	£4000	—
1839 Proof	—	—	—	—	£3000
1840	386,496	£35	£170	£400	£1000
1841	42,768	£300	£600	£1500	£3000
1842	486,288	£35	£100	£400	£900
1843	454,608	£70	£200	£700	£1200
1844	1,999,008	£25	£50	£300	£750
1845	2,231,856	£25	£50	£300	£750
1846	1,539,668	£30	£60	£300	£750
1848 Plain 8	367,488	£70	£175	£600	£2000
1848/6	incl. above	£6050	£150	£500	£1800
1849	261,360	£45	£90	£400	£900
1849 Small date	incl. above	£60	£150	£600	£1000
1850	484,613	£35	£90	£400	£1000
1853 Proof only	—	—	—	—	£2000
1874	2,188,599	£15	£35	£160	£350
1875	1,113,483	£15	£35	£160	£350
1876	633,221	£15	£35	£160	£350
1876/5 6 over 5	incl. above	£20	£50	£200	£350
1877	447,059	£15	£35	£180	£350
1878	1,466,323	£15	£35	£180	£350
1879	901,356	£20	£40	£200	£350
1880	1,346,350	£15	£40	£140	£350
1881	2,301,495	£15	£40	£140	£325
1882	808,227	£15	£40	£140	£325
1883	2,982,779	£15	£40	£140	£300
1884	1,569,175	£15	£40	£140	£300
1885	1,628,438	£15	£40	£140	£300
1886	891,767	£15	£40	£140	£300
1887	1,438,046	£15	£40	£140	£300

JUBILEE HEAD ISSUES

DATE	MINTAGE	F	VF	EF	UNC
1887	incl. above	£5	£8	£16	£40
1887 Proof	1,084	—	—	—	£160
1888	1,428,787	£8	£15	£35	£70
1889	4,811,954	£8	£14	£35	£70
1890	3,228,111	£8	£14	£45	£100
1891	2,284,632	£8	£15	£45	£100
1892	1,710,946	£8	£14	£50	£110

OLD HEAD ISSUES

DATE	MINTAGE	F	VF	EF	UNC
1893	1,792,600	£7	£15	£40	£85
1893 Proof	1,312	—	—	—	£150
1894	1,524,960	£10	£25	£60	£150
1895	1,772,662	£8	£18	£50	£130
1896	2,148,505	£7	£15	£45	£130
1897	1,678,643	£7	£15	£40	£120
1898	1,870,055	£7	£15	£40	£120
1899	2,865,872	£7	£15	£40	£120
1900	4,479,128	£7	£15	£40	£120
1901	1,516,570	£7	£15	£40	£120

EDWARD VII (1901–10)

DATE	MINTAGE	F	VF	EF	UNC
1902	1,316,008	£8	£20	£60	£90
1902 "Matt Proof"	15,123	—	£300	—	£150
1903	274,840	£80	£300	£900	£1950
1904	709,652	£50	£175	£400	£1000
1905	166,008	£200	£600	£1250	£3000
1906	2,886,206	£10	£35	£150	£550
1907	3,693,930	£10	£35	£150	£550
1908	1,758,889	£15	£50	£275	£800
1909	3,051,592	£10	£50	£200	£600
1910	2,557,685	£8	£30	£85	£340

GEORGE V (1910–36)

First issue

DATE	MINTAGE	F	VF	EF	UNC
1911	2,914,573	£7	£20	£50	£100
1911 Proof	6,007	—	—	—	£95
1912	4,700,789	£6	£14	£40	£90

George V first type reverse

DATE	MINTAGE	F	VF	EF	UNC
1913	4,090,169	£6	£12	£50	£110
1914	18,333,003	£3	£8	£30	£60
1915	32,433,066	£3	£8	£25	£55
1916	29,530,020	£3	£8	£25	£50
1917	11,172,052	£3	£8	£28	£70
1918	29,079,592	£3	£8	£20	£50
1919	10,266,737	£4	£10	£25	£70

Second issue—debased silver

1920	17,982,077	£2	£7	£20	£60
1921	23,677,889	£2	£7	£16	£50
1922	16,396,724	£2	£7	£16	£50
1923	26,308,526	£6	£7	£15	£35
1924	5,866,294	£7	£15	£50	£150
1925	1,413,461	£14	£45	£175	£550
1926	4,473,516	£4	£15	£40	£120

Third issue — Modified effigy

1926	incl. above	£4	£10	£30	£75
1927	6,837,872	£3	£8	£25	£45

Fourth issue—New shield reverse

1927 Proof	15,000	—	—	—	£60
1928	18,762,727	£2	£5	£12	£35
1929	17,632,636	£2	£5	£12	£35
1930	809,051	£8	£35	£170	£450
1931	11,264,468	£2	£5	£15	£35
1932	4,793,643	£2	£5	£20	£75
1933	10,311,494	£2	£5	£15	£40
1934	2,422,399	£3	£8	£40	£120
1935	7,022,216	£2	£5	£12	£20
1936	7,039,423	£2	£5	£10	£18

George V, fourth issue, new shield reverse

GEORGE VI (1936–52)

1937	9,106,440	—	£2	£4	£10
1937 Proof	26,402	—	—	—	£12
1938	6,426,478	£1	£3	£10	£17
1939	15,478,635	—	£1.50	£4	£8
1940	17,948,439	—	£1.50	£4	£6
1941	15,773,984	—	£1.50	£4	£6
1942	31,220,090	—	£1.50	£4	£6
1943	15,462,875	—	£1.50	£4	£6
1944	15,255,165	—	£1.50	£4	£6
1945	19,849,242	—	£1.50	£4	£6
1946	22,724,873	—	£1.50	£4	£6

Cupro-nickel

1947	21,911,484	—	£1	£2	£4
1948	71,164,703	—	£1	£2	£4
1949	28,272,512	—	£1	£2	£6
1950	28,335,500	—	£1	£2	£6
1950 Proof	17,513	—	£1	£2	£9
1951	9,003,520	—	£1	£2	£6
1951 Proof	20,000	—	—	—	£9
1952				Only one known	

ELIZABETH II (1952–)

1953	4,333,214	—	—	£1	£3
1953 Proof	40,000	—	—	—	£5
1954	11,614,953	—	£1	£3	£15
1955	23,628,726	—	—	£1	£4
1956	33,934,909	—	—	£1	£4
1957	34,200,563	—	—	£1	£4
1958	15,745,668	—	£1	£3	£16
1959	9,028,844	—	£1	£5	£18
1960	19,929,191	—	—	£1	£2
1961	25,887,897	—	—	—	£1
1961 Polished dies	incl. above	—	—	£1	£2
1962	24,013,312	—	—	—	£1
1963	17,625,200	—	—	—	£1
1964	5,973,600	—	—	—	£1
1965	9,778,440	—	—	—	£1
1966	13,375,200	—	—	—	£1
1967	33,058,400	—	—	—	—

FLORINS

"Gothic" florin

DATE	MINTAGE	F	VF	EF	UNC

VICTORIA (1837–1901)

YOUNG (CROWNED) HEAD ISSUES

"Godless" type (without D.G.—"Dei Gratia")

1848 "Godless" Pattern only plain edge	—			Very rare	
1848 "Godless" Pattern only milled edge	—			Extremely rare	
1849	413,820	£15	£40	£110	£300

(Beware of recent forgeries)

"Gothic" type i.e. date in Roman numerals in obverse legend

"brit." in legend. No die no.

1851 mdcccli Proof	1,540			Extremely rare	
1852 mdccclii	1,014,552	£20	£50	£170	£400
1853 mdcccliii	3,919,950	£20	£50	£170	£400
1853 — Proof	incl. above	—	—	—	£1800
1854 mdcccliv	550,413	£500	—	—	—
1855 mdccclv	831,017	£20	£50	£170	£450
1856 mdccclvi	2,201,760	£20	£50	£170	£450
1857 mdccclvii	1,671,120	£20	£50	£170	£450
1858 mdccclviii...........................	2,239,380	£20	£50	£170	£450
1859 mdccclix	2,568,060	£20	£50	£170	£450
1860 mdccclx...............................	1,475,100	£25	£70	£220	£475
1862 mdccclxii	594,000	£90	£270	£700	£2200
1863 mdccclxiii	938,520	£300	£700	£2000	£3500

"brit" in legend. Die no. below bust

1864 mdccclxiv	1,861,200	£20	£50	£170	£400
1864 Gothic Piedfort flan	incl. above			Extremely rare	
1865 mdccclxv	1,580,044	£20	£50	£170	£475
1866 mdccclxvi	914,760	£20	£50	£170	£475
1867 mdccclxvii	423,720	£40	£100	£300	£700
1867—only 42 arcs in border	incl. above			Extremely rare	

"britt" in legend. Die no. below bust

1868 mdccclxviii...........................	896,940	£20	£50	£170	£400
1869 mdccclxix	297,000	£25	£60	£220	£600
1870 mdccclxx	1,080,648	£20	£50	£170	£350
1871 mdccclxxi	3,425,605	£20	£50	£170	£350
1872 mdccclxxii	7,199,690	£20	£50	£150	£350
1873 mdccclxxiii...........................	5,921,839	£20	£50	£150	£350
1874 mdccclxxiv	1,642,630	£20	£50	£150	£350
1874 — iv over iii in date	incl. above	£25	£60	£200	£350
1875 mdccclxxv	1,117,030	£18	£50	£160	£350
1876 mdccclxxvi	580,034	£22	£60	£175	£350
1877 mdccclxxvii...........................	682,292	£20	£50	£125	£350
1877 — 48 arcs in border no W.W.	incl. above	£20	£50	£170	£370
1877 — 42 arcs	incl. above	£20	£50	£170	£370
1877 — — no die number	incl. above			Extremely rare	
1878 mdccclxxviii with die number	1,786,680	£18	£50	£170	£375
1879 mdccclxxix no die no	1,512,247			Extremely rare	
1879 — 48 arcs in border............	incl. above	£18	£50	£170	£375
1879 — no die number...............	incl. above			Extremely rare	
1879 — 38 arcs, no W.W..	incl. above	£18	£50	£170	£375
1880 mdccclxxx Younger portrait	—			Extremely rare	
1880 — 34 arcs, Older portrait....	2,167,170	£18	£50	£160	£340
1881 mdccclxxxi — —	2,570,337	£18	£50	£180	£340
1881 — xxri broken puncheon ...	incl. above	£22	£70	£170	£400
1883 mdccclxxxiii — —..............	3,555,667	£16	£45	£150	£350
1884 mdccclxxxiv — —	1,447,379	£16	£45	£150	£350
1885 mdccclxxxv — —	1,758,210	£16	£45	£150	£350
1886 mdccclxxxvi — —	591,773	£16	£45	£150	£350
1887 mdccclxxxvii — —..............	1,776,903	£35	£100	£240	£550
1887 — 46 arcs	incl. above	£35	£100	£275	£600

189

DATE	MINTAGE	F	VF	EF	UNC
JUBILEE HEAD ISSUES					
1887	incl. above	£4	£8	£18	£40
1887 Proof.....	1,084	—	—	—	£140
1888.....	1,547,540	£5	£10	£35	£90
1889.....	2,973,561	£5	£12	£35	£90
1890.....	1,684,737	£8	£22	£70	£200
1891.....	836,438	£15	£50	£140	£350
1892.....	283,401	£22	£60	£200	£500
VICTORIA — OLD HEAD ISSUES					
1893.....	1,666,103	£5	£14	£32	£75
1893 Proof.....	1,312	—	—	—	£140
1894.....	1,952,842	£8	£22	£55	£150
1895.....	2,182,968	£7	£20	£55	£130
1896.....	2,944,416	£6	£16	£40	£100
1897.....	1,699,921	£6	£16	£40	£100
1898.....	3,061,343	£6	£16	£40	£100
1899.....	3,966,953	£6	£16	£40	£100
1900.....	5,528,630	£6	£16	£40	£100
1901.....	2,648,870	£6	£16	£40	£100

EDWARD VII (1901–10)

DATE	MINTAGE	F	VF	EF	UNC
1902.....	2,189,575	£7	£15	£40	£80
1902 "Matt Proof"	15,123	—	—	—	£90
1903.....	1,995,298	£10	£35	£110	£500
1904.....	2,769,932	£10	£35	£110	£375
1905.....	1,187,596	£50	£150	£500	£1100
1906.....	6,910,128	£10	£35	£110	£425
1907.....	5,947,895	£11	£35	£110	£425
1908.....	3,280,010	£12	£50	£300	£700
1909.....	3,482,829	£10	£45	£200	£550
1910.....	5,650,713	£8	£28	£90	£240

GEORGE V (1910–36)

DATE	MINTAGE	F	VF	EF	UNC
First issue					
1911.....	5,951,284	£4	£8	£30	£75
1911 Proof.....	6,007	—	—	—	£70
1912.....	8,571,731	£3	£11	£30	£90
1913.....	4,545,278	£5	£16	£35	£110
1914.....	21,252,701	£3	£14	£22	£45
1915.....	12,367,939	£3	£14	£22	£45
1916.....	21,064,337	£3	£14	£22	£45
1917.....	11,181,617	£3	£14	£25	£60
1918.....	29,211,792	£3	£14	£22	£45
1919.....	9,469,292	£3	£15	£30	£70
Second issue — debased silver					
1920.....	15,387,833	£2	£12	£32	£70
1921.....	34,863,895	£2	£12	£30	£50
1922.....	23,861,044	£2	£12	£30	£50
1923.....	21,546,533	£2	£10	£25	£55
1924.....	4,582,372	£6	£18	£60	£150
1925.....	1,404,136	£12	£40	£175	£500
1926.....	5,125,410	£5	£15	£40	£85
Fourth issue — new reverse					
1927 Proof only	101,497	—	—	—	£50
1928.....	11,087,186	£2	£4	£12	£25
1929.....	16,397,279	£2	£4	£12	£25
1930.....	5,753,568	£2	£5	£15	£40
1931.....	6,556,331	£2	£5	£12	£30
1932.....	717,041	£8	£20	£150	£400
1933.....	8,685,303	£2	£5	£15	£35
1935.....	7,540,546	£2	£5	£10	£20
1936.....	9,897,448	£2	£4	£9	£20

DATE	MINTAGE	F	VF	EF	UNC

GEORGE VI (1936–52)

1937	13,006,781	—	£1	£3	£6
1937 Proof	26,402	—	—	—	£8
1938	7,909,388	£1	£2	£9	£18
1939	20,850,607	£1	£2	£4	£6
1940	18,700,338	£1	£2	£4	£6
1941	24,451,079	£1	£2	£4	£6
1942	39,895,243	£1	£2	£4	£6
1943	26,711,987	£1	£2	£4	£6
1944	27,560,005	£1	£2	£4	£6
1945	25,858,049	£1	£2	£4	£6
1946	22,300,254	£1	£2	£4	£6

Cupro-nickel

1947	22,910,085	—	—	£1	£3
1948	67,553,636	—	—	£1	£3
1949	28,614,939	—	—	£1	£5
1950	24,357,490	—	—	£2	£7
1950 Proof	17,513	—	—	£1	£8
1951	27,411,747	—	—	£2	£8
1951 Proof	20,000	—	—	—	£8

ELIZABETH II (1952–)

1953	11,958,710	—	—	—	£2
1953 Proof	40,000	—	—	—	£5
1954	13,085,422	—	—	£5	£25
1955	25,887,253	—	—	£1	£3
1956	47,824,500	—	—	£1	£3
1957	33,071,282	—	—	£4	£25
1958	9,564,580	—	—	£3	£15
1959	14,080,319	—	—	£4	£25
1960	13,831,782	—	—	£1	£3
1961	37,735,315	—	—	£1	£2
1962	35,147,903	—	—	£1	£2
1963	26,471,000	—	—	£1	£2
1964	16,539,000	—	—	£1	£2
1965	48,163,000	—	—	—	£1.50
1966	83,999,000	—	—	—	£1.50
1967	39,718,000	—	—	—	£1.50

SHILLINGS

OLIVER CROMWELL

1658		£500	£1000	£2100	—
1658 Dutch Copy				Extremely rare

CHARLES II (1660–85)

1663 First bust	£75	£275	£900	—
1663 — GARTIA error			Extremely rare	
1663 — Irish & Scottish shields transposed	£200	—	—	—
1666 — Elephant below bust	£400	£1250	£4000	—
1666 "Guinea" head, elephant	£1800	£3700	—	—
1666 Second bust			Extremely rare	
1668	£70	£220	£850	—
1668/7 — 8 over 7	£80	£275	—	—
1668 Second bust	£75	£250	£850	—
1669/6 First bust variety			Extremely rare	
1669			Extremely rare	
1669 Second bust			Extremely rare	
1670 —	£80	£325	£1000	—
1671 —	£100	£350	£1200	—
1671 — Plume below, plume in centre rev.	£300	£700	£2750	—
1672 —	£75	£225	£900	—
1673 —	£90	£350	£900	—

DATE	F	VF	EF	UNC
1673 — Plume below, plume in centre rev.	£260	£700	£2700	—
1673/2 — 3 over 2...	£120	£500	—	—
1674/3 — 4 over 3...	£120	£500	—	—
1674 —	£90	£300	£1000	—
1674 — Plume below bust, plume in centre rev.	£275	£700	£2700	—
1674 — Plume rev. only....................................	£300	£700	£2700	—
1674 Third bust	£250	£750	—	—
1675 Second bust	£110	£400	—	—
1675/4 — 5 over 4...	£150	£600	—	—
1675 — Plume below bust, plume in centre rev.	£275	£700	£3000	—
1675 Third bust	£225	£600	—	—
1675/3 — 5 over 3...	£225	£600	—	—
1676 Second bust	£80	£240	£900	—
1676/5 — 6 over 5...	£100	£400	—	—
1676 — Plume below bust, plume in centre rev.	£275	£750	£2750	—
1677 —	£75	£275	£1000	—
1677 — Plume below bust	£275	£750	£2750	—
1678 —	£90	£300	£1000	—
1678/7 — 8 over 7...	£100	£600	—	—
1679 —	£80	£275	£950	—
1679 — Plume below bust, plume in centre rev.	£325	£800	£3000	—
1679 — Plume below bust	£300	£750	£2750	—
1679 — 9 over 7...	£100	£500	—	—
1680 —			Extremely rare	
1680 — Plume below bust, plume in centre rev.	£350	£850	£3100	—
1680/79 — — 80 over 79	£325	£1000	—	—
1681 —	£150	£500	£1500	—
1681 — 1 over 0...	£140	£500	£1500	—
1681/0 Elephant & Castle below bust	£2500	—	—	—
1682/1 — 2 over 1...	£500	£1500	—	—
1683 —			Extremely rare	
1683 Fourth (Larger) bust................................	£200	£600	£2200	—
1684 —	£140	£500	£1750	—

JAMES II (1685–88)

	F	VF	EF	UNC
1685...	£110	£400	£1400	—
1685 Plume in centre rev. rev			Extremely rare	
1685 No stops on rev.	£160	£650	—	—
1686..	£170	£400	£1400	—
1686/5 6 over 5	£170	£400	£1400	—
1687..	£150	£400	£1500	—
1687/6 7 over 6	£120	£400	£1500	—
1688..	£120	£400	£1500	—
1688/7 last 8 over 7...	£130	£400	£1500	—

WILLIAM & MARY (1688–94)

	F	VF	EF	UNC
1692	£140	£425	£1800	—
1692 inverted 1..	£170	£425	£1850	—
1693..	£140	£425	£1800	—

WILLIAM III (1694–1702)

Provincially produced shillings carry privy marks or initials below the bust:
B: Bristol. C: Chester. E: Exeter. N: Norwich. Y or y: York.

	F	VF	EF	UNC
1695 First bust	£35	£100	£500	—
1696 —	£30	£80	£375	—
1696 — no stops on rev.	£50	£120	£650	—
1696 — MAB for MAG			Extremely rare	
1696 — 1669 error			Extremely rare	
1696 — 1669 various GVLELMVS errors			Extremely rare	
1696 — B below bust	£40	£120	£600	—
1696 — C..	£40	£120	£600	—
1696 — E..	£45	£140	£700	—
1696 — N..	£40	£120	£600	—

DATE	F	VF	EF	UNC
1696 — y	£35	£110	£600	—
1696 — Y	£35	£110	£600	—
1696 Second bust			Only one known	
1696 Third bust C below	£160	£400	£1000	—
1696 — Y			Extremely rare	
1697 First bust	£40	£90	£350	—
1697 — GRI for GRA error			Extremely rare	
1697 — Scottish & Irish shields transposed			Extremely rare	
1697 — Irish arms at date			Extremely rare	
1697 — no stops on rev	£45	£150	£600	—
1697 — GVLELMVS error			Extremely rare	
1697 — B	£45	£130	£625	—
1697 — C	£40	£120	£625	—
1697 — E	£45	£120	£625	—
1697 — N	£40	£110	£625	—
1697 — — no stops on obv			Extremely rare	
1697 — y	£40	£120	£550	—
1697 — — arms of France & Ireland transposed			Extremely rare	
1697 — Y	£40	£120	£550	—
1697 Third bust	£35	£110	£500	—
1697 — B	£40	£110	£500	—
1697 — C	£40	£110	£500	—
1697 — — Fr.a error	£100	£300	—	—
1697 — — no stops on obv	£70	£200	—	—
1697 — — arms of Scotland at date			Extremely rare	
1697 — E	£40	£110	£600	—
1697 — N	£40	£110	£600	—
1697 — y	£50	£120	£500	—
1697 Third bust variety	£40	£90	£350	—
1697 — B	£40	£120	£600	—
1697 — C	£90	£400	—	—
1698 —	£70	£200	£750	—
1698 — Plumes in angles of rev	£200	£500	£1200	—
1698 Fourth bust "Flaming hair"	£140	£400	£1400	—
1699 —	£90	£300	£1000	—
1699 Fifth bust	£80	£200	£700	—
1699 — Plumes in angles on rev	£100	£325	£1000	—
1699 — Roses in angles on rev	£95	£275	£900	—
1700 —	£45	£100	£400	—
1700 — Small round oo in date	£45	£100	£400	—
1700 — no stop after DEI			Extremely rare	
1700 — Plume below bust	£1500	£3000	—	—
1701 —	£75	£200	£500	—
1701 — Plumes in angles on rev	£100	£300	£1000	—

William III First bust

ANNE (1702–14)

	F	VF	EF	UNC
1702 First bust (pre-Union with Scotland)	£60	£300	£600	—
1702 — Plumes in angles on rev	£70	£275	£600	—
1702 — VIGO below bust	£70	£220	£600	—
1702 — — colon before ANNA			Extremely rare	
1703 Second bust, VIGO below	£55	£170	£500	—
1704 — Plain	£500	£1400	—	—
1704 — Plumes in angles on rev	£65	£175	£700	—
1705 — Plain	£60	£175	£600	—
1705 — Plumes in angles on rev	£55	£175	£600	—
1705 — Roses & Plumes in angles on rev	£55	£175	£600	—
1707 —	£50	£170	£550	—
1707 Second bust (post-Union) E below bust	£40	£100	£450	—
1707 — E* below bust	£70	£200	£650	—
1707 Third bust, Plain	£35	£90	£350	—
1707 — Plumes in angles on rev	£40	£150	£700	—
1707 — E below bust	£35	£80	£400	—
1707 "Edinburgh" bust, E* below			Extremely rare	
1708 Second bust, E below	£40	£80	£400	—
1708 — E* below bust	£45	£150	£600	—
1708/7 — — 8 over 7			Extremely rare	
1708 — Roses & Plumes in angles on rev	£80	£250	£600	—

Anne, VIGO below bust

DATE	MINTAGE	F	VF	EF	UNC
1708 Third bust, Plain		£35	£85	£325	—
1708 — Plumes in angles on rev.		£50	£150	£450	—
1708 Third bust, E below bust		£50	£160	£500	—
1708/7 — — 8 over 7		£80	£240	—	—
1708 — Roses & Plumes in angles on rev.		£60	£160	£500	—
1708 "Edinburgh" bust, E* below		£50	£150	£500	—
1709 Third bust, Plain		£40	£90	£450	—
1709 "Edinburgh" bust, E* below		£45	£150	£550	—
1709 — E no star (filled in die?)........................		£70	£160	£500	—
1710 Third bust, Roses & Plumes in angles		£50	£120	£550	—
1710 Fourth bust, Roses & Plumes in angles ...		£50	£140	£550	—
1711 Third bust, Plain		£60	£120	£375	—
1711 Fourth bust, Plain		£25	£55	£160	—
1712 — Roses & Plumes in angles on rev.		£50	£100	£350	—
1713 — —		£50	£100	£300	—
1713/2 — 3 over 2..		£50	£160	—	—
1714 — —		£55	£85	£300	—
1714/3 — —				Extremely rare	

GEORGE I (1714–27)

1715 First bust, Roses & Plumes in angles on rev.		£70	£200	£700	—
1716 — —		£80	£300	£1000	—
1717 — —		£55	£200	£900	—
1718 — —		£50	£120	£650	—
1719 — —		£110	£270	£1100	—
1720 — —		£40	£110	£400	—
1720/18 — —		£100	£300	£1000	—
1720 — Plain		£35	£100	£400	—
1721 — Roses & Plumes in angles on rev.		£50	£160	£700	—
1721/0 — — 1 over 0		£50	£160	£600	—
1721 — Plain		£100	£350	£1000	—
1721/19 — — 21 over 19		£125	£250	—	—
1722 — Roses & Plumes in angles on rev.		£70	£200	£700	—
1723 — —		£70	£200	£700	—
1723 — SSC rev., Arms of France at date		£70	£150	£700	—
1723 — SSC in angles on rev		£20	£150	£180	—
1723 Second bust, SSC in angles on rev.		£40	£110	£400	—
1723 — Roses & Plumes in angles		£60	£175	£750	—
1723 — WCC (Welsh Copper Co) below bust ..		£325	£900	£3200	—
1724 — Roses & Plumes in angles on rev.		£60	£175	£550	—
1724 — WCC below bust.................................		£325	£900	£3200	—
1725 — Roses & Plumes in angles on rev.		£50	£175	£750	—
1725 — — no stops on obv...............................		£70	£200	£700	—
1725 — WCC below bust.................................		£350	£1100	£3750	—
1726 —		£350	£1000	£3750	—
1726 — Roses & Plumes in angles on rev.		£300	£1500	—	—
1727 — —				Extremely rare	
1727 — — no stops on obv...............................				Extremely rare	

GEORGE II (1727–60)

1727 Young head, Plumes in angles on rev.		£55	£250	£500	—
1727 — Roses & Plumes in angles on rev.		£55	£150	£500	—
1728 — —		£55	£150	£500	—
1728 — Plain		£60	£200	£625	—
1729 — Roses & Plumes in angles on rev.		£50	£150	£500	—
1731 — —		£60	£150	£500	—
1731 — Plumes in angles on rev.		£60	£300	£800	—
1732 — Roses & Plumes in angles on rev.		£50	£150	£500	—
1734 — —		£50	£150	£500	—
1735 — —		£50	£150	£500	—
1736 — —		£50	£150	£500	—
1736/5 — — 6 over 5		£60	£200	£650	—
1737 — —		£50	£150	£550	—
1739 — Roses in angles on rev.		£35	£100	£350	—
1739/7 — — 9 over 7				Extremely rare	
1741 — —		£35	£100	£350	—
1741/39 — — 41 over 39				Extremely rare	
1743 Old head, Roses in angles on rev.		£25	£75	£300	—
1745 — —		£25	£75	£300	—
1745 — — LIMA beow bust		£20	£75	£275	—

*George II
Young head*

DATE	MINTAGE	F	VF	EF	UNC
1745/3 — — — 5 over 3		£50	£150	£400	—
1746 — — —		£50	£150	£600	—
1746/5 — — — 6 over 5		£100	£275	—	—
1746 — Plain, Proof		—	—	£1200	—
1747 — Roses in angles on rev.		£35	£90	£350	—
1750 — Plain		£35	£120	£350	—
1750/6 — — 0 over 6		£50	£140	£475	—
1751 — —		£100	£250	£650	—
1758 — —		£15	£40	£105	—

George II Old head

GEORGE III (1760–1820)

		F	VF	EF	UNC
1763 "Northumberland" bust		£300	£600	£1100	—
1787 rev. no semée of hearts in 4th shield		£15	£30	£80	—
1787 — No stop over head		£15	£30	£80	—
1787 — No stop at date		£15	£30	£80	—
1787 — No stops on obv		£18	£35	£85	—
1787 rev. with semée of hearts in shield		£15	£30	£80	—
1798 "Dorrien Magens" bust		—	—	£8000	—

NEW COINAGE—shield in garter reverse

		F	VF	EF	UNC
1816	—	£8	£18	£50	£100
1817	3,031,360	£8	£18	£50	£100
1817 GEOE for GEOR	incl. above	£100	£220	£400	—
1818	1,342,440	£8	£20	£80	£150
1819	7,595,280	£8	£18	£50	£100
1819/8 9 over 8	incl. above	£10	£30	£70	—
1820	7,975,440	£8	£18	£45	£100

GEORGE IV (1820–30)

		F	VF	EF	UNC
1821 First bust, first reverse	2,463,120	£10	£40	£140	£325
1821 — — Proof	incl. above	—	—	—	£750
1823 — Second reverse	693,000	£20	£55	£200	£375
1824 — —	4,158,000	£10	£40	£125	£350
1825 — —	2,459,160	£20	£40	£125	£475
1825/3 — — 5 over 3	incl. above			Extremely rare	
1825 Second bust, third reverse .	incl. above	£4	£14	£50	£130
1825 — — Roman I	incl. above			Extremely rare	
1826 — —	6,351,840	£4	£14	£45	£130
1826 — — Proof	incl. above	—	—	—	£400
1827 — —	574,200	£20	£50	£140	£400
1829 — —	879,120	£15	£50	£140	£375

WILLIAM IV (1830–37)

		F	VF	EF	UNC
1831 Proof only		—	—	—	£500
1834	3,223,440	£12	£35	£125	£350
1835	1,449,360	£12	£35	£125	£350
1836	3,567,960	£12	£35	£125	£350
1837	478,160	£15	£40	£125	£450

VICTORIA (1837–1901)

YOUNG HEAD ISSUES

First head

		F	VF	EF	UNC
1838 WW on truncation	1,956,240	£10	£30	£140	£300
1839 —	5,666,760	£10	£30	£140	£300

Second head

		F	VF	EF	UNC
1839 WW on truncation, Proof only	incl. above	—	—	—	£500
1839 no WW	incl. above	£10	£30	£110	£300
1840	1,639,440	£10	£30	£110	£300
1841	875,160	£10	£30	£110	£300
1842	2,094,840	£10	£30	£110	£300
1843	1,465,200	£10	£35	£120	£300
1844	4,466,880	£8	£30	£100	£275
1845	4,082,760	£8	£30	£100	£275
1846	4,031,280	£8	£30	£100	£275
1848 last 8 of date over 6	1,041,480	£45	£100	£500	£800
1849	845,480	£15	£45	£150	£425

Coin Yearbook 2008

DATE	MINTAGE	F	VF	EF	UNC
1850	685,080	£350	£700	£1500	£3500
1851	470,071	£25	£110	£250	£550
1851/49 51 over 49	incl. above	£125	£600	—	—
1852	1,306,574	£10	£30	£100	£275
1853	4,256,188	£10	£30	£100	£275
1853 Proof	incl. above	—	—	—	£400
1854	552,414	£70	£150	£550	£1400
1854/1 4 over 1	incl. above	£140	£500	—	—
1855	1,368,400	£8	£30	£100	£220
1856	3,168,000	£8	£30	£100	£220
1857	2,562,120	£8	£30	£100	£220
1857 error F:G with inverted G	incl. above	£110	£325	—	—
1858	3,108,600	£8	£30	£110	£220
1859	4,561,920	£8	£30	£110	£220
1860	1,671,120	£8	£30	£110	£250
1861	1,382,040	£9	£35	£125	£350
1862	954,360	£40	£100	£250	£800
1863	859,320	£90	£220	£500	£1250
1863/1 3 over 1				Extremely rare	

Die no. added above date up to 1879

1864	4,518,360	£8	£25	£80	£170
1865	5,619,240	£8	£25	£80	£200
1866	4,984,600	£8	£25	£80	£200
1866 error BBITANNIAR	incl. above	£70	£200	—	—
1867	2,166,120	£8	£30	£90	£200

Third head—with die no

1867	incl. above	£50	£100	—	—
1868	3,330,360	£8	£30	£80	£200
1869	736,560	£8	£30	£80	£200
1870	1,467,471	£8	£30	£80	£200
1871	4,910,010	£8	£30	£80	£200
1872	8,897,781	£8	£30	£80	£200
1873	6,489,598	£8	£30	£80	£200
1874	5,503,747	£8	£30	£80	£200
1875	4,353,983	£8	£30	£80	£200
1876	1,057,487	£8	£30	£80	£200
1877	2,989,703	£8	£30	£80	£200
1878	3,127,131	£8	£30	£80	£200
1879	3,611,507	£20	£55	£200	£450

Victoria Jubilee head

Fourth head—no die no

1879 no Die no.	incl. above	£7	£22	£65	£175
1880	4,842,786	£7	£22	£65	£175
1881	5,255,332	£7	£22	£65	£175
1882	1,611,786	£12	£50	£170	£350
1883	7,281,450	£6	£22	£55	£140
1884	3,923,993	£6	£22	£55	£140
1885	3,336,526	£6	£22	£55	£140
1886	2,086,819	£6	£22	£55	£140
1887	4,034,133	£7	£24	£55	£140

JUBILEE HEAD ISSUES

1887	incl. above	£2	£5	£10	£25
1887 Proof	1,084	—	—	—	£70
1888	4,526,856	£4	£9	£20	£50
1889	7,039,628	£25	£80	£275	—
1889 Large bust (until 1892)	incl. above	£5	£10	£40	£70
1890	8,794,042	£5	£10	£40	£70
1891	5,665,348	£5	£10	£40	£75
1892	4,591,622	£5	£10	£40	£80

OLD HEAD ISSUES

1893	7,039,074	£4	£8	£22	£55
1893 small lettering	incl. above	£3	£8	£22	£55
1893 Proof	1,312	—	—	—	£85
1894	5,953,152	£7	£20	£50	£100
1895	8,880,651	£6	£18	£40	£100
1896	9,264,551	£6	£15	£40	£70
1897	6,270,364	£5	£10	£40	£70
1898	9,768,703	£5	£10	£40	£60
1899	10,965,382	£5	£10	£40	£60
1900	10,937,590	£5	£10	£40	£70
1901	3,426,294	£5	£10	£40	£60

Victoria Old or Veiled head

DATE	MINTAGE	F	VF	EF	UNC

EDWARD VII (1901–10)

DATE	MINTAGE	F	VF	EF	UNC
1902	7,809,481	£3	£12	£45	£65
1902 Proof matt	13,123	—	—	—	£70
1903	2,061,823	£8	£35	£100	£400
1904	2,040,161	£8	£35	£100	£400
1905	488,390	£50	£150	£600	£1500
1906	10,791,025	£3	£10	£40	£100
1907	14,083,418	£3	£10	£40	£100
1908	3,806,969	£8	£20	£120	£350
1909	5,664,982	£8	£20	£90	£320
1910	26,547,236	£2	£8	£40	£85

GEORGE V (1910–36)

First issue

DATE	MINTAGE	F	VF	EF	UNC
1911	20,065,901	£2	£6	£16	£40
1911 Proof	6,007	—	—	—	£55
1912	15,594,009	£2	£7	£22	£60
1913	9,011,509	£4	£15	£40	£90
1914	23,415,843	£1	£5	£20	£40
1915	39,279,024	£1	£5	£20	£40
1916	35,862,015	£1	£5	£20	£40
1917	22,202,608	£1	£5	£20	£40
1918	34,915,934	£1	£5	£20	£40
1919	10,823,824	£1	£6	£25	£45

Second issue — debased silver

DATE	MINTAGE	F	VF	EF	UNC
1920	22,825,142	—	£2	£15	£35
1921	22,648,763	—	£2	£15	£35
1922	27,215,738	—	£2	£15	£35
1923	14,575,243	—	£2	£15	£30
1924	9,250,095	£3	£6	£35	£90
1925	5,418,764	£2	£5	£30	£90
1926	22,516,453	—	£4	£18	£85

George V First obverse

Third issue — Modified bust

DATE	MINTAGE	F	VF	EF	UNC
1926	incl. above	—	£3	£20	£40
1927 —	9,247,344	£1	£3	£20	£40

Fourth issue — large lion and crown on rev., date in legend

DATE	MINTAGE	F	VF	EF	UNC
1927	incl. above	£1	£2	£15	£35
1927 Proof	15,000	—	—	—	£35
1928	18,136,778	—	£2	£10	£30
1929	19,343,006	—	£2	£12	£30
1930	3,172,092	—	£2	£15	£40
1931	6,993,926	—	£2	£10	£30
1932	12,168,101	—	£2	£10	£35
1933	11,511,624	—	£2	£10	£30
1934	6,138,463	—	£2	£12	£40
1935	9,183,462	—	£2	£6	£16
1936	11,910,613	—	£2	£4	£12

GEORGE VI (1936–52)

George V Second obverse

E = England rev. (lion standing on large crown). S = Scotland rev. (lion seated on small crown holding sword and mace)

DATE	MINTAGE	F	VF	EF	UNC
1937 E	8,359,122	—	£1	£2	£6
1937 E Proof	26,402	—	—	—	£12
1937 S	6,748,875	—	£1	£2	£5
1937 S Proof	26,402	—	—	—	£12
1938 E	4,833,436	—	£1	£7	£14
1938 S	4,797,852	—	£1	£7	£14
1939 E	11,052,677	—	£1	£2	£6
1939 S	10,263,892	—	£1	£2	£6
1940 E	11,099,126	—	—	£2	£6
1940 S	9,913,089	—	£2	£2	£6

DATE	MINTAGE	F	VF	EF	UNC
1941 E	11,391,883	—	—	£2	£6
1941 S	8,086,030	—	—	£2	£4
1942 E	17,453,643	—	—	£2	£4
1942 S	13,676,759	—	—	£2	£4
1943 E	11,404,213	—	—	£2	£4
1943 S	9,824,214	—	—	£2	£4
1944 E	11,586,751	—	—	£2	£4
1944 S	10,990,167	—	—	£2	£4
1945 E	15,143,404	—	—	£2	£5
1945 S	15,106,270	—	—	£2	£5
1946 E	16,663,797	—	—	£2	£5
1946 S	16,381,501	—	—	£2	£5
Cupro-nickel					
1947 E	12,120,611	—	—	—	£2
1947 S	12,283,223	—	—	—	£2
1948 E	45,576,923	—	—	—	£2
1948 S	45,351,937	—	—	—	£2
1949 E	19,328,405	—	—	—	£5
1949 S	21,243,074	—	—	—	£5
1950 E	19,243,872	—	—	—	£5
1950 E Proof	17,513	—	—	—	£15
1950 S	14,299,601	—	—	—	£5
1950 S Proof	17,513	—	—	—	£15
1951 E	9,956,930	—	—	—	£5
1951 E Proof	20,000	—	—	—	£15
1951 S	10,961,174	—	—	—	£5
1951 S Proof	20,000	—	—	—	£15

English reverse

Scottish reverse

ELIZABETH II (1952–)

E = England rev. (shield with three lions). S = Scotland rev. (shield with one lion).

DATE	MINTAGE	F	VF	EF	UNC
1953 E	41,942,894	—	—	—	£1
1953 E Proof	40,000	—	—	—	£3
1953 S	20,663,528	—	—	—	£1
1953 S Proof	40,000	—	—	—	£3
1954 E	30,262,032	—	—	—	£2
1954 S	26,771,735	—	—	—	£2
1955 E	45,259,908	—	—	—	£2
1955 S	27,950,906	—	—	—	£2
1956 E	44,907,008	—	—	—	£10
1956 S	42,853,639	—	—	—	£10
1957 E	42,774,217	—	—	—	£1
1957 S	17,959,988	—	—	—	£10
1958 E	14,392,305	—	—	—	£10
1958 S	40,822,557	—	—	—	£1
1959 E	19,442,778	—	—	—	£1
1959 S	1,012,988	£1	£2	£5	£20
1960 E	27,027,914	—	—	—	£1
1960 S	14,376,932	—	—	—	£1
1961 E	39,816,907	—	—	—	£1
1961 S	2,762,558	—	—	—	£3
1962 E	36,704,379	—	—	—	£1
1962 S	17,475,310	—	—	—	£1
1963 E	49,433,607	—	—	—	£1
1963 S	32,300,000	—	—	—	£1
1964 E	8,590,900	—	—	—	£1
1964 S	5,239,100	—	—	—	£1
1965 E	9,216,000	—	—	—	£1
1965 S	2,774,000	—	—	—	£2
1966 E	15,002,000	—	—	—	£1
1966 S	15,604,000	—	—	—	£1

English reverse

English reverse

Scottish reverse

SIXPENCES

DATE	F	VF	EF	UNC

OLIVER CROMWELL

1658 Patterns by Thos. Simon & Tanner
   Four varieties .... Extremely rare

CHARLES II (1660–85)

	F	VF	EF	UNC
1674..	£60	£275	£800	—
1675..	£60	£275	£800	—
1675/4 5 over 4	£80	£290	£825	—
1676..	£60	£275	£800	—
1676/5 6 over 5	£80	£275	£800	—
1677..	£60	£275	£800	—
1678/7	£60	£270	£800	—
1679..	£55	£275	£800	—
1680..	£80	£400	£1000	—
1681..	£60	£275	£800	—
1682/1	£60	£275	£900	—
1682..	£70	£275	£875	—
1683..	£60	£275	£875	—
1684..	£60	£275	£850	—

JAMES II (1685–88)

	F	VF	EF	UNC
1686 Early shields	£100	£400	£1000	—
1687/6 — 7 over 6..	£100	£400	£1000	—
1687 Late shields	£100	£400	£950	—
1687/6 — 7 over 6	£90	£400	£1000	—
1688 —	£95	£400	£1000	—

WILLIAM & MARY (1688–94)

	F	VF	EF	UNC
1693	£100	£425	£900	—
1693 error inverted 3	£110	£425	£900	—
1694..	£110	£425	£1000	—

WILLIAM III (1694–1702)

Provincially produced sixpences carry privy marks or initials below the bust:
B: Bristol. C: Chester. E: Exeter. N: Norwich. Y or y: York.

	F	VF	EF	UNC
1695 First bust, early harp in 4th shield on rev.	£35	£100	£400	—
1696 — —	£35	£100	£325	—
1696 — — French arms at date	Extremely rare			
1696 — — Scottish arms at date	Extremely rare			
1696 — — DFI for DEI.....................................	Extremely rare			
1696 — — No stops on obv.	£25	£100	£375	—
1696 — — B..	£40	£100	£400	—
1696 — — — B over E	Extremely rare			
1696 — — C..	£35	£100	£425	—
1696 — — E..	£40	£100	£425	—
1696 — — N..	£40	£100	£425	—
1696 — — y...	£40	£110	£475	—
1696 — — Y...	£45	£200	£500	—
1696 — Later harp	£45	£175	£400	—
1696 — — B..	£60	£225	£500	—
1696 — — — no stops on obv.........................	£60	£225	£500	—
1696 — — C..	£65	£350	£850	—
1696 — — N..	£60	£300	—	—
1696 Second bust..	£200	£550	—	—
1697 First bust, later harp	£30	£75	£300	—
1697 — — Arms of France & Ireland transposed	Extremely rare			

DATE	MINTAGE	F	VF	EF	UNC
1697 — — B		£40	£100	£400	—
1697 — — C		£40	£100	£425	—
1697 — — Irish shield at date		Extremely rare			
1697 — — E		£40	£100	£400	—
1697 — — N		£40	£100	£400	—
1697 — — error GVLIEMVS		Extremely rare			
1697 — — y		£40	£110	£425	—
1697 — — Irish shield at date		Extremely rare			
1697 Second bust		£95	£300	£1000	—
1697 Third bust		£25	£ 65	£275	—
1697 — error GVLIEIMVS		Extremely rare			
1697 — B		£40	£100	£450	—
1697 — — IRA for FRA		Extremely rare			
1697 — C		£40	£200	£500	—
1697 — E		£40	£200	£500	—
1697 — Y		£40	£200	£500	—
1698 —		£40	£170	£450	—
1698 — Plumes in angles on rev.		£50	£175	£600	—
1699 —		£60	£240	£650	—
1699 — Plumes in angles on rev.		£60	£240	£650	—
1699 — Roses in angles on rev.		£70	£225	£650	—
1699 — — error G ˙LIELMVS		Extremely rare			
1700 —		£40	£90	£350	—
1700 — Plume below bust	£1750	—	—	—	—
1701 —		£50	£110	£400	—

ANNE (1702–14)

1703 VIGO below bust Before Union with Scotland	£40	£125	£375	—	
1705 Plain		£50	£170	£500	—
1705 Plumes in angles on rev.		£45	£140	£400	—
1705 Roses & Plumes in angles on rev.		£60	£140	£425	—
1707 Roses & Plumes in angles on rev.		£40	£140	£350	—
1707 (Post-Union), Plain		£30	£70	£275	—
1707 E (Edinburgh) below bust		£30	£80	£300	—
1707 Plumes in angles on rev.		£30	£100	£300	—
1708 Plain		£30	£80	£300	—
1708 E below bust		£30	£80	£300	—
1708 E* below bust		£40	£90	£350	—
1708 "Edinburgh" bust E* below		£35	£100	£350	—
1708 Plumes in angles on rev.		£40	£110	£350	—
1710 Roses & Plumes in angles on rev.		£35	£110	£370	—
1711 Plain		£25	£60	£170	—

GEORGE I (1714–27)

1717 Roses & Plumes in angles on rev.		£80	£220	£650	—
1717 Plain edge		Extremely rare			
1720 —		£80	£220	£600	—
1723 SSC in angles on rev.		£20	£50	£175	—
1723 Larger lettering		£20	£50	£175	—
1726 Small Roses & Plumes in angles on rev.		£80	£225	£650	—

GEORGE II (1727–60)

1728 Young head, Plain		£70	£240	£525	—
1728 — Proof		—	—	£2750	—
1728 — Plumes in angles on rev.		£40	£140	£400	—
1728 — Roses & Plumes in angles on rev.		£35	£125	£300	—
1731 — —		£35	£125	£300	—
1732 — —		£35	£125	£300	—
1734 — —		£35	£140	£350	—
1735 — —		£35	£140	£350	—
1735/4 5 over 4		£40	£150	£400	—
1736 — —		£35	£140	£350	—
1739 — Roses in angles on rev.		£30	£80	£210	—
1741 —		£28	£80	£210	—

DATE	MINTAGE	F	VF	EF	UNC
1743 Old head, Roses in angles on rev.............		£20	£70	£225	—
1745 — —		£20	£70	£225	—
1745 — — 5 over 3		£30	£80	£250	—
1745 — Plain, LIMA below bust......................		£20	£70	£200	—
1746 — — —..		£20	£70	£200	—
1746 — — Proof..		—	—	£800	—
1750 — —		£30	£120	£325	—
1751 — —		£35	£150	£350	—
1757 — —		£12	£25	£60	—
1758 — —		£12	£25	£60	—

GEORGE III (1760–1820)

1787 rev. no semée of hearts on 4th shield		£10	£25	£55	—
1787 rev. with semée of hearts		£10	£25	£55	—

NEW COINAGE

1816	—	£6	£14	£40	£95
1817	10,921,680	£6	£14	£40	£95
1818..	4,284,720	£8	£22	£80	£160
1819..	4,712,400	£6	£14	£40	£75
1819 very small 8 in date	incl. above	£6	£14	£40	£100
1820..	1,488,960	£6	£14	£40	£100

GEORGE IV (1820–30)

1821 First bust, first reverse	863,280	£12	£25	£80	£250
1821 error BBRITANNIAR............		£50	£200	£650	—
1821 — — Proof...........................	incl. above	—	—	—	£500
1824 — Second (garter) reverse .	633,600	£12	£25	£80	£225
1825 —	483,120	£12	£25	£75	£200
1826 — —	689,040	£20	£60	£200	£400
1826 Second bust, third (lion on crown) reverse	incl. above	£10	£25	£75	£150
1826 — — Proof..........................	incl. above	—	—	—	£250
1827 — —	166,320	£18	£55	£200	£400
1828 — —	15,840	£16	£40	£125	£275
1829 — —	403,290	£12	£40	£110	£275

WILLIAM IV (1830–37)

1831..	1,340,195	£11	£25	£100	£260
1831 Proof...................................	incl. above	—	—	—	£400
1834..	5,892,480	£11	£25	£100	£260
1835..	1,552,320	£11	£25	£100	£260
1836..	1,987,920	£11	£30	£125	£300
1837..	506,880	£15	£35	£150	£400

VICTORIA (1837–1901)

YOUNG HEAD ISSUES

First head

1838..	1,607,760	£8	£25	£80	£200
1839	3,310,560	£8	£25	£70	£200
1839 Proof...................................	incl. above	—	—	—	£375
1840..	2,098,800	£8	£25	£75	£200
1841..	1,386,000	£8	£27	£80	£220
1842..	601,920	£8	£25	£80	£220
1843..	3,160,080	£8	£27	£70	£200
1844..	3,975,840	£8	£22	£45	£200
1844 Large 44 in date.................	incl. above	£12	£40	£100	£270
1845..	3,714,480	£8	£24	£60	£200
1846..	4,226,880	£8	£24	£60	£200
1848..	586,080	£30	£90	£275	£700
1848/6 final 8 over 6....................	incl. above	£40	£90	£300	—
1850..	498,960	£8	£28	£70	£200
1850/3 0 over 3	incl. above	£15	£28	£80	£270

DATE	MINTAGE	F	VF	EF	UNC
1851	2,288,107	£8	£25	£70	£185
1852	904,586	£8	£25	£70	£200
1853	3,837,930	£8	£25	£70	£175
1853 Proof	incl above	—	—	—	£450
1854	840,116	£50	£150	£500	£1000
1855	1,129,684	£8	£24	£70	£160
1855/3 last 5 over 3	incl. above	£10	£35	£70	£200
1856	2,779,920	£8	£24	£70	£170
1857	2,233,440	£8	£24	£70	£170
1858	1,932,480	£8	£24	£70	£170
1859	4,688,640	£8	£24	£75	£170
1859/8 9 over 8	incl. above	£10	£30	£80	£200
1860	1,100,880	£9	£22	£80	£200
1862	990,000	£30	£100	£300	£700
1863	491,040	£30	£75	£250	£700
Die no. added above date from 1864 to 1879					
1864	4,253,040	£8	£25	£70	£175
1865	1,631,520	£8	£25	£70	£170
1866	4,140,080	£8	£25	£70	£170
1866 no Die no.	incl. above	£25	£100	—	—
Second head					
1867	1,362,240	£7	£20	£70	£200
1868	1,069,200	£7	£20	£60	£150
1869	388,080	£7	£20	£60	£150
1870	479,613	£7	£20	£60	£150
1871	3,662,684	£6	£20	£50	£140
1871 no Die no.	incl. above	£6	£20	£50	£140
1872	3,382,048	£6	£20	£50	£140
1873	4,594,733	£6	£20	£50	£140
1874	4,225,726	£6	£20	£50	£140
1875	3,256,545	£6	£20	£50	£140
1876	841,435	£6	£20	£55	£140
1877	4,066,486	£6	£20	£55	£140
1877 no Die no	incl. above	£6	£20	£55	£140
1878	2,624,525	£6	£20	£55	£120
1878 Dritanniar Error	incl. above	£60	£200	—	—
1879	3,326,313	£6	£18	£50	£140
1879 no Die no	incl. above	£5	£18	£50	£140
1880 no Die no	3,892,501	£5	£18	£50	£130
Third head					
1880	incl above	£6	£18	£50	£110
1881	6,239,447	£6	£18	£50	£110
1882	759,809	£10	£30	£100	£270
1883	4,986,558	£6	£16	£35	£90
1884	3,422,565	£6	£16	£35	£90
1885	4,652,771	£6	£16	£35	£90
1886	2,728,249	£6	£16	£35	£80
1887	3,675,607	£6	£16	£35	£80

JUBILEE HEAD ISSUES

1887 Shield reverse	incl. above	£3	£5	£10	£25
1887 — Proof	incl. above	—	—	—	£60
1887 Six Pence in wreath reverse	incl. above	£3	£5	£10	£25
1888 —	4,197,698	£4	£7	£20	£40
1889 —	8,738,928	£4	£7	£25	£50
1890 —	9,386,955	£4	£7	£25	£50
1891 —	7,022,734	£4	£7	£25	£50
1892 —	6,245,746	£4	£8	£28	£60
1893 —	7,350,619	£300	£850	£2500	—

OLD HEAD ISSUES

1893	incl. above	£4	£8	£18	£45
1893 Proof	1,312	—	—	—	£65
1894	3,467,704	£7	£14	£40	£75
1895	7,024,631	£6	£14	£35	£65
1896	6,651,699	£4	£9	£30	£50
1897	5,031,498	£4	£9	£30	£50
1898	5,914,100	£4	£9	£30	£45
1899	7,996,80	£4	£9	£30	£45
1900	8,984,354	£4	£9	£30	£45
1901	5,108,757	£4	£9	£28	£45

Jubilee head, shield reverse

Jubilee head, wreath reverse

DATE	MINTAGE	F	VF	EF	UNC

EDWARD VII (1901–10)

1902	6,367,378	£3	£7	£25	£45
1902 "Matt Proof"	15,123	—	—	—	£45
1903	5,410,096	£6	£18	£50	£140
1904	4,487,098	£10	£40	£120	£320
1905	4,235,556	£7	£20	£60	£150
1906	7,641,146	£5	£10	£35	£90
1907	8,733,673	£5	£10	£40	£80
1908	6,739,491	£8	£25	£80	£275
1909	6,584,017	£6	£15	£45	£150
1910	12,490,724	£3	£5	£20	£40

Edward VII

GEORGE V (1910–36)

First issue

1911	9,155,310	£1	£3	£10	£35
1911 Proof	6,007	—	—	—	£40
1912	10,984,129	£1	£3	£20	£40
1913	7,499,833	£1	£6	£22	£50
1914	22,714,602	£1	£2	£10	£25
1915	15,694,597	£1	£3	£12	£35
1916	22,207,178	£1	£2	£8	£25
1917	7,725,475	£5	£15	£40	£80
1918	27,553,743	£1	£2	£12	£25
1919	13,375,447	£1	£3	£12	£30
1920	14,136,287	£1	£3	£10	£25

Second issue — debased silver

1920	incl. above	£1	£3	£10	£28
1921	30,339,741	£1	£3	£10	£28
1922	16,878,890	£1	£2	£10	£28
1923	6,382,793	£3	£8	£40	£85
1924	17,444,218	£1	£5	£10	£25
1925	12,720,558	£1	£2	£10	£25
1925 Broad rim	incl. above	£1	£2	£10	£25
1926 —	21,809,621	£1	£2	£10	£25

George V,
first reverse
above and
second reverse
below

Third issue — Modified bust

1926	incl. above	£1	£2	£10	£30
1927	8,924,873	—	£1	£10	£30

Fourth issue — New design (oakleaves)

1927 Proof only	15,000	—	—	—	£25
1928	23,123,384	—	£1	£7	£20
1929	28,319,326	—	£1	£7	£20
1930	16,990,289	—	£1	£8	£25
1931	16,873,268	—	£1	£7	£20
1932	9,406,117	—	£1	£8	£28
1933	22,185,083	—	£1	£7	£20
1934	9,304,009	£1	£2	£9	£22
1935	13,995,621	—	£1	£5	£10
1936	24,380,171	—	£1	£5	£10

GEORGE VI (1936–52)

First type

1937	22,302,524	—	—	£1	£4
1937 Proof	26,402	—	—	—	£5
1938	13,402,701	—	£1	£3	£12
1939	28,670,304	—	—	£1	£5
1940	20,875,196	—	—	£1	£5
1941	23,086,616	—	—	£1	£5
1942	44,942,785	—	—	£1	£4
1943	46,927,111	—	—	£1	£4
1944	36,952,600	—	—	£1	£4
1945	39,939,259	—	—	£1	£3
1946	43,466,407	—	—	£1	£3

George VI first reverse

Cupro-nickel

1947	29,993,263	—	—	£1	£3
1948	88,323,540	—	—	£1	£3

Second type — new cypher on rev.

1949	41,335,515	—	—	£1	£3

George VI second reverse

DATE	MINTAGE	F	VF	EF	UNC
1950	32,741,955	—	—	£1	£3
1950 Proof	17,513	—	—	—	£5
1951	40,399,491	—	—	£1	£3
1951 Proof	20,000	—	—	—	£5
1952	1,013,477	£4	£10	£28	£70

ELIZABETH II (1952–   )

1953	70,323,876	—	—	—	£2
1953 Proof	40,000	—	—	—	£4
1954	105,241,150	—	—	—	£3
1955	109,929,554	—	—	—	£1
1956	109,841,555	—	—	—	£1
1957	105,654,290	—	—	—	£1
1958	123,518,527	—	—	—	£3
1959	93,089,441	—	—	—	£1
1960	103,283,346	—	—	—	£3
1961	115,052,017	—	—	—	£3
1962	166,483,637	—	—	—	25p
1963	120,056,000	—	—	—	25p
1964	152,336,000	—	—	—	25p
1965	129,644,000	—	—	—	25p
1966	175,676,000	—	—	—	25p
1967	240,788,000	—	—	—	25p

GROATS OR FOURPENCES

DATE	MINTAGE	F	VF	EF	UNC

The earlier fourpences are included in the Maundy oddments section as they are generally considered to have been issued for the Maundy ceremony.

WILLIAM IV (1831–37)

1836	—	£7	£15	£40	£80
1837	962,280	£7	£15	£40	£80

VICTORIA (1838–1901)

1837	Extremely Rare Proofs or Patterns only				
1837 over last 8 on its side		£10	£18	£50	£100
1838	2,150,280	£7	£15	£30	£80
1839	1,461,240	£7	£16	£35	£80
1839 Proof	incl. above				Rare
1840	1,496,880	£7	£15	£35	£80
1840 Small 0 in date	incl. above	£7	£16	£40	£90
1841	344,520	£7	£15	£35	£80
1842/1 2 over 1	incl. above	£7	£15	£35	£80
1842	724,680	£7	£15	£35	£80
1843	1,817640	£8	£16	£40	£100
1843 4 over 5	incl. above	£7	£15	£35	£80
1844	855,360	£7	£15	£35	£90
1845	914,760	£7	£15	£35	£90
1846	1,366,200	£7	£15	£35	£90
1847 7 over 6	225,720	£12	£25	£100	—
1848	712,800	£7	£15	£30	£80
1848/6 8 over 6	incl. above	£25	£100	—	—
1848/7 8 over 7	incl. above	£8	£20	£50	£100
1849	380,160	£7	£15	£35	£80
1849/8 9 over 8	incl. above	£8	£20	£60	£125
1851	594,000	£20	£60	£175	£350
1852	31,300	£50	£120	£350	—
1853	11,880	£40	£100	£375	—
1853 Proof Milled Rim	incl. above	—	—	—	£500
1853 Plain edge Proof				Extremely rare	
1854	1,096,613	£7	£14	£35	£80
1855	646,041	£7	£14	£35	£80
1857 Proofs only				Extremely rare	
1862 Proofs only				Extremely rare	
1888 Jubilee Head	—	£7	£14	£35	£75

THREEPENCES

DATE	MINTAGE	F	VF	EF	UNC

The earlier threepences are included in the Maundy oddments section.

WILLIAM IV (1830–37)
(issued for use in the West Indies)

1834		£6	£12	£60	£120
1835		£6	£12	£60	£120
1836		£6	£12	£60	£120
1837		£8	£15	£75	£140

VICTORIA (1837–1901)
YOUNG HEAD ISSUES

1838 BRITANNIAB error			Extremely rare		
1838	—	£7	£18	£50	£120
1839	—	£7	£18	£50	£120
1940	—	£7	£18	£50	£120
1841	—	£7	£18	£55	£140
1842	—	£7	£18	£55	£140
1843	—	£7	£18	£45	£120
1843/34 43 over 34	—	£7	£18	£70	£160
1844	—	£10	£20	£60	£140
1845	1,319,208	£8	£18	£40	£125
1846	52,008	£8	£22	£70	£180
1847	4,488		Extremely rare		
1848	incl. above		Extremely rare		
1849	131,208	£8	£20	£70	£170
1850	954,888	£8	£18	£40	£90
1851	479,065	£7	£20	£50	£125
1851 5 over 8	incl. above	£10	£25	£100	—
1852	4,488		Extremely rare		
1853	36,168	£20	£50	£100	£240
1854	1,467,246	£6	£18	£50	£120
1855	383,350	£6	£18	£50	£130
1856	1,013,760	£6	£18	£55	£120
1857	1,758,240	£6	£18	£60	£140
1858	1,441,440	£6	£18	£50	£120
1858 BRITANNIAB error	incl. above		Extremely rare		
1858/6 final 8 over 6	incl. above	£8	£25	£100	—
1858/5 final 8 over 5	incl. above	£8	£25	£100	—
1859	3,579,840	£6	£18	£45	£100
1860	3,405,600	£6	£18	£50	£120
1861	3,294,720	£6	£18	£50	£110
1862	1,156,320	£6	£18	£45	£110
1863	950,400	£10	£30	£80	£160
1864	1,330,560	£6	£18	£45	£110
1865	1,742,400	£6	£18	£45	£100
1866	1,900,800	£6	£18	£45	£100
1867	712,800	£6	£18	£45	£100
1868	1,457,280	£6	£18	£45	£100
1868 RRITANNIAR error	incl. above		Extremely rare		
1869	—	£30	£60	£175	£300
1870	1,283,218	£5	£16	£45	£80
1871	999,633	£5	£16	£40	£80
1872	1,293,271	£5	£16	£40	£80
1873	4,055,550	£5	£16	£40	£80
1874	4,427,031	£5	£16	£40	£80
1875	3,306,500	£5	£16	£40	£80
1876	1,834,389	£5	£16	£40	£80
1877	2,622,393	£5	£16	£40	£80
1878	2,419,975	£5	£16	£40	£80
1879	3,140,265	£5	£16	£40	£80
1880	1,610,069	£5	£16	£40	£70
1881	3,248,265	£5	£16	£40	£70
1882	472,965	£6	£20	£60	£125
1883	4,369,971	£5	£10	£30	£50

Victoria first type

DATE	MINTAGE	F	VF	EF	UNC
1884	3,322,424	£5	£10	£30	£50
1885	5,183,653	£5	£10	£30	£50
1886	6,152,669	£5	£10	£30	£50
1887	2,780,761	£5	£10	£30	£50

JUBILEE HEAD ISSUES

1887	incl. above	£1	£3	£9	£18
1887 Proof	incl. above	—	—	—	£40
1888	518,199	£2	£5	£18	£35
1889	4,587,010	£2	£5	£18	£35
1890	4,465,834	£2	£5	£18	£35
1891	6,323,027	£2	£5	£18	£35
1892	2,578,226	£2	£5	£18	£40
1893	3,067,243	£8	£25	£100	£220

Victoria
Jubilee head

OLD HEAD ISSUES

1893	incl. above	£1	£3	£15	£30
1893 Proof	incl. above	—	—	—	£40
1894	1,608,603	£2	£6	£24	£50
1895	4,788,609	£1	£5	£22	£50
1896	4,598,442	£1	£5	£18	£35
1897	4,541,294	£1	£5	£18	£35
1898	4,567,177	£1	£5	£18	£35
1899	6,246,281	£1	£5	£18	£35
1900	10,644,480	£1	£5	£18	£35
1901	6,098,400	£1	£5	£14	£30

Victoria
Old or Veiled
head

EDWARD VII (1901–10)

1902	8,268,480	£1	£2	£7	£15
1902 "Matt Proof"	incl. above	—	—	—	£20
1903	5,227,200	£1	£4	£20	£45
1904	3,627,360	£2	£7	£35	£75
1905	3,548,160	£1	£4	£25	£60
1906	3,152,160	£1	£4	£20	£50
1907	4,831,200	£1	£4	£20	£50
1908	8,157,600	£1	£3	£20	£50
1909	4,055,040	£1	£4	£20	£50
1910	4,563,380	£1	£4	£18	£35

GEORGE V (1910–36)

First issue

1911	5,841,084	—	—	£3	£10
1911 Proof	incl. above	—	—	—	£25
1912	8,932,825	—	—	£3	£12
1913	7,143,242	—	—	£3	£12
1914	6,733,584	—	—	£3	£12
1915	5,450,617	—	—	£3	£12
1916	18,555,201	—	—	£3	£10
1917	21,662,490	—	—	£3	£10
1918	20,630,909	—	—	£3	£10
1919	16,845,687	—	—	£3	£10
1920	16,703,597	—	—	£3	£10

Second issue—debased silver

1920	incl. above	—	—	£3	£12
1921	8,749,301	—	—	£3	£12
1922	7,979,998	—	—	£3	£12
1925	3,731,859	—	—	£5	£25
1926	4,107,910	—	—	£7	£28

Third issue—Modified bust

1926	incl. above	—	—	£8	£22

Fourth issue—new design (oakleaves)

1927 Proof only	15,022	—	—	—	£50
1928	1,302,106	£2	£6	£20	£50
1930	1,319,412	£1	£3	£8	£28
1931	6,251,936	—	—	£2	£7
1932	5,887,325	—	—	£2	£7
1933	5,578,541	—	—	£2	£7
1934	7,405,954	—	—	£2	£7
1935	7,027,654	—	—	£2	£7
1936	3,328,670	—	—	£2	£7

George V,
fourth issue oak
leaves
design reverse

DATE	MINTAGE	F	VF	EF	UNC

GEORGE VI (1936–52)

Silver

1937	8,148,156	—	—	£1	£4
1937 Proof	26,402	—	—	—	£8
1938	6,402,473	—	—	£1	£4
1939	1,355,860	—	—	£4	£12
1940	7,914,401	—	—	£1	£3
1941	7,979,411	—	—	£1	£3
1942	4,144,051	£2	£5	£12	£35
1943	1,397,220	£2	£5	£12	£35
1944	2,005,553	£5	£12	£35	£80
1945	Only one known				

Brass—larger size, 12 sided, "Thrift" design

1937	45,707,957	—	—	£1	£4
1937 Proof	26,402	—	—	—	£8
1938	14,532,332	—	—	£1	£15
1939	5,603,021	—	—	£2	£40
1940	12,636,018	—	—	£1	£20
1941	60,239,489	—	—	£1	£8
1942	103,214,400	—	—	£1	£8
1943	101,702,400	—	—	£1	£8
1944	69,760,000	—	—	£1	£8
1945	33,942,466	—	—	£1	£15
1946	620,734	£4	£25	£125	£400
1948	4,230,400	—	—	£5	£35
1949	464,000	£5	£25	£150	£475
1950	1,600,000	—	£2	£20	£110
1950 Proof	17,513	—	—	—	£15
1951	1,184,000	—	£2	£20	£100
1951 Proof	20,000	—	—	—	£15
1952	25,494,400	—	—	—	£10

George VI "Thrift" design
of the brass 3d

ELIZABETH II (1952–)

1953	30,618,000	—	—	—	£1
1953 Proof	40,000	—	—	—	£6
1954	41,720,000	—	—	—	£5
1955	41,075,200	—	—	—	£5
1956	36,801,600	—	—	—	£6
1957	24,294,500	—	—	—	£5
1958	20,504,000	—	—	—	£9
1959	28,499,200	—	—	—	£6
1960	83,078,400	—	—	—	£2
1961	41,102,400	—	—	—	£1
1962	51,545,600	—	—	—	£1
1963	39,482,866	—	—	—	£1
1964	44,867,200	—	—	—	—
1965	27,160,000	—	—	—	—
1966	53,160,000	—	—	—	—
1967	151,780,800	—	—	—	—

TWO PENCES

It is generally accepted that earlier issues of the small silver twopences were only produced for inclusion with the Maundy sets, q.v., except for those listed below.

1797 "Cartwheel"	£20	£45	£250	£800
1797 Copper Proofs	Many varieties from £500+			

VICTORIA (1837–1901)

For use in the Colonies

1838	£4	£10	£18	£35
1848	£4	£12	£20	£40

THREE-HALFPENCES

DATE		F	VF	EF	UNC

WILLIAM IV (1830–37)

For use in the Colonies

DATE	F	VF	EF	UNC
1834	£6	£16	£32	£75
1835	£8	£20	£60	£200
1835 over 4	£6	£16	£32	£75
1836	£8	£18	£35	£85
1837	£12	£35	£100	£250

VICTORIA (1837–1901)

For use in the Colonies

DATE	F	VF	EF	UNC
1838	£6	£15	£35	£75
1839	£6	£15	£35	£75
1840	£7	£18	£40	£80
1841	£6	£15	£30	£65
1842	£6	£18	£35	£75
1843	£6	£15	£30	£65
1860	£9	£20	£70	£140
1862	£9	£20	£70	£140

PENNIES

DATE	MINTAGE	F	VF	EF	UNC

The earlier small silver pennies are included in the Maundy oddments section.

GEORGE III (1760–1820)

DATE	MINTAGE	F	VF	EF	UNC
1797 "Cartwheel", 10 laurel leaves	8,601,600	£15	£35	£180	£550
1797 — 11 laurel leaves	incl. above	£15	£35	£180	£550
1806 Third type	—	£6	£15	£55	£150
1807	—	£5	£15	£55	£150
1808					Unique

GEORGE IV (1820–30)

DATE	MINTAGE	F	VF	EF	UNC
1825	1,075,200	£10	£35	£130	£400
1826 (varieties)	5,913,600	£10	£35	£130	£400
1826 Proof	—	—	—	—	£375
1827	1,451,520	£100	£350	£1100	—

WILLIAM IV (1830–37)

DATE	MINTAGE	F	VF	EF	UNC
1831 (varieties)	806,400	£10	£60	£220	£600
1831 Proof	—	—	—	£220	£600
1834	322,560	£10	£50	£200	£600
1837	174,720	£10	£50	£220	£600

VICTORIA (1837–1901)

YOUNG HEAD ISSUES

Copper

DATE	MINTAGE	F	VF	EF	UNC
1839 Proof	unrecorded	—	—	—	£850
1841	913,920	£7	£15	£80	£220
1841 No colon after REG	incl. above	£7	£15	£80	£220
1843	483,840	£40	£150	£800	£1800
1844	215,040	£10	£25	£90	£220
1845	322,560	£10	£25	£100	£260

"Cartwheel" penny

DATE	MINTAGE	F	VF	EF	UNC
1846	483,840	£10	£25	£120	£300
1846 FID: DEF colon spaced	incl. above	£10	£25	£120	£300
1846 FID:DEF colon close............	incl. above	£10	£20	£120	£300
1847	430,080	£8	£20	£100	£250
1848	161,280	£8	£20	£100	£250
1848/7 final 8 over 7	incl. above	£7	£20	£100	£250
1848/6 final 8 over 6..................	incl. above	£15	£50	£200	—
1849	268,800	£60	£200	£1000	—
1851	268,800	£10	£30	£110	£350
1853	1,021,440	£5	£10	£50	£110
1853 Proof	—	—	—	—	£450
1854	6,720,000	£5	£12	£50	£110
1854/3 4 over 3	incl. above	£10	£30	£120	—
1855	5,273,856	£5	£12	£60	£130
1856	1,212,288	£20	£65	£200	£725
1857 Plain trident	752,640	£6	£16	£60	£140
1857 Ornamental trident	incl. above	£5	£16	£60	£140
1858/7 final 8 over 7..................	incl. above	£4	£14	£60	£110
1858/3 final 8 over 3..................	incl. above	£25	£80	£250	—
1858	1,599,040	£5	£15	£60	£140
1859	1,075,200	£8	£25	£70	£220
1860/59	32,256	£350	£900	£2700	—

Bronze

1860 Beaded border	5,053,440	£5	£15	£50	£150
1860 Toothed border	incl. above	£5	£15	£50	£150
1860 — Piedfort flan	—		Extremely rare		
1861	36,449,280	£4	£10	£45	£140
1862	50,534,400	£4	£10	£45	£140
1862 8 over 6............................	incl. above		Extremely rare		
1863	28,062,720	£4	£8	£40	£140
1863 Die no below date	incl. above		Extremely rare		
1864 Plain 4.............................	3,440,640	£15	£80	£450	£900
1864 Crosslet 4	incl. above	£15	£75	£450	£1100
1865	8,601,600	£6	£15	£50	£270
1865/3 5 over 3	incl. above	£20	£70	£300	—
1866	9,999,360	£5	£15	£55	£300
1867	5,483,520	£5	£15	£55	£300
1868	1,182,720	£10	£60	£200	£550
1869	2,580,480	£75	£220	£800	£2400
1870	5,695,022	£8	£30	£110	£325
1871	1,290,318	£30	£100	£400	£1500
1872	8,494,572	£6	£20	£50	£160
1873	8,494,200	£6	£20	£50	£160
1874	5,621,865	£6	£20	£50	£160
1874 H	6,666,240	£6	£20	£50	£160
1874 Later (older) bust	incl. above	£10	£25	£65	£250
1875	10,691,040	£6	£20	£65	£200
1875 H	752,640	£35	£110	£500	£1500
1876 H	11,074,560	£5	£12	£55	£180
1877	9,624,747	£5	£14	£55	£180
1878	2,764,470	£5	£14	£50	£170
1879	7,666,476	£4	£12	£50	£170
1880	3,000,831	£4	£12	£50	£170
1881	2,302,362	£5	£12	£50	£170
1881 H	3,763,200	£5	£12	£50	£170
1882 H	7,526,400	£5	£12	£50	£170
1882 no H	—		Extremely Rare		
1883	6,237,438	£5	£14	£50	£150
1884	11,702,802	£5	£14	£50	£150
1885	7,145,862	£4	£14	£50	£150
1886	6,087,759	£4	£14	£50	£150
1887	5,315,085	£4	£14	£50	£150
1888	5,125,020	£4	£14	£50	£150

Victoria copper penny

(N.B. Prices for Victoria Bun head coins will be considerably higher in mint with full lustre)

DATE	MINTAGE	F	VF	EF	UNC
1889	12,559,737	£4	£14	£50	£140
1890	15,330,840	£4	£14	£50	£125
1891	17,885,961	£4	£12	£50	£125
1892	10,501,671	£4	£12	£45	£140
1893	8,161,737	£4	£12	£45	£130
1894	3,883,452	£7	£26	£90	£240

OLD HEAD ISSUES

1895 Trident 2mm from P(ENNY)	5,395,830	£5	£24	£80	£275
1895 Trident 1mm from P	incl. above	—	£2	£15	£60
1896	24,147,156	—	£2	£15	£60
1897	20,756,620	—	£2	£15	£55
1898	14,296,836	—	£2	£16	£55
1899	26,441,069	—	£2	£14	£45
1900	31,778,109	—	£2	£13	£35
1901	22,205,568	—	£2	£7	£25

EDWARD VII (1901–10)

1902	26,976,768	—	£1	£8	£22
1902 "Low tide" to sea line	incl. above	—	£6	£28	£70
1903	21,415,296	—	£3	£15	£60
1904	12,913,152	—	£4	£20	£90
1905	17,783,808	—	£3	£14	£50
1906	37,989,504	—	£3	£15	£45
1907	47,322,240	—	£3	£15	£45
1908	31,506,048	—	£3	£16	£60
1909	19,617,024	—	£3	£20	£80
1910	29,549,184	—	£3	£15	£45

GEORGE V (1910–36)

1911	23,079,168	—	£3	£12	£35
1912	48,306,048	—	£3	£12	£35
1912 H	16,800,000	—	£3	£30	£140
1913	65,497,812	—	£3	£15	£55
1914	50,820,997	—	£3	£15	£55
1915	47,310,807	—	£3	£15	£60
1916	86,411,165	—	£3	£15	£45
1917	107,905,436	—	£3	£15	£40
1918	84,227,372	—	£3	£12	£40
1918 H	3,660,800	£1	£8	£80	£300
1918 KN	incl. above	£7	£70	£500	£1650
1919	113,761,090	—	£2	£15	£40
1919 H	5,209,600	£1	£10	£80	£300
1919 KN	incl. above	£8	£75	£550	£2000
1920	124,693,485	—	£2	£12	£30
1921	129,717,693	—	£2	£12	£30
1922	16,346,711	—	£2	£15	£55
1922 with reverse of 1927		£1000	£2500	—	—
1926	4,498,519	—	£6	£20	£80
1926 Modified effigy	incl above	£8	£30	£400	£1500
1927	60,989,561	—	£2	£8	£32
1928	50,178,00	—	£2	£8	£30
1929	49,132,800	—	£2	£8	£30
1930	29,097,600	—	£2	£15	£45
1931	19,843,200	—	£2	£8	£35
1932	8,277,600	—	£2	£10	£35
1933			Only 7 examples known		
1934	13,965,600	—	£2	£8	£35
1935	56,070,000	—	—	£2	£9
1936	154,296,000	—	—	£2	£8

DATE	MINTAGE	F	VF	EF	UNC

GEORGE VI (1936–52)

DATE	MINTAGE	F	VF	EF	UNC
1937	88,896,000	—	—	—	£3
1937 Proof	26,402	—	—	—	£6
1938	121,560,000	—	—	—	£3
1939	55,560,000	—	—	—	£4
1940	42,284,400	—	—	—	£6
1944	42,600,000	—	—	—	£6
1945	79,531,200	—	—	—	£5
1946	66,855,600	—	—	—	£3
1947	52,220,400	—	—	—	£3
1948	63,961,200	—	—	—	£3
1949	14,324,400	—	—	—	£4
1950	240,000	£4	£8	£18	£28
1950 Proof	17,513	—	—	—	£25
1951	120,000	£5	£11	£25	£50
1951 Proof	20,000	—	—	—	£30

ELIZABETH II (1952–   )

DATE	MINTAGE	F	VF	EF	UNC
1953	1,308,400	—	—	£1	£4
1953 Proof	40,000	—	—	—	£6
1954	Only one known				
1961	48,313,400	—	—	—	£1
1962	143,308,600	—	—	—	50p
1963	125,235,600	—	—	—	50p
1964	153,294,000	—	—	—	50p
1965	121,310,400	—	—	—	50p
1966	165,739,200	—	—	—	50p
1967	654,564,000	—	—	—	—

Later issues are included in the Decimal section.

HALFPENNIES

DATE		F	VF	EF	UNC

CHARLES II (1660–85)

	F	VF	EF	UNC
1672	£60	£250	£950	—
1672 CRAOLVS error			Extremely rare	
1673	£60	£250	£900	—
1673 CRAOLVS error			Extremely rare	
1673 No rev. stop	£90	£500		
1673 No stops on obv.			Extremely rare	
1675	£60	£500	£1000	—
1675 No stops on obv.	£60	£550	—	—
1675/3 5 over 3	£175	£600	—	—

JAMES II (1685–88)

	F	VF	EF	UNC
1685 (tin)	£125	£600	£2750	—
1686 (tin)	£140	£600	£2750	—
1687 (tin)	£125	£600	£2750	—

WILLIAM & MARY (1688–94)

Tin

	F	VF	EF	UNC
1689 Small draped busts, edge dated	£600	—	—	—
1690 Large cuirassed busts, edge dated	£150	£500	£2500	—
1691 — date on edge and in exergue	£150	£500	£2500	—
1692 — —	£150	£500	£2500	—

DATE	F	VF	EF	UNC

Copper

	F	VF	EF	UNC
1694 Large cuirassed busts, date in exergue ..	£45	£210	£1000	—
1694 — — GVLIEMVS error		Extremely rare		
1694 — — MΛRIΛ error		Extremely rare		
1694 — — No stops on rev.		Extremely rare		

WILLIAM III (1694–1702)

	F	VF	EF	UNC
1695 First issue (date in exergue)	£35	£125	£600	—
1695 — No stop after BRITANNIA on rev.		Extremely rare		
1696 —	£30	£140	£600	—
1696 — TERTVS error		Extremely rare		
1697 —	£30	£125	£600	—
1697 — No stop after TERTIVS on obv.	£50	£200	—	—
1698 —	£40	£150	£700	—
1698 Second issue (date in legend)	£40	£180	—	—
1698 — No stop after date	£45	£170	—	—
1699 —	£35	£140	£700	—
1699 — No stop after date	£175	—	—	—
1699 Third issue (date in exergue) (Britannia with right hand on knee)	£35	£140	£700	—
1699 — No stop after date		Extremely rare		
1699 — BRITΛNNIΛ error	£175	—	—	—
1699 — TERTVS error		Extremely rare		
1699 — No stop on rev.		Extremely rare		
1699 — No stops on obv.	£90	£300	—	—
1700 —	£35	£140	£650	—
1700 — No stops on obv.	£100	£300	—	—
1700 — No stops after GVLIELMUS	£100	£300	—	—
1700 — BRITVANNIA error		Extremely rare		
1700 — GVIELMS error	£100	£300	—	—
1700 — GVLIEEMVS error	£100	£300	—	—
*1701 —	£40	£150	£625	—
1701 — BRITΛNNIΛ error	£70	£275	—	—
1701 — No stops on obv.		Extremely rare		
1701 — inverted As for Vs	£60	£275	—	—

GEORGE I (1714–27)

	F	VF	EF	UNC
1717 "Dump" issue	£40	£130	£550	
1718 —	£35	£130	£500	—
1719 Second issue	£30	£130	£425	—
1720 —	£25	£130	£425	—
1721 —	£25	£100	£425	—
1721 — Stop after date	£40	£140	—	—
1722 —	£30	£120	£425	—
1722 — inverted A for V on obv.		Extremely rare		
1723 —	£30	£120	£425	—
1723 — No stop on rev.	£80	£330	—	—
1724 —	£25	£120	£450	—

GEORGE II (1727–60)

	F	VF	EF	UNC
1729 Young head	£22	£75	£325	—
1729 — No stop on rev.	£25	£75	£325	—
1730 —	£15	£75	£310	—
1730 — GEOGIVS error	£50	£170	£550	—
1730 — Stop after date	£25	£100	£350	—
1730 — No stop after REX on obv.	£30	£120	£400	—
1731 —	£20	£100	£300	—
1731 — No rev. stop	£25	£100	£325	—
1732 —	£20	£90	£275	—
1732 — No rev. stop	£25	£100	£325	—
1733 —	£20	£70	£275	—

DATE	MINTAGE	F	VF	EF	UNC
1734/3 — 4 over 3		£35	£190	—	—
1734 — No stop on obv.		£35	£190	—	—
1735 —		£20	£80	£300	—
1736 —		£20	£70	£275	—
1737 —		£20	£80	£285	—
1738 —		£20	£80	£285	—
1739 —		£18	£65	£220	—
1740 Old head		£15	£60	£220	—
1742 —		£15	£60	£220	—
1742/0 — 2 over 0		£22	£110	£325	—
1743 —		£15	£70	£225	—
1744 —		£15	£70	£225	—
1745 —		£15	£70	£225	—
1746 —		£15	£70	£225	—
1747 —		£15	£70	£225	—
1748 —		£15	£70	£225	—
1749 —		£15	£70	£225	—
1750 —		£15	£70	£225	—
1751 —		£15	£70	£225	—
1752 —		£15	£70	£225	—
1753 —		£15	£70	£225	—
1754 —		£15	£70	£225	—

GEORGE III (1760–1820)

First type—Royal Mint

	MINTAGE	F	VF	EF	UNC
1770		£18	£50	£250	—
1770 No stop on rev.		£25	£65	£260	—
1771		£10	£45	£250	—
1771 No stop on rev.		£20	£60	£260	—
1772 Error GEORIVS		£50	£140	£550	
1772		£10	£40	£175	—
1772 No stop on rev		£20	£60	£220	—
1773		£10	£35	£220	—
1773 No stop after REX		£25	£70	—	—
1773 No stop on rev.		£20	£60	£200	—
1774		£10	£30	£180	—
1775		£10	£30	£180	—

Second type—Soho Mint

		F	VF	EF	UNC
1799		£2	£6	£30	£80

Third type

		F	VF	EF	UNC
1806		£2	£6	£30	£80
1807		£2	£6	£30	£80

George III second type

GEORGE IV (1820–30)

	MINTAGE	F	VF	EF	UNC
1825	215,040	£10	£35	£120	£250
1826 (varieties)	9,031,630	£10	£35	£120	£250
1826 Proof	—	—	—	—	£375
1827	5,376,000	£10	£25	£100	£175

WILLIAM IV (1830–37)

	MINTAGE	F	VF	EF	UNC
1831	806,400	£8	£25	£80	£225
1831 Proof	—	—	—	—	£300
1834	537,600	£8	£25	£80	£225
1837	349,440	£8	£25	£80	£225

VICTORIA (1837–1901)

YOUNG HEAD ISSUES

Copper

	MINTAGE	F	VF	EF	UNC
1838	456,960	£5	£15	£40	£150
1839 Proof	268,800	—	—	—	£300

DATE	MINTAGE	F	VF	EF	UNC
1841	1,075,200	£5	£15	£40	£130
1843	967,680	£20	£45	£120	£325
1844	1,075,200	£5	£15	£40	£150
1845	1,075,200	£50	£130	£650	—
1846	860,160	£7	£16	£50	£160
1847	725,640	£7	£16	£50	£160
1848	322,560	£7	£16	£50	£160
1848/7 final 8 OVER 7	incl. above	£7	£15	£50	£150
1851	215,040	£5	£14	£45	£160
1852	637,056	£7	£16	£45	£160
1853	1,559,040	£4	£7	£20	£60
1853/2 3 over 2	incl. above	£15	£25	£50	£150
1853 Proof	—	—	—	—	£200
1854	12,354,048	£4	£8	£30	£65
1855	1,455,837	£4	£8	£30	£65
1856	1,942,080	£7	£18	£45	£160
1857	1,820,720	£5	£14	£40	£80
1858	2,472,960	£4	£10	£30	£80
1858/7 final 8 over 7	incl. above	£4	£10	£30	£80
1858/6 final 8 over 6	incl. above	£4	£10	£30	£80
1859	1,290,240	£5	£15	£45	£140
1859/8 9 over 8	incl. above	£5	£15	£45	£140
1860	unrecorded		£700	£2000	£5000

Victoria copper halfpenny

Bronze

1860 Beaded border	6,630,400	£3	£9	£30	£140
1860 Toothed border		£4	£12	£45	£160
1861	54,118,400	£3	£9	£30	£125
1862 Die letter A, B or C to left of lighthouse				Extremely rare	
1862	61,107,200	£3	£9	£30	£110
1863	15,948,800	£3	£9	£30	£110
1864	537,600	£3	£10	£40	£110
1865	8,064,000	£4	£18	£55	£140
1865/3 5 over 3	incl. above	£30	£75	£300	—
1866	2,508,800	£5	£15	£50	£130
1867	2,508,800	£5	£15	£45	£125
1868	3,046,400	£5	£12	£50	£150
1869	3,225,600	£7	£35	£90	£415
1870	4,350,739	£5	£15	£50	£200
1871	1,075,280	£75	£90	£220	£575
1872	4,659,410	£4	£10	£35	£110
1873	3,404,880	£4	£10	£35	£110
1874	1,347,655	£5	£25	£90	£220
1874 H	5,017,600	£3	£10	£50	£200
1875	5,430,815	£3	£8	£40	£150
1875 H	1,254,400	£4	£10	£40	£120
1876 H	5,809,600	£4	£10	£40	£120
1877	5,209,505	£3	£10	£40	£140
1878	1,425,535	£5	£20	£60	£140
1879	3,582,545	£3	£10	£35	£120
1880	2,423,465	£4	£12	£45	£150
1881	2,007,515	£4	£12	£35	£120
1881 H	1,792,000	£3	£10	£35	£110
1882 H	4,480,000	£3	£10	£30	£120
1883	3,000,725	£3	£10	£30	£100
1884	6,989,580	£3	£10	£30	£100
1885	8,600,574	£3	£10	£30	£100
1886	8,586,155	£3	£10	£30	£100
1887	10,701,305	£3	£10	£30	£100
1888	6,814,670	£3	£10	£30	£100
1889	7,748,234	£3	£10	£30	£100
1889/8 9 over 8	incl. above	£10	£30	£75	—
1890	11,254,235	£3	£10	£25	£100

Victoria bronze halfpenny

DATE	MINTAGE	F	VF	EF	UNC
1891	13,192,260	£3	£10	£30	£95
1892	2,478,335	£3	£10	£30	£100
1893	7,229,344	£3	£10	£30	£95
1894	1,767,635	£5	£15	£50	£180

OLD HEAD ISSUES

1895	3,032,154	£1	£4	£15	£40
1896	9,142,500	£1	£4	£10	£35
1897	8,690,315	£1	£4	£10	£35
1898	8,595,180	£1	£4	£10	£35
1899	12,108,001	£1	£4	£10	£35
1900	13,805,190	£1	£4	£10	£30
1901	11,127,360	£1	£2	£7	£18

EDWARD VII (1901–10)

1902	13,672,960	£2	£4	£8	£22
1902 "Low tide"	incl. above	£8	£35	£90	£225
1903	11,450,880	£2	£5	£18	£40
1904	8,131,200	£2	£5	£18	£40
1905	10,124,800	£2	£5	£18	£40
1906	16,849,280	£2	£5	£18	£40
1907	16,849,280	£2	£5	£18	£40
1908	16,620,800	£2	£5	£18	£45
1909	8,279,040	£2	£5	£18	£40
1910	10,769,920	£2	£5	£18	£40

GEORGE V (1910–36)

1911	12,570,880	—	£3	£12	£30
1912	21,185,920	—	£2	£12	£30
1913	17,476,480	—	£2	£14	£35
1914	20,289,111	—	£2	£12	£35
1915	21,563,040	£1	£3	£14	£35
1916	39,386,143	—	£2	£12	£35
1917	38,245,436	—	£2	£12	£30
1918	22,321,072	—	£2	£12	£30
1919	28,104,001	—	£2	£12	£30
1920	35,146,793	—	£2	£12	£30
1921	28,027,293	—	£2	£12	£30
1922	10,734,964	—	£2	£15	£40
1923	12,266,282	—	£2	£12	£30
1924	13,971,038	—	£2	£10	£30
1925	12,216,123	—	£2	£10	£30
1925 Modified effigy	incl. above	£2	£5	£25	£60
1926	6,172,306	—	£2	£10	£35
1927	15,589,622	—	£2	£10	£30
1928	20,935,200	—	£2	£8	£25
1929	25,680,000	—	£2	£8	£25
1930	12,532,800	—	£2	£8	£25
1931	16,137,600	—	£2	£8	£25
1932	14,448,000	—	£2	£8	£25
1933	10,560,000	—	£2	£8	£25
1934	7,704,000	—	£2	£12	£30
1935	12,180,000	—	£1	£6	£15
1936	23,008,800	—	£1	£5	£8

GEORGE VI (1936–52)

1937	24,504,000	—	—	£1	£3
1937 Proof	26,402	—	—	£1	£8
1938	40,320,000	—	—	£1	£5
1939	28,924,800	—	—	£1	£5

DATE	MINTAGE	F	VF	EF	UNC
1940	32,162,400	—	—	£1	£6
1941	45,120,000	—	—	£1	£5
1942	71,908,800	—	—	£1	£3
1943	76,200,000	—	—	£1	£3
1944	81,840,000	—	—	£1	£3
1945	57,000,000	—	—	£1	£3
1946	22,725,600	—	—	£1	£5
1947	21,266,400	—	—	£1	£3
1948	26,947,200	—	—	£1	£2
1949	24,744,000	—	—	£1	£2
1950	24,153,600	—	—	£1	£4
1950 Proof	17,513	—	—	£1	£5
1951	14,868,000	—	—	£1	£5
1951 Proof	20,000	—	—	£1	£5
1952	33,78,400	—	—	£1	£2

ELIZABETH II (1952–   )

1953	8,926,366	—	—	—	£1
1953 Proof	40,000	—	—	—	£3
1954	19,375,000	—	—	—	£3
1955	18,799,200	—	—	—	£3
1956	21,799,200	—	—	—	£3
1957	43,684,800	—	—	—	£1
1958	62,318,400	—	—	—	£1
1959	79,176,000	—	—	—	£1
1960	41,340,000	—	—	—	£1
1962	41,779,200	—	—	—	£1
1963	45,036,000	—	—	—	20p
1964	78,583,200	—	—	—	20p
1965	98,083,200	—	—	—	20p
1966	95,289,600	—	—	—	20p
1967	146,491,200	—	—	—	10p

Later issues are included in the Decimal section.

FARTHINGS

DATE		F	VF	EF	UNC

OLIVER CROMWELL

Undated (copper) Draped bust, shield rev. Variations — Extremely rare

CHARLES II (1660–85)

Copper

		F	VF	EF	UNC
1672		£40	£200	£700	—
1673		£40	£200	£600	—
1673 CAROLA for CAROLO error		£75	£375	—	—
1673 No stops on obv.				Extremely rare	
1673 No stop on rev.				Extremely rare	
1674		£40	£175	£575	—
1675		£40	£175	£575	—
1675 No stop after CAROLVS				Extremely rare	
1679		£50	£250	£700	—
1679 No stop on rev.		£60	£270	—	—

Tin

		F	VF	EF	UNC
1684 with date on edge		£175	£450	—	—
1685 —				Extremely rare	

DATE	F	VF	EF	UNC

JAMES II (1685–88)

1684 (tin) Cuirassed bust			Extremely rare	
1685 (tin) —	£150	£500	£1600	—
1686 (tin) —	£150	£500	£1600	—
1687 (tin) —			Extremely rare	
1687 (tin) Draped bust	£200	£700	—	—

WILLIAM & MARY (1688–94)

1689 (tin) Small draped busts	£500	—	—	—
1689 (tin) — with edge date 1690			Extremely rare	
1690 (tin) Large cuirassed busts	£140	£450	£2000	—
1690 (tin) — with edge date 1689			Extremely rare	
1691 (tin) —	£140	£450	—	—
1692 (tin) —	£150	£500	£2000	—
1694 (copper) —	£50	£200	£650	—
1694 No stop after MARIΛ			Extremely rare	
1694 No stop on obv.			Extremely rare	
1694 No stop on rev.			Extremely rare	
1694 Unbarred As in BRITANNIA			Extremely rare	

WILLIAM III (1694–1702)

1695 First issue (date in exergue)	£35	£150	£600	—
1695 — GVLIELMV error			Extremely rare	
1696 —	£35	£150	£600	—
1697 —	£35	£150	£575	—
1697 — GVLIELMS error			Extremely rare	
1698 —	£175	£600	—	—
1698 Second issue (date in legend)	£50	£250	£750	—
1699 First issue	£40	£200	£650	—
1699 Second issue	£40	£200	£625	—
1699 — No stop after date	£50	£225	—	—
1700 First issue	£30	£100	£525	—
1700 — error RRITANNIA			Extremely rare	

ANNE (1702–14)

1714	£250	£450	£850	—

GEORGE I (1714–27)

1717 First small "Dump" issue	£125	£400	£850	—
1719 Second issue	£25	£100	£400	—
1719 — No stop on rev.	£70	£350	—	—
1719 — No stops on obv.	£70	£350	—	—
1720 —	£25	£100	£425	—
1721 —	£25	£100	£425	—
1721/0 — Last 1 over 0	£40	£130	—	—
1722 —	£25	£100	£400	—
1723 —	£30	£110	£425	—
1723 — R over sideways R in REX			Extremely rare	
1724 —	£30	£110	£425	—

George I, first type

GEORGE II (1727–60)

1730 Young head	£15	£60	£260	—
1731 —	£15	£60	£260	—
1732 —	£15	£75	£280	—
1733 —	£15	£65	£270	—
1734 —	£15	£60	£270	—
1734 — No stop on obv.	£30	£100	£350	—
1735 —	£15	£55	£250	—

George I second type

DATE	MINTAGE	F	VF	EF	UNC
1735 — 3 over 5		£20	£90	£325	—
1736 —		£12	£50	£250	—
1737 —		£12	£50	£250	—
1739 —		£12	£50	£250	—
1741 Old Head		£12	£50	£250	—
1744 —		£11	£45	£200	—
1746 —		£11	£45	£200	—
1746 — V over LL in GEORGIVS			Extremely rare		
1749 —		£15	£45	£200	—
1750 —		£15	£45	£200	—
1754 —		£9	£30	£175	—
1754 — 4 over 0		£25	£80	£300	—

GEORGE III (1760–1820)

DATE	MINTAGE	F	VF	EF	UNC
1771 First (London) issue		£20	£60	£250	—
1773 —		£11	£40	£170	—
1773 — No stop on rev.		£18	£50	£190	—
1773 — No stop after REX		£25	£70	£200	—
1774 —		£10	£40	£170	—
1775 —		£10	£40	£170	—
1797 Second (Soho Mint) issue				Patterns only	
1799 Third (Soho Mint) issue		£2	£8	£40	£85
1806 Fourth (Soho Mint) issue		£2	£8	£40	£85
1807 —		£2	£8	£40	£85

George III, third (Soho Mint) issue

GEORGE IV (1820–30)

DATE	MINTAGE	F	VF	EF	UNC
1821 First bust (laureate, draped), first reverse (date in exergue)	2,688,000	£2	£10	£60	£100
1822 —	5,924,350	£2	£10	£60	£100
1823 —	2,365,440	£3	£10	£60	£100
1823 I for 1 in date	incl. above	£15	£70	£250	—
1825 —	4,300.800	£3	£10	£60	£100
1826 —	6,666,240	£3	£10	£60	£100
1826 Second bust (couped, date below), second reverse (ornament in exergue)	incl. above	£3	£10	£60	£100
1826 — Proof	—	—	—	—	£250
1827 —	2,365,440	£3	£10	£55	£125
1828 —	2,365,440	£3	£10	£55	£125
1829 —	1,505,280	£3	£10	£60	£125
1830 —	2,365,440	£3	£10	£55	£125

George III, fourth (Soho Mint) issue

WILLIAM IV (1830–37)

DATE	MINTAGE	F	VF	EF	UNC
1831	2,688,000	£5	£12	£45	£115
1831 Proof	—	—	—	—	£300
1834	1,935,360	£5	£12	£45	£110
1835	1.720,320	£5	£12	£45	£110
1836	1,290.240	£5	£12	£50	£110
1837	3,010,560	£5	£12	£45	£125

VICTORIA (1837–1901)

FIRST YOUNG HEAD (COPPER) ISSUES

DATE	MINTAGE	F	VF	EF	UNC
1838	591,360	£4	£12	£40	£125
1839	4,300,800	£4	£12	£40	£125
1839 Proof	—	—	—	—	£275
1840	3,010,560	£4	£12	£40	£90
1841	1,720,320	£4	£12	£40	£125
1842	1,290,240	£8	£24	£90	£260
1843	4,085,760	£5	£10	£40	£125
1843 I for 1 in date		£50	£275	—	—

DATE	MINTAGE	F	VF	EF	UNC
1844	430,080	£45	£100	£450	£1150
1845	3,225,600	£6	£10	£40	£90
1846	2,580,480	£6	£18	£50	£125
1847	3,879,720	£5	£10	£45	£90
1848	1,290,240	£5	£10	£45	£90
1849	645,120	£25	£60	£260	£550
1850	430,080	£5	£10	£35	£90
1851	1,935,360	£6	£20	£60	£195
1851 D over sideways D in DEI ...	incl. above	£25	£50	£200	—
1852	822,528	£7	£20	£50	£140
1853	1,028,628	£4	£7	£30	£60
1853 Proof	—	—	—	—	£440
1854	6,504,960	£4	£10	£35	£55
1855	3,440,640	£4	£10	£35	£55
1856	1,771,392	£8	£20	£55	£180
1856 R over E in VICTORIA	incl. above	£20	£50	£140	—
1857	1,075,200	£4	£10	£35	£70
1858	1,720,320	£4	£10	£35	£70
1859	1,290,240	£10	£25	£60	£190
1860	unrecorded	£800	£2000	£4700	—

Victoria Young Head first (copper) issue

SECOND YOUNG OR "BUN" HEAD (BRONZE) ISSUES

1860 Toothed border	2,867,200	£2	£5	£40	£100
1860 Beaded border	incl. above	£3	£7	£40	£110
1860 Toothed/Beaded border mule	incl. above			Extremely rare	
1861	8,601,600	£2	£5	£35	£100
1862	14,336,000	£1	£5	£35	£100
1862 Large 8 in date	incl. above			Extremely rare	
1863	1,433,600	£20	£50	£160	£400
1864	2,508,800	£1	£5	£30	£90
1865	4,659,200	£1	£5	£30	£80
1865 5 over 2	incl. above	£10	£18	£40	—
1866	3,584,000	£1	£5	£25	£85
1867	5,017,600	£1	£5	£25	£85
1868	4,851,210	£1	£5	£25	£885
1869	3,225,600	£1	£8	£35	£115
1872	2,150,400	£1	£5	£25	£70
1873	3,225,620	£1	£5	£25	£70
1874 H	3,584,000	£1	£5	£25	£100
1874 H both Gs over sideways G	incl. above	£150	£275	£795	—
1875	712,760	£3	£10	£35	£100
1875 H	6,092,800	£1	£5	£20	£70
1876 H	1,175,200	£3	£12	£50	£130
1878	4,008,540	£1	£4	£20	£70
1879	3,977,180	£1	£4	£20	£70
1880	1,842,710	£1	£4	£20	£70
1881	3,494,670	£1	£4	£20	£70
1881 H	1,792,000	£1	£4	£20	£70
1882 H	1,792,000	£1	£5	£20	£70
1883	1,128,680	£4	£15	£55	£120
1884	5,782,000	£1	£4	£20	£40
1885	5,442,308	£1	£4	£20	£40
1886	7.707,790	£1	£4	£20	£40
1887	1,340,800	£1	£4	£20	£40
1888	1,887,250	£1	£4	£20	£40
1890	2,133,070	£1	£4	£20	£40
1891	4,959,690	£1	£4	£20	£40
1892	887,240	£2	£10	£50	£95
1893	3,904,320	£1	£4	£20	£40
1894	2,396,770	£1	£4	£20	£40
1895	2,852,852	£10	£25	£60	£160

Victoria Young Head second (bronze) issue

DATE	MINTAGE	F	VF	EF	UNC
OLD HEAD ISSUES					
1895 Bright finish	incl. above	£1	£2	£16	£35
1896 —	3,668,610	£1	£2	£16	£25
1897 —	4,579,800	£1	£2	£16	£25
1897 Dark finish	incl. above	£1	£2	£16	£25
1898 —	4,010,080	£1	£2	£16	£25
1899 —	3,864,616	£1	£2	£16	£25
1900 —	5,969,317	£1	£2	£16	£25
1901 —	8,016,460	£1	£2	£10	£20

EDWARD VII (1901–10)

1902...	5,125,120	50p	£1	£10	£15
1903...	5,331,200	50p	£1	£12	£20
1904...	3,628,800	£1	£2	£15	£35
1905...	4,076,800	50p	£1	£12	£25
1906...	5,340,160	50p	£1	£12	£20
1907...	4,399,360	50p	£1	£10	£20
1908...	4,264,960	50p	£1	£10	£20
1909...	8,852,480	50p	£1	£10	£20
1910...	2,298,400	£1	£7	£20	£55

GEORGE V (1910–36)

1911...	5,196,800	25p	50p	£5	£10
1912...	7,669,760	25p	50p	£8	£10
1913...	4,184,320	25p	50p	£5	£100
1914...	6,126,988	25p	50p	£4	£10
1915...	7,129,255	25p	50p	£4	£12
1916...	10,993,325	25p	50p	£4	£10
1917...	21,434,844	25p	50p	£4	£10
1918...	19,362,818	25p	50p	£4	£10
1919...	15,089,425	25p	50p	£4	£10
1920...	11,480,536	25p	50p	£4	£8
1921...	9,469,097	25p	50p	£4	£8
1922...	9,956,983	25p	50p	£4	£8
1923...	8,034,457	25p	50p	£4	£8
1924...	8,733,414	25p	50p	£4	£8
1925...	12,634,697	25p	50p	£4	£8
1926 Modified effigy...................	9,792,397	25p	50p	£4	£8
1927	7,868,355	25p	50p	£4	£8
1928	11,625,600	25p	50p	£4	£8
1929	8,419,200	25p	50p	£4	£8
1930	4,195,200	25p	50p	£4	£8
1931	6,595,200	25p	50p	£4	£8
1932	9,292,800	25p	50p	£4	£8
1933	4,560,000	25p	50p	£4	£8
1934	3,052,800	25p	50p	£4	£8
1935	2.227,200	£1	£2	£8	£20
1936	9,734,400	25p	50p	£3	£6

GEORGE VI (1936–52)

1937...	8,131,200	—	—	50p	£1
1937 Proof..................................	26,402	—	—	£1	£4
1938...	7,449,600	—	—	£1	£6
1939...	31,440,000	—	—	50p	£1
1940...	18,360,000	—	—	50p	£1
1941...	27,312,000	—	—	50p	£1
1942...	28,857,600	—	—	50p	£1
1943...	33,345,600	—	—	50p	£1
1944...	25,137,600	—	—	50p	£1
1945...	23,736,000	—	—	50p	£1

DATE	MINTAGE	F	VF	EF	UNC
1946	24,364,800	—	—	50p	£1
1947	14,745,600	—	—	50p	£1
1948	16,622,400	—	—	50p	£1
1949	8,424,000	—	—	50p	£1
1950	10,324,800	—	—	50p	£1
1950 Proof	17,513	—	—	50p	£8
1951	14,016,000	—	—	50p	£1
1951 Proof	20,000	—	—	50p	£8
1952	5,251,200	—	—	50p	£1

ELIZABETH II (1952–   )

1953	6,131,037	—	—	—	£1
1953 Proof	40,000	—	—	—	£5
1954	6,566,400	—	—	—	£1
1955	5,779,200	—	—	—	£1
1956	1,996,800	—	50p	£1	£3

HALF FARTHINGS

DATE	MINTAGE	F	VF	EF	UNC

GEORGE IV (1820–30)

1828 (two different obverses) (issued for Ceylon)	7,680,000	£9	£20	£45	£125
1830 (large or small date) (issued for Ceylon)	8,766,320	£9	£20	£45	£125

WILLIAM IV (1830–37)

1837 (issued for Ceylon)	1,935,360	£20	£55	£140	£225

VICTORIA (1837–1901)

1839	2,042,880	£5	£10	£30	£75
1842	unrecorded	£4	£8	£25	£75
1843	3,440,640	£3	£6	£20	£45
1844	6,451,200	£3	£6	£15	£45
1844 E over N in REGINA	incl. above	£10	£45	£100	—
1847	3,010,560	£6	£12	£30	£65
1851	unrecorded	£5	£12	£35	£75
1851 5 over 0	unrecorded	£8	£20	£60	£135
1852	989,184	£5	£12	£40	£85
1853	955,224	£5	£15	£45	£100
1853 Proof	incl. above	—	—	—	£175
1854	677,376	£8	£25	£70	£150
1856	913,920	£8	£25	£70	£150
1868	unrecorded	—	—	—	Rare
1868	unrecorded	—	—	—	Rare

THIRD FARTHINGS

DATE	MINTAGE	F	VF	EF	UNC

GEORGE IV (1820–30)

DATE	MINTAGE	F	VF	EF	UNC
1827 (issued for Malta)	unrecorded	£7	£15	£40	£100

WILLIAM IV (1830–37)

1835 (issued for Malta)	unrecorded	£7	£16	£40	£125

VICTORIA (1837–1901)

1844 (issued for Malta)	1,301,040	£10	£24	£70	£155
1844 RE for REG	incl. above	£30	£60	£250	—
1866	576,000	£6	£14	£30	£60
1868	144,000	£6	£14	£30	£60
1876	162,000	£6	£14	£30	£60
1878	288,000	£6	£14	£30	£60
1881	144,000	£6	£14	£30	£60
1884	144,000	£6	£14	£30	£60
1885	288,000	£6	£14	£30	£60

EDWARD VII (1902–10)

1902 (issued for Malta)	288,000	£3	£7	£20	£35

GEORGE V (1911–36)

1913 (issued for Malta)	288,000	£3	£7	£20	£35

QUARTER FARTHINGS

DATE	MINTAGE	F	VF	EF	UNC

VICTORIA (1837–1901)

1839 (issued for Ceylon)	3,840,000	£15	£30	£65	£125
1851 (issued for Ceylon)	2,215,680	£15	£30	£65	£125
1852 (issued for Ceylon)	incl. above	£15	£30	£65	£125
1853 (issued for Ceylon)	incl. above	£15	£30	£65	£125
1853 Proof	—	—	—	—	£425

EMERGENCY ISSUES

DATE	F	VF	EF	UNC

GEORGE III (1760–1820)

To alleviate the shortage of circulating coinage during the Napoleonic Wars the Bank of England firstly authorised the countermarking of other countries' coins, enabling them to pass as English currency. The coins, countermarked with punches depicting the head of George III, were mostly Spanish American 8 reales of Charles III. Although this had limited success it was later decided to completely overstrike the coins with a new English design on both sides — specimens that still show traces of the original host coin's date are avidly sought after by collectors. This overstriking continued for a number of years although all the known coins are dated 1804. Finally, in 1811 the Bank of England issued silver tokens which continued up to 1816 when a completely new regal coinage was introduced.

DOLLAR
Oval countermark of George III

	F	VF	EF	UNC
On "Pillar" type 8 reales	£165	£650	£1000	—
*On "Portrait" type.............	£200	£350	£750	—

Octagonal countermark of George III

	F	VF	EF	UNC
On "Portrait" type	£200	£600	£850	—

HALF DOLLAR
Oval countermark of George III

	F	VF	EF	UNC
On "Portrait" type 4 reales	£200	£400	£850	—

FIVE SHILLINGS OR ONE DOLLAR
These coins were overstruck on Spanish-American coins

	F	VF	EF	UNC
1804...................................	£100	£250	£450	—

— With details of original coin still visible add from 10%.

BANK OF ENGLAND TOKENS

THREE SHILLINGS

	F	VF	EF	UNC
1811 Draped bust..............	£35	£45	£100	—
1812 —	£35	£50	£125	—
1812 Laureate bust	£35	£45	£100	—
1813 —	£35	£45	£100	—
1814 —	£35	£45	£100	—
1815 —	£35	£45	£100	—
1816 —	£125	£250	£850	—

ONE SHILLING AND SIXPENCE

	F	VF	EF	UNC
1811 Draped bust..............	£20	£45	£75	£145
1812 —	£20	£45	£75	£145
1812 Laureate bust	£20	£45	£75	£145
1812 Proof in platinum				Unique
1813 —	£20	£35	£65	£125
1813 Proof in platinum				Unique
1814 —	£20	£35	£65	£125
1815 —	£20	£35	£65	£125
1816 —	£20	£35	£65	£125

NINEPENCE

	F	VF	EF	UNC
1812 Pattern only	—	—		Very Rare

MAUNDY SETS

DATE	F	VF	EF	UNC
CHARLES II (1660–85)				
Undated	£160	£280	£575	—
1670	£145	£250	£520	—
1671	£135	£230	£490	—
1672	£135	£230	£500	—
1673	£135	£225	£490	—
1674	£140	£240	£510	—
1675	£135	£235	£490	—
1676	£150	£250	£505	—
1677	£125	£225	£480s	—
1678	£185	£340	£610	—
1679	£150	£255	£535	—
1680	£140	£240	£495	—
1681	£160	£255	£520	—
1682	£150	£240	£495	—
1683	£150	£240	£500	—
1684	£200	£340	£630	—
JAMES II (1685–88)				
1686	£170	£280	£570	—
1687	£170	£280	£590	—
1688	£185	£310	£610	—
WILLIAM & MARY (1688–94)				
1689	£565	£750	£1250	—
1691	£525	£875	£1100	—
1692	£450	£610	£1000	—
1693	£315	£480	£825	—
1694	£275	£435	£750	—
WILLIAM III (1694–1702)				
1698	£190	£325	£685	—
1699	£410	£560	£1050	—
1700	£205	£350	£725	—
1701	£185	£325	£675	—
ANNE (1702–14)				
1703	£160	£310	£580	—
1705	£145	£285	£545	—
1706	£140	£270	£525	—
1708	£425	£625	£1050	—
1709	£190	£320	£620	—
1710	£195	£355	£635	—
1713	£155	£320	£570	—
GEORGE I (1714–27)				
1723	£160	£315	£615	—
1727	£155	£300	£570	—
GEORGE II (1727–60)				
1729	£130	£230	£485	—
1731	£130	£235	£485	—
1732	£125	£225	£435	—
1735	£120	£220	£435	—
1737	£125	£230	£445	—
1739	£125	£220	£435	—
1740	£115	£215	£420	—
1743	£180	£310	£615	—
1746	£110	£200	£420	—
1760	£130	£220	£445	—

DATE	MINTAGE	F	VF	EF	UNC
GEORGE III (1760–1820)					
1763	£110	£200	£370	—	
1763 Proof	—	Extremely rare			
1766	£120	£200	£385	—	
1772	£120	£205	£380	—	
1780	£115	£200	£360	—	
1784	£115	£200	£360	—	
1786	£120	£210	£375	—	
1792 Wire	£160	£260	£460	£625	
1795	£85	£120	£180	£300	
1800	£80	£110	£170	£275	
New Coinage					
1817	£105	£140	£210	£350	
1818	£100	£125	£200	£320	
1820	£100	£130	£205	£335	
GEORGE IV (1820–30)					
1822	—	£100	£170	£295	
1823	—	£95	£170	£295	
1824	—	£100	£170	£290	
1825	—	£95	£165	£290	
1826	—	£95	£165	£290	
1827	—	£95	£165	£290	
1828	—	£95	£165	£290	
1828 Proof	—	—	—£2000		
1829	—	£95	£160	£290	
1830	—	£95	£165	£295	
WILLIAM IV (1830–37)					
1831	—	£115	£185	£310	
1831 Proof	—	—	—	£800	
1831 Proof Gold	—	—	£22000		
1832	—	£115	£195	£325	
1833	—	£115	£185	£325	
1834	—	£115	£195	£325	
1835	—	£115	£185	£315	
1836	—	£115	£195	£325	
1837	—	£130	£210	£345	
VICTORIA (1837–1901)					
YOUNG HEAD ISSUES					
1838	4,158	—	—	£135	£230
1838 Proof	unrecorded	—	—	£1100	
1838 Proof Gold	—	—	£18000		
1839	4,125	—	—	£145	£250
1839 Proof	unrecorded	—	—	£325	£650
1840	4,125	—	—	£180	£260
1841	2,574	—	—	£195	£325
1842	4,125	—	—	£2005	£360
1843	4,158	—	—	£140	£250
1844	4,158	—	—	£180	£315
1845	4,158	—	—	£120	£225
1846	4,158	—	—	£350	£525
1847	4,158	—	—	£350	£550
1848	4,158	—	—	£350	£550
1849	4,158	—	—	£200	£325
1850	4,158	—	—	£140	£250
1851	4,158	—	—	£155	£260
1852	4,158	—	—	£400	£570
1853	4,158	—	—	£425	£650
1853 Proof	unrecorded	—	—	—	£850
1854	4,158	—	—	£150	£260
1855	4,158	—	—	£160	£300

DATE	MINTAGE	EF	UNC
1856	4,158	£130	£230
1857	4,158	£160	£300
1858	4,158	£135	£245
1859	4,158	£120	£230
1860	4,158	£140	£270
1861	4,158	£130	£245
1862	4,158	£145	£260
1863	4,158	£160	£325
1864	4,158	£145	£240
1865	4,158	£145	£250
1866	4,158	£140	£250
1867	4,158	£130	£260
1867 Proof	unrecorded	—	£1100
1868	4,158	£130	£220
1869	4,158	£165	£285
1870	4,458	£120	£200
1871	4,488	£115	£195
1871 Proof	unrecorded	—	£1200
1872	4,328	£110	£180
1873	4,162	£110	£175
1874	4,488	£105	£175
1875	4,154	£105	£175
1876	4,488	£100	£165
1877	4,488	£95	£160
1878	4,488	£95	£160
1878 Proof	unrecorded	—	£1200
1879	4,488	£95	£165
1879 Proof	unrecorded	—	£1800
1880	4,488	£95	£165
1881	4,488	£95	£165
1881 Proof	unrecorded	—	£1200
1882	4,146	£110	£195
1882 Proof	unrecorded	—	£1300
1883	4,488	£85	£150
1884	4,488	£85	£150
1885	4,488	£85	£150
1886	4,488	£85	£150
1887	4,488	£110	£175

JUBILEE HEAD ISSUES

DATE	MINTAGE	EF	UNC
1888	4,488	£90	£130
1888 Proof	unrecorded	—	£1100
1889	4,488	£85	£120
1890	4,488	£90	£130
1891	4,488	£85	£125
1892	4,488	£85	£130s

OLD HEAD ISSUES

DATE	MINTAGE	EF	UNC
1893	8,976	£65	£95
1894	8,976	£75	£110
1895	8,976	£70	£95
1896	8,976	£70	£95
1897	8,976	£70	£95
1898	8,976	£70	£95
1899	8,976	£70	£95
1900	8,976	£60	£90
1901	8,976	£60	£90

EDWARD VII (1902–110)

DATE	MINTAGE	EF	UNC
1902	8,976	£50	£80
1902 Matt proof	15,123	—	£95
1903	8,976	£55	£90
1904	8,976	£65	£95
1905	8,976	£65	£100
1906	8,800	£60	£90
1907	8,760	£55	£90
1908	8,769	£55	£90
1909	1,983	£90	£155
1910	1,440	£100	£160

GEORGE V (1911–136)

DATE	MINTAGE	EF	UNC
1911	1,786	£75	£120
1911 Proof	6,007	—	£130
1912	1,246	£85	£130

DATE AND PLACE OF ISSUE	MINTAGE	EF	UNC
1913	1,228	£80	£125
1914	982	£95	£140
1915	1,293	£85	£125
1916	1,128	£80	£125
1917	1,237	£80	£125
1918	1,375	£80	£125
1919	1,258	£80	£125
1920	1,399	£80	£130
1921	1,386	£85	£130
1922	1,373	£80	£125
1923	1,430	£80	£125
1924	1,515	£80	£125
1925	1,438	£75	£125
1926	1,504	£75	£125
1927	1,647	£80	£125
1928	1,642	£85	£130
1929	1,761	£85	£130
1930	1,724	£80	£125
1931	1,759	£80	£125
1932	1,835	£80	£125
1933	1,872	£80	£125
1934	1,887	£80	£125
1935	1,928	£85	£135
1936	1,323	£95	£150

GEORGE VI (1936–52)

DATE	MINTAGE	EF	UNC
1937	1,325	£60	£90
1937 Proof	20,900	£60	£100
1938	1,275	£80	£125
1939	1,234	£80	£125
1940	1,277	£80	£125
1941	1,253	£85	£130
1942	1,231	£80	£125
1943	1,239	£80	£125
1944	1,259	£80	£125
1945	1,355	£80	£125
1946	1,365	£80	£125
1947	1,375	£85	£130
1948	1,385	£85	£130
1949	1,395	£85	£130
1950	1,405	£85	£130
1951	1,468	£85	£130
1952	1,012	£100	£145

ELIZABETH II (1952–   )

DATE	MINTAGE	EF	UNC
1953 St. Paul's Cathedral	1,025	—	£525
1953 Proof in gold	unrecorded	Ex. rare	
1953 Proof Matt		Very rare	
1954 Westminster Abbey	1,020	—	£110
1955 Southwark Cathedral	1,036	—	£110
1955 Proof Matt		—	£1200
1956 Westminster Abbey	1,088	—	£110
1957 St. Albans Cathedral	1,094	—	£110
1958 Westminster Abbey	1,100	—	£110
1959 St. George's Chapel, Windsor	1,106	—	£110
1960 Westminster Abbey	1,112	—	£110
1961 Rochester Cathedral	1,118	—	£110
1962 Westminster Abbey	1,125	—	£110
1963 Chelmsford Cathedral	1,131	—	£110
1964 Westminster Abbey	1,137	—	£110
1965 Canterbury Cathedral	1,143	—	£110
1966 Westminster Abbey	1,206	—	£110
1967 Durham Cathedral	986	—	£115
1968 Westminster Abbey	964	—	£115
1969 Selby Cathedral	1,002	—	£115
1970 Westminster Abbey	980	—	£115

Later issues are listed in the Decimal section.
Sets in contemporary dated boxes are usually worth a higher premium. For example approximately £55 can be added to sets from Victoria to George VI in contemporary undated boxes and above £20 for dated boxes.

MAUNDY ODDMENTS
SINGLE COINS

DATE	F	VF	EF

FOUR PENCE
CHARLES II (1660–85)

	F	VF	EF
Undated	£40	£60	£125
1670	£45	£70	£135
1671	£33	£55	£115
1672/1	£33	£55	£115
1673	£33	£55	£110
1674	£35	£55	£115
1674 7 over 6	£40	£65	£130
1675	£30	£55	£110
1675/4	£40s	£65	£135
1676	£32	£55	£115
1676 7 over 6	£45	£70	£125
1677	£30	£50	£105
1678	£30	£50	£105
1678 8 over 7	£40	£60	£120
1679	£27	£45	£100
1680	£32	£50	£110
1681	£35	£55	£115
1682	£30	£45	£120
1682/1	£40	£65	£130
1683	£33	£50	£120
1684	£33	£50	£120
1684 4 over 3	£30	£50	£125

JAMES II (1685–88)

	F	VF	EF
1686	£40	£65	£130
1686 Date over crown	£50	£70	£135
1687	£40	£60	£120
1687 7 over 6	£45	£65	£130
1688	£40	£60	£120
1688 1 over 8	£45	£65	£135

WILLIAM & MARY (1688–94)

	F	VF	EF
1689	£33	£50	£120
1689 GV below bust	£40	£60	£135
1689 GVLEELMVS	£70	£140	£250
1690	£45	£65	£140
1690 6 over 5	£50	£75	£150
1691	£45	£70	£145
1691 1 over 0	£50	£75	£150
1692	£55	£80	£175
1692 Mar.ia	£110	£160	£225
1692 2 over 1	£60	£85	£185
1693	£55	£85	£170
1693 3 over 2	£50	£80	£165
1694	£45	£80	£155

WILLIAM III (1694–1702)

	F	VF	EF
1698	£50	£80	£155
1699	£40	£70	£140
1700	£50	£75	£145
1701	£45	£80	£145
1702	£50	£90	£140

ANNE (1702–14)

	F	VF	EF
1703	£42	£70	£135
1704	£35	£65	£120
1705	£45	£70	£130	—

It is nowadays considered that the early small denomination silver coins 4d–1d were originally struck for the Maundy ceremony although undoubtedly many subsequently circulated as small change—therefore they are listed here under "Maundy silver single coins".

DATE	F	VF	EF	UNC
1706	£40	£65	£120	—
1708	£40	£65	£130	—
1709	£45	£70	£130	—
1710	£30	£55	£100	—
1713	£40	£65	£125	—

GEORGE I (1714–27)

	F	VF	EF	UNC
1717	£35	£65	£120	—
1721	£33	£65	£120	—
1723	£45	£70	£130	—
1727	£40	£65	£125	—

GEORGE II (1727–60)

	F	VF	EF	UNC
1729	£40	£60	£100	—
1731	£40	£60	£100	—
1732	£35	£60	£95	—
1735	£35	£55	£95	—
1737	£40	£55	£95	—
1739	£40	£5	£95	—
1740	£35	£55	£95	—
1743	£65	£110	£175	—
1743 3 over 0	£70	£115	£180	
1746	£35	£50	£85	—
1760	£40	£65	£95	—

GEORGE III (1760–1820)

	F	VF	EF	UNC
1763 Young head	£30	£55	£80	—
1763 Proof	—	—	Extremely rare	
1765	£350	£600	£875	—
1766	£35	£60	£95	—
1770	£90	£140	£200	—
1772	£50	£80	£125	—
1776	£50	£75	£120	—
1780	£35	£60	£90	—
1784	£35	£55	£90	—
1786	£35	£55	£95	—
1792 Older head, Thin 4	£50	£80	£130	£200
1795	—	£30	£55	£80
1800	—	£25	£50	£70
1817 New coinage	—	£25	£50	£75
1818	—	£30	£50	£75
1820	—	£30	£55	£80

GEORGE IV (1820–30)

	F	VF	EF	UNC
1822	—	—	£45	£90
1823	—	—	£40	£75
1824	—	—	£40	£80
1826	—	—	£40	£70
1827	—	—	£40	£70
1828	—	—	£40	£70
1829	—	—	£40	£70
1830	—	—	£40	£70

WILLIAM IV (1830–37)

	F	VF	EF	UNC
1831–37	—	—	£45	£80

VICTORIA (1837–1901)

	F	VF	EF	UNC
1838–87 (Young Head)	—	—	£20	£33
1841 & 1857	—	—	£32	£45
1888–92 (Jubilee Head)	—	—	£15	£25
1893–1909 (Old Head	—	—	£12	£20

DATE	F	VF	EF	UNC

EDWARD VII (1901–10)

1902–08....................................	—	—	£12	£20
1909 & 1910	—	—	£20	£35

GEORGE V (1910–36)

1911–36....................................			£15	£26

GEORGE VI (1936–52)

1937–52....................................	—	—	£15	£27

ELIZABETH II (1952–   )

1953..	—	—	£75	£110
1954–85....................................	—	—	£20	£30
1986–2007................................	—	—	£25	£35
2002 in Gold Proof	—	—	£300	£400

THREEPENCE

CHARLES II (1660–85)

Undated....................................	£40	£60	£135	—
1670..	£32	£55	£105	—
1671..	£32	£55	£105	—
1671 GRVTIA...........................	£45	£65	£175	—
1672..	£32	£55	£110	—
1673..	£32	£55	£100	—
1674..	£30	£50	£105	—
1675..	£35	£55	£110	—
1676..	£35	£60	£110	—
1676 ERA for FRA	£50	£70	£150	—
1677..	£35	£55	£115	—
1678..	£30	£55	£110	—
1679..	£30	£45	£90	—
1679 O/A in CAROLVS	£50	£75	£170	—
1680..	£30	£55	£115	—
1681..	£33	£55	£115	—
1682..	£35	£55	£115	—
1683..	£35	£55	£115	—
1684..	£35	£55	£120	—
1684/3	£40	£55	£125	—

JAMES II (1685–88)

1685..	£40	£65	£130	—
1685 Struck on fourpence flan	£70	£105	£190	—
1686..	£35	£55	£115	—
1687..	£30	£55	£110	—
1687 7 over 6...........................	£40	£60	£115	—
1688..	£45	£80	£155	—
1688 8 over 7...........................	£50	£85	£170	—

WILLIAM & MARY (1688–94)

1689..	£35	£55	£120	—
1689 No stop on reverse........	£40	£65	£135	—
1689 LMV over MVS (obverse)	£60	£80	£170	—
1690..	£50	£75	£140	—
1690 6 over 5...........................	£55	£85	£150	—
1691 First bust	£310	£460	£625	—
1691 Second bust	£235	£375	£475	—
1692..	£55	£85	£160	—
1692 G below bust.................	£60	£90	£170	—
1692 GV below bust...............	£60	£85	£135	—
1692 GVL below bust.............	£60	£85	£175	—
1693..	£95	£150	£220	—
1693 3 over 2...........................	£100	£160	£225	—
1694..	£55	£80	£145	—
1694 Marla error	£70	£100	£190	—

DATE	F	VF	EF	UNC

WILLIAM III (1694–1702)

	F	VF	EF	UNC
1698	£45	£75	£130	—
1699	£40	£70	£120	—
1700	£50	£80	£140	—
1701	£45	£60	£120	—
1701 GBA instead of GRA	£50	£70	£130	—

ANNE (1702–14)

	F	VF	EF	UNC
1703	£45	£65	£120	—
1703 7 of date above crown	£50	£70	£125	—
1704	£38	£55	£100	—
1705	£45	£60	£120	—
1706	£38	£55	£110	—
1707	£38	£55	£105	—
1708	£35	£55	£115	—
1709	£35	£55	£115	—
1710	£33	£55	£95	—
1713	£40	£65	£115	—

GEORGE I (1714–27)

	F	VF	EF	UNC
1717	£40	£55	£100	—
1721	£45	£60	£115	—
1723	£45	£60	£120	—
1727	£45	£65	£120	—

GEORGE II (1727–60)

	F	VF	EF	UNC
1729	£40	£60	£95	—
1731	£40	£55	£95	—
1731 Small lettering	£42	£65	£100	—
1732	£40	£60	£95	—
1731 Stop over head	£40	£60	£95	—
1735	£36	£55	£95	—
1737	£40	£55	£95	—
1739	£37	£55	£95	—
1740	£35	£45	£90	—
1743	£35	£50	£90	—
1743 Stop over head	£40	£60	£100	—
1746	£33	£50	£80	—
1746 6 over 3	£38	£55	£90	—
1760	£40	£60	£100	—

GEORGE III (1760–1820)

	F	VF	EF	UNC
1762	£16	£30	£45	—
1763	£16	£30	£45	—
1763 Proof	—	—	Extremely rare	
1765	£270	£400	£625	—
1766	£35	£55	£90	—
1770	£40	£60	£100	—
1772	£30	£50	£75	—
1780	£35	£50	£80	—
1784	£35	£50	£90	—
1786	£35	£55	£85	—
1792	£45	£70	£130	£225
1795	—	£25	£45	£70
1800	—	£30	£50	£80
1817	—	£30	£50	£100
1818	—	£28	£45	£95
1820	—	£30	£50	£100

GEORGE IV (1820–30)

	F	VF	EF	UNC
1822	—	—	£50	£100
1823	—	—	£50	£95
1824	—	—	£50	£100
1825–30	—	—	£50	£95

DATE	F	VF	EF	UNC

WILLIAM IV (1830–37)

1831–1836.............................	–	–	£60	£120
1837......................................	–	–	£70	£135

VICTORIA (1837–1901)

1838......................................	–	–	£70	£135
1839......................................	–	–	£85	£165
1840......................................	–	–	£90	£190
1841......................................	–	–	£110	£215
1842......................................	–	–	£120	£230
1843......................................	–	–	£75	£140
1844......................................	–	–	£100	£195
1845......................................	–	–	£55	£115
1846......................................	–	–	£225	£400
1847......................................	–	–	£260	£450
1848......................................	–	–	£260	£450
1849......................................	–	–	£115	£225
1850......................................	–	–	£85	£160
1851......................................	–	–	£90	£170
1852......................................	–	–	£310	£500
1853......................................	–	–	£310	£500
1854......................................	–	–	£85	£180
1855......................................	–	–	£90	£190
1856......................................	–	–	£70	£185
1857......................................	–	–	£100	£195
1858......................................	–	–	£75	£155
1859......................................	–	–	£60	£120
1860......................................	–	–	£85	£170
1861......................................	–	–	£80	£155
1862......................................	–	–	£185	£165
1863......................................	–	–	£100	£200
1864......................................	–	–	£80	£165
1865......................................	–	–	£85	£165
1866......................................	–	–	£80	£160
1867......................................	–	–	£85	£160
1868......................................	–	–	£70	£140
1869......................................	–	–	£95	£185
1870......................................	–	–	£70	£125
1871......................................	–	–	£70	£125
1872......................................	–	–	£65	£115
1873......................................	–	–	£60	£105
1874......................................	–	–	£60	£100
1875......................................	–	–	£50	£95
1876......................................	–	–	£50	£100
1877......................................	–	–	£50	£100
1878......................................	–	–	£55	£100
1879......................................	–	–	£60	£105
1880......................................	–	–	£55	£100
1881......................................	–	–	£50	£100
1882......................................	–	–	£80	£155
1883......................................	–	–	£50	£95
1884......................................	–	–	£45	£90
1885......................................	–	–	£45	£90
1886......................................	–	–	£40	£85
1887......................................	–	–	£55	£110
1888–1892 (Jubilee Head)......	–	–	£37	£60
1893–1901 (Old Head)...........	–	–	£25	£45

EDWARD VII (1901–10)

1902......................................	–	–	£20	£45
1903......................................	–	–	£30	£60
1904......................................	–	–	£38	£75
1905......................................	–	–	£45	£75
1906......................................	–	–	£35	£65
1907......................................	–	–	£35	£65

DATE	F	VF	EF	UNC
1908..................................	—	—	£30	£60
1909..................................	—	—	£35	£85
1910..................................	—	—	£50	£90

GEORGE V (1910–36)

1911–34.............................	—	—	£25	£45
1935..................................	—	—	£30	£55
1936..................................	—	—	£45	£75

GEORGE VI (1936–52)

1937–52.............................	—	—	£35	£60

ELIZABETH II (1952–)

1953..................................	—	—	£80	£145
1954–85.............................	—	—	£30	£50
1986–2007..........................	—	—	£37	£55
2002 In gold (proof)	—	—	—	£275

TWOPENCE

CHARLES II (1660–85)

	F	VF	EF	UNC
Undated...............................	£35	£55	£110	—
1668..................................	£42	£60	£125	—
1670..................................	£33	£50	£100	—
1671..................................	£30	£50	£100	—
1672..................................	£30	£50	£100	—
1672/1	£33	£50	£115	—
1673..................................	£33	£50	£105	—
1674..................................	£33	£55	£110	—
1675..................................	£30	£50	£100	—
1676..................................	£35	£55	£105	—
1677..................................	£30	£50	£100	—
1678..................................	£25	£45	£95	—
1679..................................	£25	£40	£85	—
1680..................................	£30	£50	£95	—
1681..................................	£28	£45	£100	—
1682..................................	£30	£50	£105	—
1682/1 ERA for FRA	£35	£55	£155	—
1683..................................	£30	£50	£110	—
1684..................................	£33	£55	£115	—

JAMES II (1685–88)

	F	VF	EF	UNC
1686..................................	£35	£60	£115	—
1686 reads IACOBVS	£40	£70	£150	—
1687..................................	£40	£60	£120	—
1687 ERA for FRA	£45	£65	£135	—
1688..................................	£33	£50	£105	—
1688/7	£35	£60	£115	—

WILLIAM & MARY (1688–94)

	F	VF	EF	UNC
1689..................................	£26	£50	£95	—
1691..................................	£30	£50	£95	—
1692..................................	£55	£95	£145	—
1693..................................	£40	£65	£115	—
1693 Below bust	£45	£70	£125	—
1693/2	£45	£70	£125	—
1694..................................	£32	£50	£105	—
1694 Marla error	£45	£70	£195	—
1694 HI for HIB....................	£35	£70	£140	—
1694 GVLI under bust	£40	£65	£130	—
1694 GVL under bust	£40	£65	£130	—

WILLIAM III (1694–1702)

	F	VF	EF	UNC
1698..................................	£45	£75	£125	—
1699..................................	£30	£55	£95	—
1700..................................	£35	£65	£115	—
1701..................................	£40	£65	£115	—

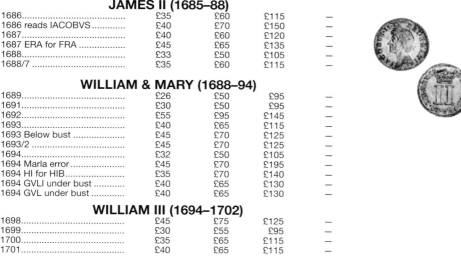

DATE	F	VF	EF	UNC

ANNE (1702–14)

	F	VF	EF	UNC
1703	£37	£60	£120	—
1704	£30	£45	£90	—
1704 No stops on obverse	£37	£50	£105	—
1705	£35	£60	£110	—
1706	£35	£60	£110	—
1707	£30	£45	£95	—
1708	£30	£50	£95	—
1709	£45	£70	£130	—
1710	£27	£45	£85	—
1713	£45	£70	£125	—

GEORGE I (1714–27)

	F	VF	EF	UNC
1717	£30	£50	£85	—
1721	£30	£50	£80	—
1723	£30	£60	£100	—
1726	£25	£45	£90	—
1727	£30	£52	£90	—

GEORGE II (1727–60)

	F	VF	EF	UNC
1729	£27	£45	£75	—
1731	£27	£45	£75	—
1732	£30	£50	£80	—
1735	£25	£45	£75	—
1737	£25	£45	£75	—
1739	£28	£50	£77	—
1740	£25	£45	£77	—
1743	£25	£45	£70	—
1743/0	£27	£50	£85	—
1746	£25	£45	£70	—
1756	£23	£40	£65	—
1759	£23	£40	£65	—
1760	£28	£45	£70	—

GEORGE III (1760–1820)

	F	VF	EF	UNC
1763	£20	£40	£60	—
1763 Proof			Extremely rare	
1765	£275	£425	£700	—
1766	£23	£40	£55	—
1772	£22	£35	£55	—
1780	£22	£35	£50	—
1784	£22	£35	£50	—
1786	£24	£35	£50	—
1792	—	£50	£70	£120
1795	—	£20	£35	£50
1800	—	£20	£30	£40
1817	—	£25	£40	£55
1818	—	£20	£30	£45
1820	—	£20	£30	£45

GEORGE IV (1820–30)

	F	VF	EF	UNC
1822–30	—	—	£25	£40
1825 TRITANNIAR	—	—	£45	£75

WILLIAM IV (1830–37)

	F	VF	EF	UNC
1831–37	—	—	£27	£45

VICTORIA (1837–1901)

	F	VF	EF	UNC
1838–87 (Young Head)	—	—	£17	£25
1859 BEITANNIAR	—	—	£40	£75
1861 6 over 1	—	—	£20	£40
1888–92 (Jubilee Head)	—	—	£15	£25
1893–1901 (Old Head)	—	—	£11	£20

DATE	F	VF	EF	UNC

EDWARD VII (1901–10)

DATE	F	VF	EF	UNC
1902–08	−	−	£12	£18
1909	−	−	£20	£40
1910	−	−	£17	£35

GEORGE V (1910–36)

1911–34	−	−	£15	£25
1935	−	−	£20	£30
1936	−	−	£22	£35

GEORGE VI (1936–52)

1937–47	−	−	£15	£25
1948–52	−	−	£17	£28

ELIZABETH II (1952–   )

1953	−	−	£52	£95
1954–85	−	−	£20	£30
1986–2007	−	−	£20	£30
2002 Gold Proof	−	−	−	£215

PENNY

CHARLES II (1660–85)

	F	VF	EF	UNC
Undated	£40	£65	£120	−
1670	£32	£65	£110	−
1671	£32	£65	£115	−
1672/1	£32	£65	£110	−
1673	£32	£65	£110	−
1674	£35	£65	£115	−
1674 Gratia (error)	£45	£80	£195	−
1675	£32	£65	£105	−
1675 Gratia (error)	£45	£80	£190	−
1676	£42	£65	£130	−
1676 Gratia (error)	£50	£90	£195	−
1677	£32	£60	£140	−
1677 Gratia (error)	£40	£70	£175	−
1678	£115	£195	£275	−
1678 Gratia (error)	£130	£210	£315	−
1679	£55	£80	£140	−
1680	£40	£65	£120	−
1681	£65	£95	£155	−
1682	£42	£70	£125	−
1682 ERA for FRA	£45	£85	£185	−
1683	£42	£70	£125	−
1683/1	£45	£80	£165	−
1684	£170	£230	£350	−
1684/3	£175	£255	£320	−

Charles II

JAMES II (1685–88)

	F	VF	EF	UNC
1685	£40	£65	£110	−
1686	£40	£60	£110	−
1687	£45	£65	£130	−
1687/8	£45	£65	£135	−
1688	£42	£55	£110	−
1688/7	£45	£65	£135	−

James II

WILLIAM & MARY (1688–94)

	F	VF	EF	UNC
1689	£375	£525	£800	−
1689 GVIELMVS (Error)	£350	£500	£725	−
1690	£55	£85	£130	−
1691	£50	£80	£135	−
1692	£150	£260	£400	−
1692/1	£150	£260	£425	−

DATE	F	VF	EF	UNC
1693....................................	£60	£95	£155	—
1694....................................	£50	£80	£135	—
1694 HI for HIB......................	£65	£105	£185	—
1694 No stops on obverse	£60	£95	£170	—

WILLIAM III (1694–1702)

1698....................................	£55	£85	£135	—
1698 HI. BREX (Error).............	£60	£105	£175	—
1699....................................	£225	£330	£500	—
1700....................................	£60	£90	£145	—
1701....................................	£60	£90	£130	—

ANNE (1702–14)

1703....................................	£48	£75	£130	—
1705....................................	£45	£70	£120	—
1706....................................	£40	£60	£110	—
1708....................................	£275	£350	£500	—
1709....................................	£42	£60	£100	—
1710....................................	£95	£150	£235	—
1713/0	£50	£75	£125	—

GEORGE I (1714–27)

1716....................................	£30	£55	£80	—
1718....................................	£30	£50	£80	—
1720....................................	£37	£50	£85	—
1720 HIPEX (Error).................	£45	£70	£140	—
1723....................................	£45	£70	£110	—
1725....................................	£40	£60	£85	—
1726....................................	£40	£60	£85	—
1727....................................	£40	£70	£110	—

GEORGE II (1727–60)

1729....................................	£35	£60	£85	—
1731....................................	£35	£50	£80	—
1732....................................	£27	£40	£65	—
1735....................................	£27	£40	£60	—
1737....................................	£30	£40	£65	—
1739....................................	£30	£47	£65	—
1740....................................	£28	£45	£70	—
1743....................................	£35	£55	£70	—
1746....................................	£38	£60	£75	—
1746/3	£38	£60	£80	—
1750....................................	£25	£37	£50	—
1752....................................	£25	£37	£50	—
1753....................................	£22	£37	£50	—
1754....................................	£22	£37	£55	—
1755....................................	£25	£40	£60	—
1756....................................	£24	£40	£55	—
1757....................................	£24	£40	£50	—
1757 No colon after Gratia	£30	£50	£70	—
1758....................................	£22	£35	£50	—
1759....................................	£24	£33	£50	—
1760....................................	£30	£45	£70	—

George II

GEORGE III (1760–1820)

1763....................................	£25	£45	£65	—
1763 Proof.............................	—	—	Extremely rare	
1766....................................	£25	£40	£55	—
1772....................................	£25	£40	£50	—
1780....................................	£26	£45	£50	—
1781....................................	£20	£32	£50	—
1784....................................	£20	£35	£55	—
1786....................................	£20	£35	£55	—
1792....................................	£22	£40	£60	£85

DATE	F	VF	EF	UNC
1795	—	£20	£30	£40
1800	—	£19	£30	£40
1817	—	£18	£22	£35
1818	—	£18	£22	£35
1820	—	£18	£23	£37

George III

GEORGE IV (1820–30)

	F	VF	EF	UNC
1822–30	—	—	£18	£35

WILLIAM IV (1830–37)

	F	VF	EF	UNC
1831–37	—	—	£19	£37

VICTORIA (1837–1901)

	F	VF	EF	UNC
1838–87 (Young Head)	—	—	£12	£22
1888–92 (Jubilee Head)	—	—	£11	£20
1893–1901 (Old Head)	—	—	£10	£17

EDWARD VII (1901–10)

	F	VF	EF	UNC
1902–08	—	—	£10	£16
1909	—	—	£15	£25
1910	—	—	£20	£45

GEORGE V (1910–36)

	F	VF	EF	UNC
1911–14	—	—	£15	£25
1915	—	—	£16	£30
1916–19	—	—	£15	£25
1920	—	—	£16	£30
1921–28	—	—	£15	£25
1929	—	—	£17	£35
1930–34	—	—	£15	£25
1935	—	—	£17	£30
1936	—	—	£20	£35

GEORGE VI (1936–52)

	F	VF	EF	UNC
1937–40	—	—	£16	£30
1941	—	—	£17	£33
1942–47	—	—	£16	£33
1948–52	—	—	£18	£35

ELIZABETH II (1952–   )

	F	VF	EF	UNC
1953	—	—	£150	£250
1965–85	—	—	£20	£35
1986–2007	—	—	£24	£40
2005 Proof in gold	—	—	—	£285

The new hardback
Banknote Yearbook
5th Edition

DECIMAL COINAGE

Since the introduction of the Decimal system in the UK, many coins have been issued for circulation purposes in vast quantities. In addition, from 1982 sets of coins to non-proof standard, and including examples of each denomination found in circulation, have been issued each year. For 1982 and 1983 they were to "circulation" standard and described as "Uncirculated". Individual coins from these sets are annotated "Unc" on the lists that follow. From 1984 to the present day they were described as "Brilliant Uncirculated" (BU on the lists), and from around 1986 these coins are generally distinguishable from coins intended for circulation. They were from then produced by the Proof Coin Division of the Royal Mint (rather than by the Coin Production Room which produces circulation-standard coins). For completeness however, we have included the annotations Unc and BU back to 1982, the start year for these sets.

It is emphasised that the abbreviations Unc and BU in the left-hand columns adjacent to the date refer to an advertising description or to an engineering production standard, not the preservation condition or grade of the coin concerned. Where no such annotation appears adjacent to the date, the coin is circulation-standard for issue as such.

We have included the "mintage" figures for circulation coins down to Twenty-five pence. Strictly speaking, these figures are for coins issued by the Royal Mint up to December 31, 2005. The figure given for the 1997 Two Pounds, for example, is considerably less than the actual quantity struck, because many were scrapped before issue due to failing an electrical conductivity test. Figures are not available for commemorative £5, £2 and 50p coins dated 2000 or since, their totals are included in the definitive version of the coins concerned. We have included the figures for non-circulation-standard coins where known. Where a coin is available in uncirculated grade at, or just above, face value no price has been quoted.

Base metal Proof issues of circulation coinage (£2 or £1 to one or half penny) of the decimal series were only issued, as with Unc or BU, as part of Year Sets, but many of these sets have been broken down into individual coins, hence the appearance of the latter on the market.

The lists do not attempt to give details of die varieties, except where there was an obvious intention to change the appearance of a coin, e.g. 1992 20p.

HUNDRED POUNDS AND BELOW
(Britannia Gold series)

In 1987 the gold £100 coin was introduced, known as the Britannia. It contained one Troy ounce of fine gold, alloyed to 22 carat, and this has continued to the present day. At the same time, and also continuing, coins of face value £50, £25 and £10 appeared, containing a half ounce, quarter ounce and one tenth of an ounce of fine gold respectively. From 1987 to 1989 the alloy was of equal weights of silver and copper, (Red Gold), whereas from 1990 to the present day the alloy has been silver only (yellow gold). Below (Britannia Silver Series)" section below.

Proof sets of these coins are listed in the "Proof and Specimen Sets" section. In addition, non-proof coins have been minted, it is believed for each of the four coins for every year. The one ounce £100 Britannia is primarily issued as a bullion coin in the non-proof standard, originally in competition with the South African Krugerrand. Its price is quoted daily on the financial pages of some newspapers.

There were five reverse designs by Philip Nathan:- 1987-1996 Standing Britannia, 1997 Chariot, 1998-2000 Standing Britannia, 2001 Una and the Lion, 2002 Standing Britannia, 2003 Britannia's Helmeted Head, 2004 Standing Britannia, 2005 Britannia seated, 2006 Standing Britannia. For 2007 the design is a Seated Britannia with lion at her feet, by Christopher Le Brun.

In general the proof coins have reverse features frosted, The proofs with Standing Britannia and Una and the Lion reverses include P NATHAN on the reverse, whereas the equivalent bullion coins include NATHAN. The other three reverses have PN on both proofs and bullion coins.

FIVE POUNDS (Sovereign series)

This series is all minted in gold, and, except where stated, have the Pistrucci St George and Dragon reverse. BU coins up to 2001 bear a U in a circle.

DATE	Mintage	UNC
1980 Proof	10,000	£450
1981 Proof	5,400	£450
1982 Proof	2,500	£480
1984 BU	15,104	£400
1984 Proof	8,000	£475
1985 New portrait BU	13,626	£400
1985 — Proof	6,130	£480
1986 BU	7,723	£400
1987 Uncouped portrait BU	5,694	£400
1988 BU	3,315	£400
1989 500th Anniversary of the Sovereign. Enthroned portrayal obverse and Crowned shield reverse BU	2,937	£550
1989 — Proof	5000	£650
1990 Reverts to couped portrait BU	1,226	£400
1990 Proof	1,721	£500
1991 BU	976	£400
1991 Proof	1,336	£550
1992 BU	797	£400
1992 Proof	1,165	£550
1993 BU	906	£400
1993 Proof	1,078	£550
1994 BU	1,000	£400
1994 Proof	918	£550
1995 BU	1,000	£400
1995 Proof	1,250	£550
1996 BU	901	£400
1996 Proof	742	£550
1997 BU	802	£400
1997 Proof	860	£600
1998 New portrait BU	825	£425
1998 Proof	789	£650
1999 BU	991	£425
1999 Proof	1,000	£650
2000 ("Bullion")	10,000	£350
2000 BU	994	£450
2000 Proof	3,000	£650

Pistrucci's famous rendering of St George and the Dragon.

The obverse of the 1989 gold coins portray HM the Queen enthroned

238

DATE	Mintage	UNC
2001 BU	1,000	£450
2001 Proof	3,500	£650
2002 Shield rev. ("Bullion")	—	£350
2002 BU	—	£450
2002 Proof	3,000	£650
2003 BU	—	£450
2003 Proof	—	£550
2004 Proof	—	£550
2005 Noad's heraldic St George and Dragon BU	—	£550
2005 — Proof	—	£650
2006 BU	—	£724
2006 Proof	—	—
2007 Proof	—	—

FIVE POUNDS (Crown series)

This series commenced in 1990 when the "Crown" was declared legal tender at £5, instead of 25p as all previous issues continued to be. Mintage is in cupro-nickel unless otherwise stated. BU includes those in individual presentation folders, and those in sets sold with stamp covers and/or banknotes.

DATE	Mintage	UNC
1990 Queen Mother's 90th Birthday.	2,761,431	£8
1990 — BU	48,477	£10
1990 — Silver Proof	56,800	£34
1990 — Gold Proof	2,500	£525
1993 Coronation 40th Anniversary	1,834,655	£8
1993 — BU	—	£10
1993 — Proof	—	£15
1993 — Silver Proof	100,000	£32
1993 — Gold Proof	2,500	£525
1996 HM the Queen's 70th Birthday	2,396,100	£8
1996 — BU	—	£10
1996 — Proof	—	£15
1996 — Silver Proof	70,000	£32
1996 — Gold Proof	2,127	£650
1997 Royal Golden Wedding	1,733,000	£8
1997 — BU	—	£10
1997 — — with £5 note	5,000	£55
1997 — Proof	—	£20
1997 — Silver Proof	75,000	£32
1997 — Gold Proof	2,750	£650
1998 Prince of Wales 50th birthday	1,407,300	£7
1998 — BU	—	£12
1998 — Proof	—	£20
1998 — Silver Proof	—	£40
1998 — Gold Proof	—	£650
1999 Princess of Wales Memorial.	1,600,000	£9
1999 — BU	—	£12
1999 — Proof	—	£20
1999 — Silver Proof	350,000	£40
1999 — Gold Proof	7,500	£650
1999 Millennium	3,796,300	£8
1999 — BU	—	£15
1999 — Proof	—	£22
1999 — Silver Proof	100,000	£40
1999 — Gold Proof	2,500	£600
2000 —	3,147,092*	£8
2000 — BU	—	£15
2000 — — with special Millennium Dome mintmark	—	£12
2000 — Proof	—	£22
2000 — Silver Proof with gold highlight	50,000	£40
2000 — Gold Proof	2,500	£575
2000 Queen Mother's 100th Birthday	*incl. above**	£7
2000 — BU	—	£12

DATE	Mintage	UNC
2000 — Silver Proof	100,000	£40
2000 — — — Piedfort	14,850	£175
2000 — Gold Proof	3,000	£550
2001 Victorian Era.	851,491	£7
2001 — BU	—	£12
2001 — Proof	—	£20
2001 — Silver Proof	100,000	£40
2001 — Gold Proof	3,000	£550
2001 — — with frosted relief	750	£850
2002 Golden Jubilee	3,687,882*	£7
2002 — BU	—	£12
2002 — Proof	—	£20
2002 — Silver Proof	75,000	£40
2002 — Gold Proof	5,502	£550
2002 Queen Mother Memorial	*incl. above**	£7
2002 — BU	—	£12
2002 — Silver Proof	25,000	£40
2002 — Gold Proof	3,000	£550
2003 Coronation Jubilee	1,307,010	£7
2003 — BU	—	£10
2003 — Proof	—	£20
2003 — Silver Proof	—	£40
2003 — Gold Proof	—	£550
2004 Entente Cordiale Centenary	—	£6
2004 — Proof Reverse Frosting	—	£15
2004 — Silver Proof	—	£35
2004 — Gold Proof	—	£550
2004 — Platinum Proof Piedfort	501	£3000
2005 Trafalgar Bicentenary	—	—
2005 — BU	—	—
2005 — Proof	—	—
2005 — Silver Proof	—	—
2005 — — — Piedfort	—	—
2005 — Gold Proof	—	£550
2005 Bicentenary of the Death of Nelson	—	—
2005 — BU	—	—
2005 — Proof	—	—
2005 — Silver Proof	—	—
2005 — — — Piedfort	—	—
2005 — Gold Proof	—	£550
2005 — Platinum Proof Piedfort	200	£3450
2006 Queen's 80th birthday	—	—
2006 — BU	—	£10
2006 — Proof	—	—
2006 — Silver Proof	—	—
2006 — — — Piedfort, selective gold plating on reverse	—	£80
2006 — Gold Proof	—	£745
2006 — Platinum Proof Piedfort	250	£3450
2007 Queen's Diamond Wedding BU	—	—
2007 — Proof	—	—
2007 — Silver Proof	—	—
2007 — — — Piedfort	—	—
2007 — Gold Proof	—	—

DOUBLE SOVEREIGN

As with the Sovereign series Five Pound coins, those listed under this heading bear the Pistrucci St George and Dragon reverse, except where otherwise stated, and are minted in gold. They are, and always have been, legal tender at £2, and have a diameter indentical to that of the base metal Two Pound coins listed further below under a different heading. The denomination does not appear on Double Sovereigns.

DATE	Mintage	UNC
1980 Proof	10,000	£250
1982 Proof	2,500	£250
1983 Proof	12,500	£200
1985 New Portrait Proof	5,849	£250
1987 Proof	14,301	£225
1988 Proof	12,743	£200
1989 500th Anniversary of the Sovereign. Enthroned portrayal obverse and Crowned shield reverse Proof	14,936	£285
1990 Proof	4,374	£250
1991 Proof	3,108	£275
1992 Proof	2,608	£275
1993 Proof	2,155	£275
1996 Proof	3,167	£275
1998 New Portrait Proof	4,500	£285
2000 Proof	2,250	£275
2002 Shield reverse Proof	8,000	£300
2003 Proof	2,250	£300
2004 Proof	—	—
2005 Noad heraldic St George and Dragon Proof	—	—
2006 Proof	—	—
2007 Proof	—	—

TWO POUNDS AND BELOW
(Britannia Silver Series)

This series commenced in 1997, and, as with the Gold Britannia series, sets of the coins are listed in the "Proof and Specimen Sets" section. Coins contain one Troy ounce of fine silver (£2) alloyed to Britannia standard, i.e. 95.8 per cent fine silver, or fractions of one ounce as follows: half ounce (£1), quarter ounce (50 pence) and one tenth of an ounce (20 pence). Six different reverses have been used, all four coins of any particular date being of the same design. The reverses by Philip Nathan appear as follows:
1997 Chariot, 1998 Standing Britannia, 1999 Chariot, 2000 Standing Britannia, 2001 Una and the Lion, 2002 Standing Brittania, 2003 Britannia's Helmeted Head, 2004 Standing Britannia, 2005 Britannia Seated, 2006 Standing Britannia (also see under "Proof and Specimen Sets" section). The 2007 design is by Christopher Le Brun, and features a Seated Britannia with Lion at her feet.
Two pounds Britannia coins to BU or "bullion" standard have been issued as individual coins for each year from 1998 onwards.

TWO POUNDS

This series commenced in 1986 with nickel-brass commemorative coins, with their associated base metal and precious metal BU and proof coins. From 1997 (actually issued in 1998) a thinner bi-metal version commenced with a reverse theme of the advance of technology, and from this date the coin was specifically intended to circulate. This is true also for the parallel issues of anniversary and commemorative Two Pound issues in 1999 and onwards. All have their BU and proof versions, as listed below.

DATE	Mintage	UNC
1986 Commonwealth Games	8,212,184	£6
1986 — BU		£7
1986 — Proof		£10
1986 — Silver BU		£15
1986 — — Proof		£18
1986 — Gold Proof		£250
1989 Tercentenary of Bill of Rights.	4,392,825	£7
1989 — BU (issued in folder with Claim of Right)		£20
1989 — Proof (issued as pair with Claim of Right)		£28
1989 — Silver Proof (Pair as above)		£40
1989 — — — Piedfort (Pair as above)		£60
1989 Tercentenary of Claim of Right (issued in Scotland)	381,400	£12
1989 — BU (see above)		£20
1989 — Proof (see above)		£28
1989 — Silver Proof (see above)		£40
1989 — — — Piedfort (see above)		£60

1994 Tercentenary of the Bank of England	1,443,116	£5
1994 — BU		£7
1994 — Proof		£10
1994 — Silver Proof		£28
1994 — — — Piedfort		£65
1994 — Gold Proof		£400
1994 — — — with Double Sovereign obverse (no denomination)		£575
1995 50th Anniversary of End of WWII.	4,394,566	£5
1995 — BU		£6
1995 — Proof		£10
1995 — Silver Proof		£35
1995 — — — Piedfort		£55
1995 — Gold Proof		£450

1995 50th Anniversary of The United Nations	1,668,575	£5
1995 — BU		£6
1995 — Proof		£10
1995 — Silver Proof		£35
1995 — — Piedfort		£60
1995 — Gold Proof		£450
1996 European Football Championships.	5,195,350	£6
1996 — BU		£7
1996 — Proof		£8
1996 — Silver Proof		£32
1996 — — — Piedfort		£55
1996 — Gold Proof		£450

1997	13,734,625	£4
1997 BU		£8
1997 Proof		£12
1997 Silver Proof		£25
1997 — — Piedfort		£45
1997 Gold Proof (red (outer) and yellow (inner) 22ct)		£400
1998 *New Portrait*		£3
1998 BU	91,110,375	£7
1998 Proof		£10
1998 Silver Proof		£34

DATE	Mintage	UNC
1999	33,719,000	£3
1999 Rugby World Cup	4,933,000	£3
1999 — BU		£4
1999 — Silver Proof (gold plated ring)		£32
1999 — — Piedfort (Hologram)		£85
1999 — Gold Proof		£355
2000	25,770,000	£3
2000 BU		£4
2000 Proof		£10
2000 Silver Proof		£32
2000 Gold Proof		£355
2001	37,843,500*	—
2001 BU		£3
2001 Proof		£10
2001 Marconi	*Incl. in above**	£3
2001 — BU		£4
2001 — Proof		£10
2001 — Silver Proof (gold plated ring)		£30
2001 — — Piedfort		£85
2001 — Gold Proof		£355
2002	15,521,000*	—
2002 BU		£3
2002 Proof		£10
2002 Commonwealth Games (4 versions)	*Incl in above**	£3
2002 — BU (issued in set of 4)		£4
2002 — Proof (issued in set of 4)		£10
2002 — Silver Proof (issued in set of 4)		£32
2002 — — Piedfort (painted) (issued in set of 4)		£85
2002 — Gold (issued in set of 4)		£350
2003	21,830,250*	—
2003 BU		£4
2003 Proof		£12
2003 DNA Double Helix	*Incl in above**	—
2003 — BU		£4
2003 — Proof		£10
2003 — Silver Proof (Gold-plated ring)		£30
2003 — — Piedfort		£80
2003 — Gold Proof		£300
2004	13,904,500*	—
2004 BU		£4
2004 Proof		£12
2004 Trevithick Steam Locomotive	*Incl in above**	—
2004 — BU		£4
2004 — Proof		£12
2004 — Silver BU		£25
2004 — — Proof (Gold-plated ring)		£30
2004 — — Piedfort		£100
2004 — Gold Proof		£350
2005		—
2005 BU		—
2005 Proof		—
2005 Gunpowder Plot		—
2005 — BU		—
2005 — Proof		—
2005 — Silver Proof		—
2005 — — Piedfort		—
2005 — Gold Proof		—
2005 End of World War II		—
2005 — BU		—
2005 — Silver Proof		—
2005 — — Piedfort		—
2005 — Gold Proof		—

DATE	Mintage	UNC

2006 .... —
2006 Proof... —
2006 Brunel, The Man (Portrait) .... —
2006 — BU.. —
2006 — Proof .... —
2006 — Silver Proof .... —
2006 — — — Piedfort .... —
2006 —Gold Proof.. —
2006 Brunel, His Achievements (Paddington Station) .... —
2006 — BU.. —
2006 — Proof .... —

2006 — Silver Proof .... —
2006 — — — Piedfort .... —
2006 —Gold Proof.. —
2007 .... —
2007 Proof... —
2007 Tercentenary of the Act of Union............................... —
2007 BU .... —
2007 — Proof .... —
2007 — Silver Proof .... —
2007 — — — Piedfort .... —

2007 — Gold Proof.. —
2007 Bicentenary of the Abolition of the Slave Trade .... —
2007 — BU.. —
2007 — Proof .... —
2007 — Silver Proof .... —
2007 — — — Piedfort .... —
2007 — Gold Proof.. —

SOVEREIGN

All are minted in gold, bear the Pistrucci St George and Dragon reverse except where stated, and are legal tender at one pound.

	Mintage	UNC
1974..	5,002,566	£55
1976..	4,150,000	£55
1978..	6,550,000	£55
1979..	9,100,000	£55
1979 Proof..	50,000	£75
1980..	5,100,000	£55
1980 Proof..	91,200	£75
1981..	5,000,000	£55
1981 Proof..	32,960	£75
1982..	2,950,000	£55
1982 Proof..	22,500	£80
1983 Proof	21,250	£80
1984 Proof	19,975	£90
1985 New portrait Proof	17,242	£100
1986 Proof	17,579	£90
1987 Proof	22,479	£90
1988 Proof	18,862	£120
1989 500th Anniversary of the Sovereign—details as Five Pounds (Sov. Series). Proof	23,471	£350
1990 Proof	8,425	£150
1991 Proof	7,201	£150
1992 Proof	6,854	£165
1993 Proof	6,090	£165
1994 Proof	7,165	£165
1995 Proof	9,500	£165

DATE	Mintage	UNC
1996 Proof	9,110	£165
1997 Proof	9,177	£175
1998 New Portrait Proof	11,349	£175
1999 Proof	11,903	£200
2000 (first Unc issue since 1982)	129,069	£65
2000 Proof	12,159	£140
2001	49,462	£65
2001 Proof	10,000	£140
2002 Shield Rev. ("bullion")	74,263	£65
2002 Proof	20,500	£140
2003 ("bullion")	43,208	£65
2003 Proof	—	£140
2004 ("bullion")	28,821	£65
2004 Proof	—	£150
2005 Noad heraldic St George and Dragon	—	£85
2005 — Proof	—	£140
2006 ("bullion")	—	£110
2006 Proof	—	£179
2007 ("bullion")	—	—
2007 Proof	—	—

HALF SOVEREIGN

Legal Tender at 50 pence, otherwise the notes for the Sovereign apply.

1980 Proof only	86,700	£45
1982	2,500,000	£45
1982 Proof	21,590	£50
1983 Proof	19,710	£50
1984 Proof	19,505	£50
1985 New portrait Proof	15,800	£45
1986 Proof	17,075	£45
1987 Proof	20,687	£45
1988 Proof	18,266	£55
1989 500th Anniversary of the Sovereign—details as Five Pounds (Sov. Series) Proof	21,824	£100
1990 Proof	7,889	£55
1991 Proof	6,076	£55
1992 Proof	5,915	£65
1993 Proof	4,651	£65
1994 Proof	7,167	£70
1995 Proof	7,500	£70
1996 New Portrait Proof	7,340	£70
1997 Proof	9,177	£70
1998 Proof	7,496	£70
1999 Proof	9,403	£70
2000	146,822	£40
2000 Proof	9,708	£70
2001	98,763	£40
2001 Proof	7,500	£70
2002 Shield reverse ("bullion")	61,347	£70
2002 Proof	—	£40
2003 ("bullion")	47,805	£40
2003 Proof	—	£70
2004 ("bullion")	32,479	£40
2004 Proof	—	£70
2005 Noad heralldic St George and Dragon	—	£45
2005 — Proof	—	£80
2006 ("bullion")	—	£57
2006 Proof	—	£97
2006 ("bullion")	—	—
2007 Proof	—	—

ONE POUND

Introduced into circulation in 1983 to replace the £1 note, all are minted in nickel-brass unless otherwise stated. The reverse changes yearly, the Royal coat of arms being the "definitive" version. Unc or BU may come either in a presentation folder or from a set. Collectors and others should be aware of the many different counterfeit £1 coin versions in circulation, a high proportion of which do not have matching obverses, although many do.

DATE	Mintage	UNC
1983 Royal coat of arms	443,053,510	£5
1983 — Unc	1,134,000	£7
1983 — Proof	107,800	£10
1983 — Silver Proof	50,000	£30
1983 — — Piedfort	10,000	£120
1984 Scottish Thistle	146,256,501	£4
1984 — BU	199,430	£6
1984 — Proof	106,520	£7
1984 — Silver Proof	44,855	£32
1984 — — Piedfort	15,000	£60
1985 New portrait. Welsh Leek	228,430,749	£3
1985 — BU	213,679	£6
1985 — Proof	102,015	£7
1985 — Silver Proof	50,000	£30
1985 — — Piedfort	15,000	£50
1986 Northern Ireland Flax	10,409,501	£3
1986 — BU		£6
1986 — Proof		£8
1986 — Silver Proof		£35
1986 — — Piedfort		£55
1987 English Oak	39,298,502	£3
1987 — BU		£6
1987 — Proof		£10
1987 — Silver Proof		£30
1987 — — Piedfort		£50
1988 Crowned Royal Arms	7,118,825	£2
1988 — BU		£6
1988 — Proof		£10
1988 — Silver Proof		£32
1988 — — Piedfort		£55
1989 Scottish Thistle	70,580,501	£2
1989 — BU		£6
1989 — Proof		£8
1989 — Silver Proof		£28
1989 — — Piedfort		£50
1990 Welsh Leek		£2
1990 — BU	97,269,302	£5
1990 — Proof		£8
1990 — Silver Proof		£28
1991 Northern Ireland Flax	38,443,575	£2
1991 — BU		£6
1991 — Proof		£8
1991 — Silver Proof		£32
1992 English Oak	36,320,487	£2
1992 — BU		£5
1992 — Proof		£8
1992 — Silver Proof		£32
1993 Royal Coat of Arms	114,744,500	£2
1993 — BU		£5
1993 — Proof		£10
1993 — Silver Proof		£34
1993 — — Piedfort		£65

1983, 1993, 1998, 2003

1984, 1989

1985, 1990

1986, 1991

1987, 1992

DATE	Mintage	UNC
1994 Scottish Lion	29,752,525	£2
1994 — BU		£6
1994 — Proof		£8
1994 — Silver Proof		£32
1994 — — — Piedfort		£65
1995 Welsh Dragon	34,503,501	£2
1995 — BU		£6
1995 — — (Welsh)		£8
1995 — Proof		£10
1995 — Silver Proof		£34
1995 — — — Piedfort		£65
1996 Northern Ireland Celtic-style Cross	89,886,000	£3
1996 — BU		£6
1996 — Proof		£8
1996 — Silver Proof		£33
1996 — — — Piedfort		£65
1997 English Lions	57,117,450	£3
1997 — BU		£6
1997 — Proof		£8
1997 — Silver Proof		£35
1997 — — — Piedfort		£70
1998 New portrait. Royal Coat of Arms. BU		£7
1998 — Proof		£8
1998 — Silver Proof		£30
1998 — — — Piedfort		£45
1999 Scottish Lion. BU		£6
1999 — Proof		£8
1999 — Silver Proof		£35
1999 — — — Reverse Frosting		£45
1999 — — — Piedfort		£75
2000 Welsh Dragon	109,496,500	£2
2000 — BU		£6
2000 — Proof		£8
2000 — Silver Proof		£35
2000 — — — Reverse Frosting		£40
2000 — — — Piedfort		£45
2001 Northern Ireland Celtic-style Cross.		£2
2001 — BU	58,093,731	£6
2001 — Proof		£8
2001 — Silver Proof		£35
2001 — — — Piedfort		£45
2002 English Lions	77,818,000	£2
2002 — BU		£6
2002 — Proof		£8
2002 — Silver Proof		£32
2002 — — — Piedfort		£50
2002 — Gold Proof		£160
2003 Royal Coat of Arms	61,596,500	£2
2003 — BU		£6
2003 — Proof		£10
2003 — Silver Proof		£40
2003 — — — Piedfort		£50
2004 Forth Railway Bridge	37,286,000	£3
2004 — BU		£6
2004 — Proof		£10
2004 — Silver Proof		£40
2004 — — — Piedfort		£55
2004 — Gold Proof		£175
2005 Menai Bridge		—
2005 — BU		—
2005 — Proof		—
2005 — Silver Proof		—
2005 — — — Piedfort		—
2005 — Gold Proof		—

1988

1994, 1999

1995, 2000

1996, 2001

1997, 2002

2004

DATE	Mintage	UNC
2006 Egyptian Arch		—
2006 — BU..		—
2006 — Proof		—
2006 — Silver Proof		—
2006 — — — Piedfort		—
2006 — Gold Proof..		—
2007 Gateshead Millennium Bridge		—
2007 — BU..		—
2007 — Proof		—
2007 — Silver Proof		—
2007 — — — Piedfort		—
2007 — Gold Proof..		—

FIFTY PENCE

Introduced as legal tender for 10 shillings to replace the banknote of that value prior to decimalisation, coins of the original size are no longer legal tender. Unless otherwise stated, i.e. for commemoratives, the reverse design is of Britannia. The reverse legend of NEW PENCE became FIFTY PENCE from 1982.

DATE	Mintage	UNC
1969..	188,400,000	£3
1970..	19,461,500	£4
1971 Proof..		£8
1972 Proof..		£8
1973 Accession to EEC	89,775,000	£3
1973 — Proof		£5
1973 — Silver Proof Piedfort		£1000
1974 Proof..		£5
1975 Proof..		£5
1976..	43,746,500	£3
1976 Proof		£5
1977..	49,536,000	£3
1977 Proof..		£5
1978..	72,005,000	£3
1978 Proof..		£5
1979..	58,680,000	£3
1979 Proof		£5
1980..	89,086,000	£3
1980 Proof		£5
1981..	74,002,000	£2
1981 Proof		£5
1982	51,312,000	£1
1982 Unc		£2
1982 Proof		£5
1983..	62,824,000	£1
1983 Unc		£3
1983 Proof		£5
1984 BU		£3
1984 Proof		£5
1985 New portrait .... estimated approx 3,400,000		£1
1985 BU		£3
1985 Proof		£5
1986 BU		£4
1986 Proof		£5
1987 BU		£4
1987 Proof		£5
1988 BU		£4
1988 Proof		£5

DATE	Mintage	UNC
1989 BU		£4
1989 Proof		£5
1990 BU		£4
1990 Proof		£5
1991 BU		£5
1991 Proof		£6
1992 BU		£9
1992 — Proof		£15
1992 Presidency of EC Council and EC accession 20th anniversary (includes 1993 date)	109,000	£10
1992 — BU		—
1992 — Proof		—
1992 — Silver Proof		£30
1992 — — — Piedfort		£50
1992 — Gold Proof		£425
1993 BU		£5
1993 Proof		—
1994 50th Anniversary of the Normandy Landings	6,705,520	£8
1994 — BU (also in presentation folder)		£10
1994 — Proof		£12
1994 — Silver Proof		£35
1994 — — — Piedfort		£75
1994 — Gold Proof		£455
1995 BU		£5
1995 Proof		£8
1996 BU		£5
1996 Proof		£7
1996 Silver Proof		£22
1997 BU		£8
1997 Proof		£10
1997 Silver Proof		£30
1997 new reduced size	456,364,100	£4
1997 BU		—
1997 Proof		£6
1997 Silver Proof		£28
1997 — — Piedfort		£40
1998 New portrait	64,306,500	£2
1998 BU		—
1998 Proof		£5
1998 Presidency and 25th anniversary of EU entry	5,043,000	£2
1998 — BU		£4
1998 — Proof		£7
1998 — Silver Proof		£25
1998 — — — Piedfort		£75
1998 — Gold Proof		£300
1998 50th Anniversary of the National Health Service	5,001,000	£2
1998 — BU		£4
1998 — Silver Proof (believed not issued as Cu-Ni proof)		£25
1998 — — — Piedfort		£85
1998 — Gold Proof		£300
1999	24,905,000	£2
1999 BU		£4
1999 Proof		£5
2000	39,172,000*	£1
2000 BU		£2
2000 Proof		£5
2000 150th Anniversary of Public Libraries	*Incl in above**	£1
2000 — BU		£3
2000 — Proof		£8
2000 — Silver Proof		£30
2000 — — — Piedfort		£45
2000 — Gold proof		£250
2001	84,999,500	£1
2001 BU		£2

DATE	Mintage	UNC
2001 Proof...		£5
2002..	23,907,500	—
2002 BU		£1
2002 Proof..		£5
2002 Gold Proof..		£150
2003..	26,557,030*	—
2003 BU		£4
2003 Proof..		£6
2003 Suffragette..*Incl. in above**		—
2003 — BU...		£4
2003 — Proof		£8
2003 — Silver Proof		£30
2003 — — — Piedfort...		£50
2003 — Gold Proof...		£200
2004..	13,904,500*	—
2004 BU		£6
2004 Proof..		£8
2004 Roger Bannister..*Incl in above**		—
2004 — BU...		£4
2004 — Proof		£8
2004 — Silver Proof		£25
2004 — — — Piedfort...		£50
2004 — Gold Proof...		£200
2005..		—
2005 BU...		—
2005 Proof..		—
2005 Samuel Johnson...		—
2005 — BU...		—
2005 — Proof		—
2005 — Silver Proof		—
2005 — — — Piedfort...		—
2005 — Gold Proof...		—
2006		—
2006 Proof..		—
2006 Silver Proof...		—
2006 Victoria Cross, The Award		—
2006 — BU...		—
2006 — Proof		—
2006 — Silver Proof		—
2006 — — — — Piedfort		—
2006 — Gold Proof...		—
2006 Victoria Cross, Heroic Acts		—
2006 — BU...		—
2006 — Proof		—
2006 — Silver Proof		—
2006 — — — — Piedfort		—
2006 — Gold Proof...		—
2007		—
2007 BU		—
2007 Proof..		—
2007 Centenary of Scout Movement		—
2007 — BU...		—
2007 — Proof		—
2007 — Silver Proof		—
2007 — — — Piedfort		—
2007 — Gold Proof...		—

TWENTY-FIVE PENCE (CROWN)

This series is a continuation of the pre-decimal series, there having been four crowns to the pound. The coins below have a legal tender face value of 25p to this day, and are minted in cupro-nickel except where stated otherwise.

1972 Royal Silver Wedding	7,452,100	£2
1972 — Proof	150,000	£6
1972 — Silver Proof	100,000	£20
1977 Silver Jubilee	37,061,160	£2

DATE	Mintage	UNC
1977 — in Presentation folder	Incl. above	£3
1977 — Proof	193,000	£5
1977 — Silver Proof	377,000	£15
1980 Queen Mother 80th Birthday	9,306,000	£1.50
1980 — in Presentation folder	Incl. above	£3
1980 — Silver Proof	83,670	£28
1981 Royal Wedding	26,773,600	£2
1981 — in Presentation folder	Incl. above	£3
1981 — Silver Proof	218,140	£25

TWENTY PENCE

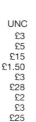

The series commenced in 1982, some 11 years after the introduction of decimal coinage. Its presence from introduction date meant that there was no requirement for ten pence circulation—standard coins until the latter's size was reduced in 1992. Unlike the circulation coins on either side of it in face value, it's alloy is 84% copper and 16% nickel.

DATE	UNC	DATE	UNC
1982	£1	1995 Proof	£4
1982 Unc	£2	1996	£1
1982 Proof	£5	1996 BU	£2
1982 Silver Proof Piedfort	£40	1996 Proof	£4
1983	£1	1996 Silver Proof	£15
1983 Unc	£2	1997	£1
1983 Proof	£5	1997 BU	£2
1984	£1	1997 Proof	£4
1984 BU	£2	1998 New portrait	£1
1984 Proof	£5	1998 BU	£2
1985 New portrait	£1	1998 Proof	£4
1985 BU	£2	1999	£1
1985 Proof	£6	1999 BU	£2
1986 BU	£4	1999 Proof	£4
1986 Proof	£5	2000	£1
1987	£1	2000 BU	£2
1987 BU	£2	2000 Proof	£4
1987 Proof	£4	2000 Silver Proof	£25
1988	£1	2001	£1
1988 BU	£2	2001 BU	£2
1988 Proof	£4	2001 Proof	£4
1989	£1	2002	£1
1989 BU	£2	2002 BU	£2
1989 Proof	£4	2002 Proof	£4
1990	£1	2002 Gold Proof	£125
1990 BU	£1	2003	£1
1990 Proof	£4	2003 BU	£1
1991	£1	2003 Proof	£5
1991 BU	£2	2004	—
1991 Proof	£5	2004 BU	£2
1992	£4	2004 Proof	£5
1992 Enhanced effigy	£2	2005	—
1992 — BU	£2	2005 BU	£2
1992 — Proof	£4	2005 Proof	£5
1993	£1	2006	—
1993 BU	£2	2006 BU	—
1993 Proof	£4	2006 Proof	—
1994	£1	2006 Silver Proof	—
1994 BU	£2	2007	—
1994 Proof	£4	2007 BU	—
1995	£1	2007 Proof	—
1995 BU	£2		

TEN PENCE

The series commenced before decimalisation with the legend NEW PENCE, this changed to TEN PENCE from 1982. These "florin-sized" coins up to 1992 are no longer legal tender.

DATE	UNC	DATE	UNC
1968	£1	1992 Proof	£4
1969	£2	1992 Silver Proof	£17
1970	£2	1992 − − Piedfort	£40
1971	£2	1993 BU	£2
1971 Proof	£2	1993 Proof	£3
1972 Proof	£3	1994 BU	£2
1973	£2	1994 Proof	£3
1973 Proof	£4	1995	£1
1974	£2	1995 BU	£2
1974 Proof	£4	1995 Proof	£3
1975	£2	1996	£1
1975 Proof	£4	1996 BU	£2
1976	£2	1996 Proof	£3
1976 Proof	£4	1996 Silver Proof	£22
1977	£2	1997	£1
1977 Proof	£4	1997 BU	£2
1978 Proof	£5	1997 Proof	£3
1979	£2	1998 New portrait BU	£4
1979 Proof	£4	1998 Proof	£3
1980	£2	1999 BU	£3
1980 Proof	£3	1999 Proof	£3
1981	£2	2000	£1
1981 Proof	£3	2000 BU	£2
1982 Unc	£4	2000 Proof	£3
1982 Proof	£5	2000 Silver Proof	£24
1983 Unc	£3	2001	£1
1983 Proof	£2	2001 BU	£2
1984 BU	£2	2001 Proof	£3
1984 Proof	£3	2002	£1
1985 New portrait BU	£4	2002 BU	£2
1985 Proof	£3	2002 Proof	£3
1986 BU	£4	2002 Gold Proof	£150
1986 Proof	£3	2003	−
1987 BU	£4	2003 BU	£1
1987 Proof	£5	2003 Proof	£3
1988 BU	£4	2004	−
1988 Proof	£5	2004 BU	£1
1989 BU	£6	2004 Proof	£4
1989 Proof	£5	2005	−
1990 BU	£6	2005 BU	−
1990 Proof	£5	2005 Proof	−
1991 BU	£6	2006	−
1991 Proof	£5	2006 BU	−
1992 BU	£5	2006 Proof	−
1992 Proof	£6	2006 Silver Proof	−
1992 Silver Proof	£17	2007	−
1992 *Size reduced* (24.5mm diam)	£1	2007 BU	−
1992 BU	£2	2007 Proof	−

FIVE PENCE

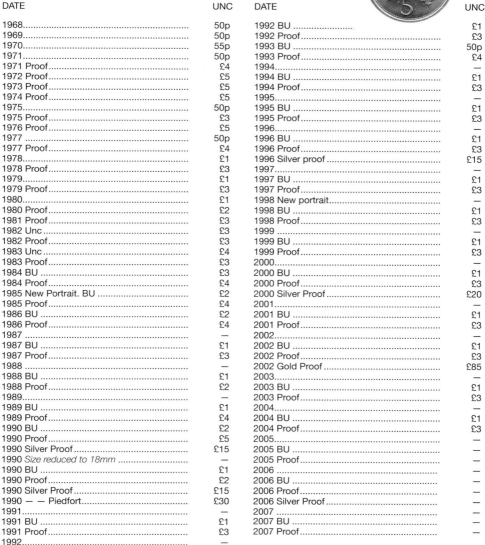

This series commenced simultaneously with the Ten Pence (qv). They were the same size and weight as their predecessor, the shilling, and such coins up to 1990 are no longer legal tender.

DATE	UNC	DATE	UNC
1968	50p	1992 BU	£1
1969	50p	1992 Proof	£3
1970	55p	1993 BU	50p
1971	50p	1993 Proof	£4
1971 Proof	£4	1994	—
1972 Proof	£5	1994 BU	£1
1973 Proof	£5	1994 Proof	£3
1974 Proof	£5	1995	—
1975	50p	1995 BU	£1
1975 Proof	£3	1995 Proof	£3
1976 Proof	£5	1996	—
1977	50p	1996 BU	£1
1977 Proof	£4	1996 Proof	£3
1978	£1	1996 Silver proof	£15
1978 Proof	£3	1997	—
1979	£1	1997 BU	£1
1979 Proof	£3	1997 Proof	£3
1980	£1	1998 New portrait	—
1980 Proof	£2	1998 BU	£1
1981 Proof	£3	1998 Proof	£3
1982 Unc	£3	1999	—
1982 Proof	£3	1999 BU	£1
1983 Unc	£4	1999 Proof	£3
1983 Proof	£3	2000	—
1984 BU	£3	2000 BU	£1
1984 Proof	£4	2000 Proof	£3
1985 New Portrait. BU	£2	2000 Silver Proof	£20
1985 Proof	£4	2001	—
1986 BU	£2	2001 BU	£1
1986 Proof	£4	2001 Proof	£3
1987	—	2002	—
1987 BU	£1	2002 BU	£1
1987 Proof	£3	2002 Proof	£3
1988	—	2002 Gold Proof	£85
1988 BU	£1	2003	—
1988 Proof	£2	2003 BU	£1
1989	—	2003 Proof	£3
1989 BU	£1	2004	—
1989 Proof	£4	2004 BU	£1
1990 BU	£2	2004 Proof	£3
1990 Proof	£5	2005	—
1990 Silver Proof	£15	2005 BU	—
1990 *Size reduced to 18mm*	—	2005 Proof	—
1990 BU	£1	2006	—
1990 Proof	£2	2006 BU	—
1990 Silver Proof	£15	2006 Proof	—
1990 — — Piedfort	£30	2006 Silver Proof	—
1991	—	2007	—
1991 BU	£1	2007 BU	—
1991 Proof	£3	2007 Proof	—
1992	—		

TWO PENCE

Dated from 1971, and legal tender from Decimal Day that year, early examples are found in the blue Specimen decimal set wallets of 1968. They were minted in bronze up to 1991, and mainly in copper-plated steel from 1992. However details of where this rule does not totally apply (1992, 1996, 1998–2000 and 2002) are given below. As with other denominations, "NEW" was replaced by the quantity of pence in word from 1982.

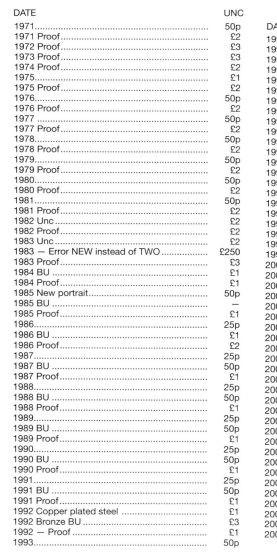

DATE	UNC
1971	50p
1971 Proof	£2
1972 Proof	£3
1973 Proof	£3
1974 Proof	£2
1975	£1
1975 Proof	£2
1976	50p
1976 Proof	£2
1977	50p
1977 Proof	£2
1978	50p
1978 Proof	£2
1979	50p
1979 Proof	£2
1980	50p
1980 Proof	£2
1981	50p
1981 Proof	£2
1982 Unc	£2
1982 Proof	£2
1983 Unc	£2
1983 — Error NEW instead of TWO	£250
1983 Proof	£3
1984 BU	£1
1984 Proof	£1
1985 New portrait	50p
1985 BU	—
1985 Proof	£1
1986	25p
1986 BU	£1
1986 Proof	£2
1987	25p
1987 BU	50p
1987 Proof	£1
1988	25p
1988 BU	50p
1988 Proof	£1
1989	25p
1989 BU	50p
1989 Proof	£1
1990	25p
1990 BU	50p
1990 Proof	£1
1991	25p
1991 BU	50p
1991 Proof	£1
1992 Copper plated steel	£1
1992 Bronze BU	£3
1992 — Proof	£1
1993	50p

DATE	UNC
1993 BU	£1
1993 Proof	£2
1994	25p
1994 BU	50p
1994 Proof	£2
1995	—
1995 BU	50p
1995 Proof	£2
1996	—
1996 BU	50p
1996 Proof	£2
1996 Silver Proof	£18
1997	—
1997 BU	50p
1997 Proof	£2
1998 New portrait	—
1998 BU	50p
1998 Proof	£4
1998 Bronze	£1
1999	£1
1999 Bronze BU	£4
1999 — Proof	£5
2000	—
2000 BU	50p
2000 Proof	£4
2000 Silver Proof	£15
2001	—
2001 BU	50p
2001 Proof	£4
2002	—
2002 BU	50p
2002 Proof	£4
2002 Gold Proof	£85
2003	—
2003 BU	50p
2003 Proof	£2
2004	—
2004 BU	50p
2004 Proof	£2
2005	—
2005 BU	—
2005 Proof	—
2006	—
2006 BU	—
2006 Proof	—
2006 Silver Proof	—
2007	—
2007 BU	—
2007 Proof	—

ONE PENNY

The history of this coin is very similar to that of the Two Pence coin (qv) except that all 1998 examples were of copper-plated steel.

DATE	UNC
1971	25p
1971 Proof	£1
1972 Proof	£2
1973	£1
1973 Proof	£2
1974	£1
1974 Proof	£2
1975	£1
1975 Proof	£2
1976	£1
1976 Proof	£2
1977	50p
1977 Proof	£1
1978	£1
1978 Proof	£2
1979	£1
1979 Proof	£2
1980	£1
1980 Proof	£2
1981	£1
1981 Proof	£2
1982 Legend changed to ONE PENNY	50p
1982 Unc	£1
1982 Proof	£2
1983	50p
1983 Unc	£1
1983 Proof	£1
1984	50p
1984 BU	£1
1984 Proof	£1
1985 New portrait	25p
1985 BU	50p
1985 Proof	£1
1986	25p
1986 BU	50p
1986 Proof	£1
1987	25p
1987 BU	50p
1987 Proof	£1
1988	25p
1988 BU	50p
1988 Proof	£3
1989	25p
1989 BU	50p
1989 Proof	£2
1990	25p
1990 BU	50p
1990 Proof	£2
1991	25p
1991 BU	50p
1991 Proof	£2
1992 Copper-plated steel	£1
1992 Bronze BU	£2
1992 — Proof	£2

DATE	UNC
1993	25p
1993 BU	50p
1993 Proof	£1
1994	25p
1994 BU	50p
1994 Proof	£1
1995	25p
1995 BU	50p
1995 Proof	£1
1996	—
1996 BU	50p
1996 Proof	£1
1996 Silver Proof	£16
1997	—
1997 BU	50p
1997 Proof	£1
1998 New portrait	25p
1998 — BU	50p
1998 Proof	£2
1999	£2
1999 Bronze BU	£3
1999 Bronze Proof	£1
2000	—
2000 BU	50p
2000 Proof	£2
2000 Silver Proof	£20
2001	—
2001 BU	£1
2001 Proof	£2
2002	—
2002 BU	£1
2002 Proof	£3
2002 Gold Proof	£65
2003	—
2003 BU	£1
2003 Proof	£3
2004	—
2004 BU	£1
2004 Proof	£3
2005	—
2005 BU	—
2005 Proof	—
2006	—
2006 BU	—
2006 Proof	—
2006 Silver Proof	—
2007	—
2007 BU	—
2007 Proof	—

HALF PENNY

No longer legal tender, its history tracks that of the Two Pence and One Penny.

DATE	UNC
1971	50p
1971 Proof	£1
1972 Proof	£5
1973	£1
1973 Proof	£3
1974	£1
1974 Proof	£2
1975	£1
1975 Proof	£2
1976	£1
1976 Proof	£2
1977	£1
1977 Proof	£2
1978	£1
1978 Proof	£2
1979	£1
1979 Proof	£2

DATE	UNC
1980	£1
1980 Proof	£2
1981	£1
1981 Proof	£2
1982 Legend changed to HALF PENNY	50p
1982 Unc	£1
1982 Proof	£3
1983	50p
1983 Unc	£1
1983 Proof	£4
1984	£4
1984 BU	£5
1984 Proof	£5

MAUNDY SETS

DATE AND PLACE OF ISSUE	MINTAGE	UNC
1971 Tewkesbury Abbey	1,018	£110
1972 York Minster	1,026	£115
1973 Westminster Abbey	1,004	£110
1974 Salisbury Cathedral	1,042	£110
1975 Peterborough Cathedral	1,050	£110
1976 Hereford Cathedral	1,158	£110
1977 Westminster Abbey	1,138	£120
1978 Carlisle Cathedral	1,178	£115
1979 Winchester Cathedral	1,188	£110
1980 Worcester Cathedral	1,198	£110
1981 Westminster Abbey	1,178	£110
1982 St David's Cathedral	1,218	£110
1983 Exeter Cathedral	1,228	£110
1984 Southwell Minster	1,238	£110
1985 Ripon Cathedral	1,248	£110
1986 Chichester Cathedral	1,378	£110
1987 Ely Cathedral	1,390	£115
1988 Lichfield Cathedral	1,402	£115
1989 Birmingham Cathedral	1,353	£115
1990 Newcastle Cathedral	1,523	£120
1991 Westminster Abbey	1,384	£120
1992 Chester Cathedral	1,424	£120
1993 Wells Cathedral	1,440	£120
1994 Truro Cathedral	1,433	£120
1995 Coventry Cathedral	1,466	£120
1996 Norwich Cathedral	1,629	£125
1997 Birmingham Cathedral	1,786	£125
1998 Portsmouth Cathedral	1,654	£125
1999 Bristol Cathedral	1,676	£125
2000 Lincoln Cathedral	1,686	£135
2000 Silver Proof	13,180	£140
2001 Westminster Abbey	1,132	£145

DATE AND PLACE OF ISSUE	MINTAGE	UNC
2002 Canterbury Cathedral	1,681	£150
2002 Gold Proof	2,002	£1350
2003 Gloucester Cathedral	1,608	£150
2004 Liverpool Cathedral	1,613	£150
2005 Wakefield Cathedral	1,685	£160
2006 Guildford Cathedral	—	£160
2006 Silver Proof	—	£170
2007 Manchester Cathedral	—	£170

In keeping with ancient tradition the Royal Maundy sets are made up of four silver coins of 4p, 3p, 2p and 1p. The designs for the reverse of the coins are a crowned numeral in a wreath of oak leaves—basically the same design that has been used for Maundy coins since Charles II.

PROOF AND SPECIMEN SETS

The following listings are an attempt to include all officially marketed products from the Royal Mint of two coins or more, but excluding those which included non-UK coins. It is appreciated that not all have been advertised as new to the public, but it is assumed that at some time they have been, or will be, available. In a few cases, therefore, the prices may be conjectural but are, nevertheless, attempts at listing realistic value, in some instances based on an original retail price. In the case of Elizabeth II sets, if no metal is stated in the listing, the coins in the sets are of the same metal as the circulation coin equivalent. In addition to the above we have excluded historical gold coin sets, such as sets of sovereigns from different mints, where the dates of the coins vary from one set to another.

DATE   FDC

GEORGE IV
1826 £5–farthing (11 coins) £18,000

WILLIAM IV
1831 Coronation £2–farthing (14 coins) £16,500

VICTORIA
1839 "Una and the Lion" £5–farthing (15 coins) £35,000
1853 Sovereign–quarter farthing, including "Gothic"crown (16 coins) £27,500
1887 Golden Jubilee £5–3d (11 coins) £7500
1887 Golden Jubilee Crown–3d (7 coins) £1250
1893 £5–3d (10 coins) £8500
1893 Crown–3d (6 coins) £1500

EDWARD VII
1902 Coronation £5–Maundy penny, matt proofs (13 coins) £2000
1902 Coronation Sovereign–Maundy penny, matt proofs (11 coins) £1000

GEORGE V
1911 Coronation £5–Maundy penny (12 coins) £2750
1911 Sovereign–Maundy penny (10 coins) £850
1911 Coronation Halfcrown–Maundy penny (8 coins) £450
1927 New types Crown–3d (6 coins) £350

DATE   FDC

GEORGE VI

1937 Coronation £5–half sovereign (4 coins) £1550
1937 Coronation Crown–farthing including Maundy money (15 coins) £175
1950 Mid-century Halfcrown–farthing (9 coins) £65
1951 Festival of Britain, Crown–farthing (10 coins) £85

ELIZABETH II

1953 Proof Coronation Crown–farthing (10 coins) £55
1953 Currency (plastic) set halfcrown–farthing (9 coins)... £12
1968 Specimen decimal set 10p, 5p and 1971-dated bronze in blue wallet (5 coins) £2.50
1970 Proof Last £sd coins (issued from 1972) Halfcrown–halfpenny (8 coins) £18
1971 Proof (issued 1973) 50p–half penny (6 coins) £12
1972 Proof (issued 1976) 50p–half penny (7 coins including Silver Wedding crown) £15
1973 Proof (issued 1976) 50p–half penny (6 coins) £14
1974 Proof (issued 1976) 50p–half penny (6 coins) £16
1975 Proof (issued 1976) 50p–half penny (6 coins) £16
1976 Proof 50p–half penny (6 coins)... £16
1977 Proof 50p–half penny (7 coins including Silver Jubilee crown) £15
1978 Proof 50p–half penny (6 coins) £15
1979 Proof 50p–half penny (6 coins) £16
1980 Proof gold sovereign series (4 coins) £750
1980 — 50p–half penny (6 coins) £15
1981 Proof £5, sovereign, Royal Wedding Silver crown, 50p–half penny (9 coins) £650
1981 — 50p–half penny (6 coins) £18
1982 Proof gold sovereign series (4 coins) £750
1982 — 50p–half penny (7 coins) £18
1982 Uncirculated 50p–half penny (7 coins) £12
1983 Proof gold double-sovereign to half sovereign (3 coins)... £350
1983 — £1–half penny (8 coins) (includes H. J. Heinz sets) £20
1983 Uncirculated £1–half penny (8 coins) (includes Benson & Hedges and Martini sets) £25
1983 — 50p–half penny (7 coins) (H. J. Heinz sets) £14
1984 Proof gold five pounds, sovereign and half-sovereigns (3 coins)... £650
1984 — £1 (Scottish rev.)–half penny (6 coins) £16
1984 BU £1 (Scottish rev.)–half penny (8 coins) £15
1985 New portrait proof gold sovereign series (4 coins).. £750
1985 Proof £1–1p in de luxe case (7 coins) £25
1985 — in standard case £18
1985 BU £1–1p (7 coins) in folder £15
1986 Proof gold Commonwealth Games £2, sovereign and half sovereign (3 coins)...................... £450
1986 — Commonwealth Games £2–1p, de luxe case (8 coins) £25
1986 — — in standard case (8 coins) £23
1986 BU £2–1p in folder (8 coins) £15
1987 Proof gold Britannia set (4 coins) £800
1987 — — — £25 and £10 (2 coins) £150
1987 — — double- to half sovereign (3 coins) £325
1987 — £1–1p in de luxe case (7 coins) £28
1987 — £1–1p in standard case (7 coins).. £20
1987 BU £1–1p in folder (7 coins) £14
1988 Proof gold Britannia set (4 coins) £800
1988 — — — £25 and £10 (2 coins) £150
1988 — — double- to half sovereign (3 coins) £325
1988 — £1–1p in de luxe case (7 coins) £30
1988 — £1–1p in standard case (7 coins).. £25
1988 BU £1–1p in folder (7 coins) (includes Bradford & Bingley sets) £12
1989 Proof gold Britannia set (4 coins) £785
1989 — — — £25 and £10 (2 coins) £150
1989 — — — 500th anniversary of the sovereign series set (4 coins) £950
1989 — — — double- to half sovereign (3 coins) £600
1989 — Silver Bill of Rights £2, Claim of Right £2 (2 coins)... £45
1989 — — Piedfort as above (2 coins) £85
1989 BU £2 in folder (2 coins) £15
1989 Proof £2 (both)–1p in de luxe case (9 coins) £35
1989 — in standard case (9 coins).. £30

DATE		FDC
1989 BU £1–1p in folder (7 coins)		£18
1990 Proof gold Britannia set (4 coins)		£800
1990 — — sovereign series set (4 coins)		£875
1990— — double- to half sovereign (3 coins)		£400
1990 — silver 5p, 2 sizes (2 coins)		£20
1990 — £1–1p in de luxe case (8 coins)		£32
1990 — £1–1p standard case (8 coins)		£25
1990 BU £1–1p in folder (8 coins)		£16
1991 Proof gold Britannia set (4 coins)		£775
1991 — — sovereign series set (4 coins)		£1000
1991 — — double- to half sovereign (3 coins)		£450
1991 — £1–1p in de luxe case (7 coins)		£30
1991 — £1–1p in standard case (7 coins)		£25
1991 BU £1–1p in folder (7 coins)		£16
1992 Proof gold Britannia set (4 coins)		£775
1992 — — sovereign series set (4 coins)		£900
1992 — — double- to half sovereign (3 coins)		£450
1992 — £1–1p including two each 50p and 10p in de luxe case (9 coins)		£35
1992 — £1–1p as above in standard case (9 coins)		£30
1992 BU £1–1p as above in folder (9 coins)		£15
1992 Proof silver 10p, two sizes (2 coins)		£35
1993 Proof gold Britannia set 1 (4 coins)		£900
1993 — — sovereign series set (4 coins plus silver Pistrucci medal)		£1000
1993 — — double- to half sovereign (3 coins)		£500
1993 — Coronation anniversary £5–1p in de luxe case (8 coins)		£38
1993 — — in standard case (8 coins)		£35
1993 BU £1–1p including 1992 EU 50p (8 coins)		£15
1994 Proof gold Britannia set (4 coins)		£825
1994 — — sovereign series set (4 coins)		£1000
1994 — — £2 to half sovereign (3 coins)		£550
1994 — Bank of England Tercentenary £2–1p in de luxe case (8 coins)		£35
1994 — — in standard case (8 coins)		£32
1994 BU £1–1p in folder (7 coins)		£16
1994 Proof gold 1992 and 1994 50p (2 coins)		£145
1994 — "Family silver" set £2–50p (3 coins)		£45
1995 Proof gold Britannia set (4 coins)		£810
1995 — — sovereign series (4 coins)		£1,250
1995 — — £2 to half sovereign (3 coins)		£525
1995 — 50th Anniversary of WWII £2–1p in de luxe case (8 coins)		£40
1995 — — as above in standard case (8 coins)		£35
1995 BU as above in folder (8 coins)		£15
1995 Proof "Family Silver" set £2 (two) and £1 (3 coins)		£50
1996 Proof gold Britannia set (4 coins)		£950
1996 — — sovereign series set (4 coins)		£1000
1996 — — double- to half sovereign (3 coins)		£525
1996 — Royal 70th Birthday £5–1p in de luxe case (9 coins)		£45
1996 — — as above in standard case (9 coins)		£40
1996 BU Football £2–1p in folder (8 coins)		£18
1996 Proof gold Britannia £10 and half-sovereign (2 coins)		£450
1996 — — sovereign and silver £1 (2 coins)		£165
1996 — — "Family silver" set £5–£1 (3 coins)		£50
1996 — silver 25th Anniversary of Decimal currency £1–1p (7 coins)		£130
1996 Circulation and BU 25th Anniversary of Decimalisation 2s 6d–halfpenny (misc.) and £1–1p in folder (14 coins)		£50
1997 Proof gold Britannia set (4 coins)		£1000
1997 — — sovereign series set (4 coins)		£950
1997 — — — £2 to half sovereign (3 coins)		£520
1997 — — Silver Britannia set (4 coins)		£100
1997 — Golden Wedding £5–1p in red leather case		£55
1997 — — as above in standard case (10 coins)		£38
1997 BU £2 to 1p in folder (9 coins)		£20
1997 Proof silver 50p set, two sizes (2 coins)		£35
1997/1998 Proof silver £2 set, both dates (2 coins)		£18

DATE	FDC
1998 Proof gold Britannia set (4 coins)	£1000
1998 — — sovereign series set (4 coins)	£1000
1998 — — — double- to half sovereign (3 coins)	£500
1998 Proof silver Britannia set (4 coins)	£95
1998 — Prince of Wales £5–1p (10 coins) in red leather case	£42
1998 — — as above in standard case (10 coins)	£36
1998 BU £2–1p in folder (9 coins)	£15
1998 Proof silver European/NHS 50p set (2 coins)	£50
1998 BU Britannia/EU 50p set (2 coins)	£5
1999 Proof gold Britannia set (4 coins)	£1000
1999 — — sovereign series set (4 coins)	£1000
1999 — — — £2 to half sovereign (3 coins)	£500
1999 — Princess Diana £5–1p in red leather case (9 coins)	£50
1999 — — as above in standard case (9 coins)	£38
1999 BU £2–1p (8 coins) in folder	£15
1999 Proof "Family Silver" set. Both £5, £2 and £1 (4 coins)	£45
1999 Britannia Millennium set. Bullion £2 and BU £5 (2 coins)	£25
1999/2000 Reverse frosted proof set, two x £1 (2 coins)	£65
2000 Proof gold Britannia set (4 coins)	£1000
2000 — — sovereign series set (4 coins)	£1000
2000 — — — double- to half sovereign (3 coins)	£500
2000 — Millennium £5–1p in red leather case (10 coins)	£50
2000 — — as above in de luxe case (10 coins)	£40
2000 — — as above in standard case (10 coins)	£35
2000 — Silver set Millennium £5 to 1p plus Maundy (13 coins)	£135
2000 BU £2–1p set in folder (9 coins)	£12
2000 Millennium "Time Capsule" BU £5 to 1p (9 coins)	£25
2001 Proof gold Britannia set (4 coins)	£825
2001 — — sovereign series set (4 coins)	£1000
2001 — — — £2–half sovereign (3 coins)	£500
2001 — silver Britannia set (4 coins)	£100
2001 — Victoria £5–1p in Executive case (10 coins)	£75
2001 — — as above in red leather case (10 coins)	£50
2001 — — as above in "Gift" case (10 coins)	£45
2001 — — as above in standard case (10 coins)	£35
2001 BU £2–1p in folder (9 coins)	£15
2002 Proof gold Britannia set (4 coins)	£850
2002 — — sovereign series set, all Shield rev. (4 coins)	£1000
2002 — — — double- to half sovereign (3 coins)	£450
2002 — — Golden Jubilee set £5–1p plus Maundy (13 coins)	£2500
2002 — Golden Jubilee £5–1p in Executive case (9 coins)	£65
2002 — — as above in red leather de luxe case (9 coins)	£45
2002 — — as above in "Gift" case (9 coins)	£40
2002 — — as above in standard case (9 coins)	£30
2002 BU £2–1p (8 coins) in folder	£15
2002 Proof Gold Commonwealth Games £2 set (4 coins)	£1250
2002 — Silver Piedfort Commonwealth Games £2 set (4 coins)	£200
2002 — — Commonwealth Games £2 set (4 coins)	£100
2002 — Commonwealth Games £2 set (4 coins)	£25
2002 BU Commonwealth Games £2 set (4 coins) in folder	£15
2003 Proof gold Britannia set (4 coins)	£950
2003 — — — £50–£10 (3 coins)	£400
2003 — — — type set, one of each £100 reverse (4 coins)	£1350
2003 — — sovereign series set (4 coins)	£1000
2003 — — — series £2–half sovereign (3 coins)	£425
2003 — silver Britannia set (4 coins)	£100
2003 — — type set (one of each £2 reverse) (4 coins)	£75
2003 — £5 to 1p, two of each £2 and 50p in Executive case (11 coins)	£75
2003 — — as above in red leather case (11 coins)	£50
2003 — — as above in standard case (11 coins)	£45
2003 BU £2 (two)–1p in folder (10 coins)	£18
2003 Proof silver Piedfort set. DNA £2, £1 and Suffragette 50p (3 coins)	£155
2003 Proof "Family Silver" set £5, Britannia and DNA £2, £1 and Suffragette 50p (5 coins)	£145

DATE	FDC
2003 Circ & BU "God Save the Queen" Coronation anniversary set 5s/0d to farthing (1953) and £5 to 1p (2003) in folder (19 coins)	£70
2003 Circulation or bullion "Royal Sovereign" collection, example of each Elizabeth II date (21 coins)	£2500
2004 Proof gold Britannia set (4 coins)	£815
2004 — — £50 to £10 (3 coins)	£395
2004 — — Sovereign series set (4 coins)	£985
2004 — — Series £2-half sovereign (3 coins)	£439
2004 (Issue date) Royal Portrait gold sovereign set, all proof except the first: Gillick, Machin, Maklouf and Rank-Broadley sovereigns, and the 2nd, 3rd and 4th of above half-sovereigns, various dates (7 coins)	£750
2004 Proof silver Britannia set (4 coins)	£95
2004 — "Family Silver" set £5, Britannia and Trevithick £2, £1 and Bannister 50p (5 coins)	£145
2004 — Silver Piedfort set, Trevithick £2, £1 and Bannister 50p (3 coins)	£145
2004 — £2 to 1p, two each of £2 and 50p in Executive case (10 coins)	£65
2004 — — as above in red leather case (10 coins)	£40
2004 — — as above in standard case (10 coins)	£30
2004 BU £2 to 1p in folder (10 coins)	£14
2004 — "New Coinage" set, Trevithick £2, £1 and Bannister 50p (3 coins)	£9
2004 BU "Season's Greetings" £2 to 1p and Royal Mint Christmas medal in folder (8 coins)	£15
2005 Proof Gold Britannia set (4 coins)	£915
2005 — — £50 to £10 (3 coins)	£415
2005 — — Sovereign series set (4 coins)	£995
2005 — — series, double to half sovereign (3 coins)	£450
2005 — Silver Britannia (4 coins)	—
2005 — Gold Trafalgar and Nelson £5 crowns (2 coins)	£1100
2005 — Silver, as above (2 coins)	£70
2005 — — Piedfort, as above (2 coins)	—
2005 — Silver Piedfort set, Gunpowder Plot and World War II £2, £1 and Johnson 50p (4 coins)	£190
2005 — £5 to 1p, two of each of £5, £2 and 50p in Executive case (12 coins)	£75
2005 — — as above in red leather case (12 coins)	£49
2005 — — as above in standard case (12 coins)	£38
2005 BU Trafalgar and Nelson £5 crowns in pack (2 coins)	£19
2005 — £2 (two) to 1p in folder (10 coins)	£15
2005 — "New Coinage" set, Gunpowder Plot £2, £1 and Johnson 50p (3 coins)	£9
2005 — "Merry Xmas" £2 to 1p and Royal Mint Christmas medal in folder (8 coins)	£17
2006 Proof Gold Britannia set (4 coins)	—
2006 — — Sovereign Series set (4 coins)	£1095
2006 — — series, double to half sovereign (3 coins)	£580
2006 — Silver Brunel £2 coin set (2 coins)	£60
2006 — — Piedfort Brunel £2 coin set (2 coins)	£98
2006 — Gold Brunel £2 coin set (2 coins)	£770
2006 — Silver VC 50p coin set (2 coins)	£55
2006 — Silver Piedfort VC 50p coin set (2 coins)	£98
2006 — Gold VC 50p coin set (2 coins)	£650
2006 — Silver proof set, £5 to 1p plus Maundy coins (13 coins)	£275
2006 — — Piedfort collection £5, with trumpets enhanced with 23 carat gold, both Brunel £2, £1, both VC 50p (6 coins) ....estimated	£295
2006 — — Britannia £2 "Golden Silhouette" collection, five different reverses, all dated 2006 (5 coins) ...	£270
2006 — £5 to 1p, three of each £2 and 50p in Executive case (13 coins)	£78
2006 — as above in red leather case (13 coins)	£50
2006 — as above in standard case (13 coins)	£40
2006 BU £2 (two), £1, 50p (two) and to 1p in folder (10 coins)	£15
2006 Proof Brunel £2 in folder (2 coins)	£10
2006 — VC 50p in folder (2 coins)	£7
2006 — Gold Half-Sovereign set dated 2005 Noad and 2006 Pistrucci St George and the Dragon (2 coins)	£193
2007 — Gold Britannia set (4 coins)	£1195
2007 — — Sovereign Series set (4 coins)	£1295
2007 — — series, double to half sovereign (3 coins)	£595
2007 — — Sovereign and half-sovereign (2 coins)	£275
2007 — "Family Silver" set, Britannia, £5 crown, Union and Slavery £2, Gateshead £1 and Scouting 50p (6 coins)	£194

DATE   FDC

2007 Proof Silver Piedfort Collection, as "Family Silver" above but excluding a Britannia (5 coins)......................£250
2007 — Silver £1 Bridge series coins, dated 2004 to 2007 (4 coins) £115
2007 — Gold £1 Bridge series coins, dated as above (4 coins) £1495
2007 — £5 to 1p, three £2 and two 50p in Executive case (12 coins) £79
2007 — as above, Deluxe in red leather case (12 coins) £50
2007 — as above, in standard case (12 coins) £40
2007 BU £2 (two) to 1p (9 coins)..£15
2007 Proof Silver Britannia (four coins) £115

In addition to the above the Royal Mint produce the BU sets detailed above in Wedding and in Baby gift packs each year.
Also the following patterns have been made available:
1999 (dated 1994) Bi-metal £2, plus three unprocessed or part-processed elements... —
2003 Proof gold £1 featuring future reverse Bridge designs, hall-marked on edge (4 coins) .... —
2003 — silver £1 as above (4 coins)... —
2004 — "Heraldic Traditions" silver £1-sized hall-marked (4 coins) £98

SCOTLAND

The coins illustrated are pennies representative of the reign, unless otherwise stated.

DAVID I (1124–53)

Berwick, Carlisle, Edinburgh and Roxburgh Mints

	F	VF
Penny	£665	£1900

HENRY (1136–52)

Bamborough, Carlisle and Corbridge Mints for the Earl of Huntingdon and Northumberland

Penny	£1450	£4600

David I

MALCOLM IV (1153–65)

Berwick and Roxburgh Mints

Penny (5 different types)	£3750	£10700

WILLIAM THE LION (1165–1214)

Berwick, Edinburgh, Dun (Dunbar?), Perth and Roxburgh Mints

Penny	£115	£240

Henry

ALEXANDER II (1214–49)

Berwick and Roxburgh Mints

Penny	£850	£1950

William the Lion

ALEXANDER III (1249–86)

FIRST COINAGE (1250–80)
Pennies struck at the Mints at

Aberdeen	£115	£360
Ayr	£115	£385
Berwick	£95	£220
"Dun" (Dumfries?)	£155	£440
Edinburgh	£65	£200
Forfar	£155	£495
Forres	£170	£480
Glasgow	£180	£530
Inverness	£180	£460
Kinghorn	£200	£535
Lanark	£180	£450
Montrose	£305	£720
Perth	£115	£220
Renfrew	£220	£750
Roxburgh	£115	£250
St Andrews	£150	£360
Sterling	£200	£595

Alexander II

Alexander III

SECOND COINAGE (1280–86)

Penny	£60	£120
Halfpenny	£115	£295
Farthing	£200	£600

JOHN BALIOL (1292–1306)

FIRST COINAGE *(Rough Surface issue)*

Penny	£145	£420
Halfpenny		Extremely rare

SECOND COINAGE *(Smooth Surface issue)*

Penny	£175	£400
Halfpenny	£260	£810
Farthing	£635	£2000

John Baliol

263

	F	VF

ROBERT BRUCE (1306–29)

Berwick Mint

	F	VF
Penny	£340	£1100
Halfpenny	£520	£1445
Farthing	Extremely Rare	

Robert Bruce

DAVID II (1329–71)

Aberdeen and Edinburgh Mints

	F	VF
Noble	Extremely Rare	
Groat	£95	£290
Halfgroat	£115	£290
Penny	£65	£155
Halfpenny	£230	£580
Farthing	£600	£1850

David II

ROBERT II (1371–90)

Dundee, Edinburgh and Perth Mints

	F	VF
Groat	£140	£250
Halfgroat	£140	£290
Penny	£110	£290
Halfpenny	£165	£520

Robert II

ROBERT III (1390–1406)

Aberdeen, Dumbarton, Edinburgh, Perth Mints

	F	VF
Lion or crown	£560	£1230
Demy lion or halfcrown	£560	£1230
Groat	£90	£245
Halfgroat	£140	£440
Penny	£230	£555
Halfpenny	£340	£1020

JAMES I (1406–37)

Aberdeen, Edinburgh, Inverness, Linlithgow, Perth, Stirling Mints

	F	VF
Demy	£450	£1175
Half demy	£560	£1150
Groat	£195	£480
Penny	£150	£415
Halfpenny	£385	£1065

JAMES II (1437–60)

Aberdeen, Edinburgh, Linlithgow, Perth, Roxburgh, Stirling Mints

	F	VF
Demy	£560	£1350
Lion	£725	£2150
Half lion	Extremely rare	
Groat	£210	£660
Halfgroat	£560	£1200
Penny (billon)	£385	£845

Robert III Lion

JAMES III (1460–88)

Aberdeen, Berwick and Edinburgh Mints

	F	VF
Rider	£955	£2250
Half rider	£1180	£3000
Quarter rider	£1295	£3000
Unicorn	£845	£2250
Groat	£230	£565
Halfgroat	£595	£1130
Penny (silver)	£260	£6725
Plack (billon)	£115	£435
Half plack	Extremely rare	
Penny (billon)	£115	£435
Farthing (copper)	£285	£460

James III Groat, Berwick Mint

JAMES IV (1488–1513)

James IV

Edinburgh Mint

	F	VF
Unicorn	£780	£1825
Half unicorn	£655	£1365
Lion or crown	£915	£2110
Half lion	£1730	£4155
Groat	£480	£950
Halfgroat	£480	£950
Penny (silver)	£480	£1480
Plack	£70	£200
Half plack	£134	£330
Penny (billon)	£70	£200

JAMES V (1513–42)

Edinburgh Mint

Unicorn	£1185	£2995
Half Unicorn	£1645	£4725
Crown	£670	£1565
Ducat or Bonnet piece	£2280	£5300
Two-thirds ducat	£2145	£3800
One -third ducat	£2830	£5285
Groat	£170	£495
One-third groat	£170	£475
Plack	£55	£120
Bawbee	£45	£145
Half bawbee	£100	£220
Quarter bawbee		Extremely rare

James V Edinburgh Groat

MARY (1542–67)

Edinburgh and Stirling Mints

FIRST PERIOD (1542–58)

Crown	£1180	£2850
Twenty shillings	£2170	£4150
Lions (Forty-four shillings)	£1050	£3000
Half lions (Twenty-two shillings)	£820	£2150
Ryals (Three pounds)	£2300	£6000
Half ryal	£3175	£7150
Portrait testoon	£1100	£4600
Non-portrait testoon	£205	£605
Half testoon	£195	£575
Bawbee	£65	£145
Half bawbee	£100	£255
Penny (facing bust)	£215	£650
Penny (no bust)		Extremely rare
Lion	£60	£190
Plack	£60	£190

SECOND PERIOD (Francis and Mary, 1558–60)

Ducat (Sixty shillings)		Extremely rare
Non-portrait testoon	£200	£595
Half testoon	£225	£665
12 penny groat	£120	£325
Lion	£60	£155

Mary First Period Testoon

THIRD PERIOD (Widowhood, 1560–65)

Portrait testoon	£950	£3000
Half testoon	£1095	£3570

FOURTH PERIOD (Henry and Mary, 1565–67)

Portrait ryal		Extremely rare
Non-portrait ryal	£240	£680
Two-third ryal	£420	£800

	F	VF
One-third ryal	£445	£1250
Testoon	£270	£1065

FIFTH PERIOD (Second widowhood, 1567)

	F	VF
Non-portrait ryal	£300	£825
Two thirds ryal	£270	£750
One-third ryal	£335	£940

JAMES VI
(Before accession to the English throne)
(1567–1603)

FIRST COINAGE (1567–71)

	F	VF
Ryal	£225	£630
Two-thirds ryal	£220	£620
One-third ryal	£225	£655

SECOND COINAGE (1571–80)

	F	VF
Twenty pounds	Extremely rare	
Noble (or half merk)	£120	£505
Half noble (or quarter merk)	£120	£375
Two merks or Thistle dollar	£1540	£2420
Merk	£1540	—

THIRD COINAGE (1580–81)

	F	VF
Ducat	£2330	£5900
Sixteen shillings	£1330	£2320
Eight shillings	£1000	£2650
Four shillings	£1000	£2675
Two shillings	Extremely rare	

James VI Fourth coinage thirty shillings

FOURTH COINAGE (1582–88)

	F	VF
Lion noble	£2870	£7650
Two-third lion noble	£2870	£7650
One-third lion noble	£3400	£9950
Forty shillings	£2860	£8800
Thirty shillings	£390	£1175
Twenty shillings	£360	£880
Ten shillings	£240	£625

FIFTH COINAGE (1588)

	F	VF
Thistle noble	£1770	£3895

SIXTH COINAGE (1591–93)

	F	VF
"Hat" piece	£2880	£7150
"Balance" half merk	£210	£500
"Balance" quarter merk	£420	£1000

SEVENTH COINAGE (1594–1601)

	F	VF
Rider	£600	£1250
Half rider	£485	£1200
Ten shillings	£120	£375
Five shillings	£155	£440
Thirty pence	£120	£375
Twelve pence	£120	£375

EIGHTH COINAGE (1601–04)

	F	VF
Sword and sceptre piece	£330	£625
Half sword and sceptre piece	£275	£565
Thistle-merk	£90	£255
Half thistle-merk	£60	£220
Quarter thistle-merk	£60	£220
Eighth thistle-merk	£60	£225

	F	VF
Billon and copper issues		
Eightpenny groat	£35	£75
Fourpenny groat	£180	—
Twopenny plack	£90	£255
Hardhead	£120	£330
Twopence	£90	£300
Penny plack	£100	£310
Penny	£160	£525

JAMES VI
(After accession to the English throne)
(1603–25)

	F	VF
Unit	£465	£930
Double crown	£605	£1750
British crown	£605	£1260
Halfcrown	£360	£885
Thistle crown	£360	£760
Sixty shillings	£345	£820
Thirty shillings	£125	£345
Twelve shillings	£125	£330
Six shillings	£330	£880
Two shillings	£65	£305
One shilling	£120	£375
Copper twopence	£45	£125
Copper penny	£45	£125

James VI after accession thirty shillings

CHARLES I (1625–49)

FIRST COINAGE (1625–36)

	F	VF
Unit	£720	£1175
Double crown	£1320	£2995
British crown	£1960	£5900
Sixty shillings	£360	£930
Thirty shillings	£100	£305
Twelve shillings	£100	£305
Six shillings	£240	£535
Two shillings	£100	£440
One shilling	£100	£405

SECOND COINAGE (1636)

	F	VF
Half merk	£65	£255
Forty penny piece	£70	£220
Twenty penny piece	£75	£375

THIRD COINAGE (1637–42)

	F	VF
Unit	£660	£1870
Half unit	£715	£2150
British crown	£605	£1825
British half crown	£440	£1250
Sixty shillings	£360	£1100
Thirty shillings	£100	£325
Twelve shillings	£80	£250
Six shillings	£75	£220
Half merk	£65	£205
Forty pence	£45	£130
Twenty pence	£40	£110
Three shillings	£60	£185
Two shillings	£60	£195
Twopence (copper)	£40	£100
Penny	Extremely rare	
Twopence (CR crowned)	£25	£65
Twopence (Stirling turner)	£25	£45

Charles I Third coinage thirty shillings

	F	VF

CHARLES II (1660–85)

FIRST COINAGE

Four merks

	F	VF
1664 Thistle above bust	£600	£1250
1664 Thistle below bust	£720	£1250
1665	Extremely rare	
1670	£480	£980
1673	£480	£1100
1674 F below bust	£545	£1210
1675	£545	£1210

Two merks

1664 Thistle above bust	£240	£750
1664 Thistle below bust	£275	£885
1670	£220	£750
1673	£220	£750
1673 F below bust	£355	£1100
1674	£280	£1100
1674 F below bust	£275	£1300
1675	£215	£625

Merk

1664	£100	£255
1665	£100	£280
1666	£180	£535
1668	£100	£280
1669	£120	£320
1670	£100	£360
1671	£90	£245
1672	£90	£250
1673	£90	£250
1674	£90	£285
1674 F Below bust	£100	£285
1675 F below bust	£120	£440
1675	£120	£440

Charles II two merks

Half merk

1664	£145	£375
1665	£120	£320
1666	£145	£440
1667	£120	£375
1668	£120	£375
1669	£145	£400
1670	£120	£445
1671	£90	£285
1672	£90	£280
1673	£100	£250
1675 F below bust	£145	£375
1675	£120	£315

SECOND COINAGE

Dollar

1676	£330	£825
1679	£330	£880
1680	£440	£1320
1681	£330	£880
1682	£325	£770

Half Dollar

1675	£275	£705
1676	£330	£880
1681	£210	£550

Quarter Dollar

1675	£110	£275
1676	£110	£280
1677	£190	£495
1678	£50	£200

	F	VF
1679	£120	£440
1680	£145	£505
1681	£120	£440
1682	£160	£440
Eighth Dollar		
1676	£90	£220
1677	£90	£220
1678/7		Rare
1679	£275	£825
1680	£120	£285
1682	£240	£625
Sixteenth Dollar		
1677	£75	£190
1678/7	£90	£225
1679/7		Rare
1680	£240	£625
1681	£120	£285
Twopence CR crowned	£45	£160
Bawbees	£80	£220
Turners	£45	£160

James VII ten shillings

JAMES VII (1685–89)

	F	VF
Sixty shillings		
1688 proof only	—	£2000
Forty shillings		
1687	£155	£565
1688	£225	£625
Ten shillings		
1687	£120	£375
1688	£155	£505

WILLIAM & MARY (1689–94)

	F	VF
Sixty shillings		
1691	£240	£930
1692	£300	£930
Forty shillings		
1689	£240	£500
1690	£120	£425
1691	£160	£500
1692	£145	£435
1693	£150	£530
1694	£155	£530
Twenty shillings		
1693	£240	£815
1694	£420	£1250
Ten shillings		
1689	Extremely rare	
1690	£240	£505
1691	£180	£300
1692	£120	£315
1694	£225	£575
Five shillings		
1691	£150	£460
1694	£90	£275
Bawbee		
1691–94	£80	£160
Bodle		
1691–94	£50	£110

William & Mary ten shillings

	F	VF

WILLIAM II (1694–1702)

	F	VF
Pistole	£2850	£6200
Half pistole	£3150	£7200
Forty shillings		
1695	£165	£495
1696	£165	£410
1697	£245	£515
1698	£190	£415
1699	£245	£825
1700	Extremely rare	
Twenty shillings		
1695	£135	£445
1696	£135	£445
1697	£220	£710
1698	£165	£710
1699	£165	£465
Ten shillings		
1695	£110	£385
1696	£110	£330
1697	£110	£330
1698	£135	£385
1699	£220	£525
Five shillings		
1695	£100	£410
1696	£70	£190
1697	£90	£330
1699	£80	£330
1700	£80	£330
1701	£110	£410
1702	£110	£410
Bawbee		
1695–97	£50	£190
Bodle		
1695–97	£55	£200

William II ten shillings

ANNE (1702–14)

PRE-UNION 1702–7

Ten shillings	F	VF
1705	£175	£415
1706	£175	£525
Five shillings		
1705	£80	£250
1706	£60	£85

Anne five shillings

POST-UNION 1707–14
See listing in English section.

JAMES VIII (The Old Pretender) (1688–1766)

A number of Guineas and Crowns in various metals were struck in 1828 using original dies prepared by Norbert Roettiers, all bearing the date 1716. These coins are extremely rare and are keenly sought after.

ISLE OF MAN

DATE	F	VF	EF	UNC

PENNY

1709 Cast	£30	£80	£200	—
1709 Silver cast Proof	—	—	—	£1560
1709 Brass	£30	£85	£195	—
1733 "Quocunque"	£25	£40	£180	£300
1733 "Ouocunoue"....................................	£25	£50	£200	£540
1733 Bath metal "Quocunque"	£15	£35	£175	—
1733 Silver Proof......................................	—	—	—	£625
1733 Bronze Proof....................................	—	—	—	£360
1733 Proof...	—	—	—	£535
1733 Cap frosted......................................	£15	£35	£198	£300
1733 Brass, cap frosted	£25	£45	£220	£420
1733 Silver Proof cap frosted....................	—	—	—	£475
1733 Bronze annulets instead of pellets	£35	£75	£285	£200
1758..	£18	£30	£165	£325
1758 Proof...	—	—	—	£505
1758 Silver Proof......................................	—	—	—	£805
1786 Engrailed edge	£22	£38	£185	£385
1786 Engrailed edge Proof	—	—	—	£425
1786 Plain edge Proof..............................	—	—	—	£800
1786 Pellet below bust..............................	£22	£45	£225	£445
1798..	£22	£45	£165	£345
1798 Proof...	—	—	—	£305
1798 Bronze Proof....................................	—	—	—	£305
1798 Copper-gilt Proof..............................	—	—	—	£1450
1798 Silver Proof......................................	—	—	—	£1975
1813..	£25	£45	£155	£300
1813 Proof...	—	—	—	£325
1813 Bronze Proof....................................	—	—	—	£300
1813 Copper-gilt Proof..............................	—	—	—	£1975
1839	£22	£35	£130	£245
1839 Proof...	—	—	—	£375

HALF PENCE

1709 Cast	£35	£80	£200	—
1709 Brass	£40	£150	£405	—
1723 Silver	£525	£1000	£2560	—
1723 Copper	£230	£475	£1450	£2000
1733 Copper	£20	£42	£195	£325
1733 Bronze	£25	£42	£195	£325
1733 Silver Proof plain cap	—	—	—	£480
1733 Silver Proof frosted cap	—	—	—	—
1733 Bronze Proof....................................	—	—	—	£360
1733 Bath metal plain cap	£25	£38	£175	—
1733 Bath metal frosted cap	£25	£38	£175	—
1758..	£25	£38	£175	£305
1758 Proof...	—	—	—	£625
1786 Engrailed edge	£15	£30	£100	£265
1786 Proof engrailed edge	—	—	—	£335
1786 Plain edge..	£25	£50	£210	£285
1786 Proof plain edge	—	—	—	£545
1786 Bronze Proof....................................	—	—	—	£350
1798..	£20	£32	£95	£265
1798 Proof...	—	—	—	£315
1798 Bronze Proof....................................	—	—	—	£310

DATE	F	VF	EF	UNC
1798 Copper-gilt Proof...............................	—	—	—	£910
1798 Silver Proof.......................................	—	—	—	£1300
1813	£18	£32	£95	£200
1813 Proof	—	—	—	£295
1813 Bronze Proof....................................	—	—	—	£255
1813 Copper-gilt Proof.............................	—	—	—	£1,000
1839	£18	£32	£65	£175
1839 Bronze Proof....................................	—	—	—	£310

FARTHING

	F	VF	EF	UNC
1839 Copper	£18	£32	£75	£185
1839 Bronze Proof	—	—	—	£305
1839 Copper-gilt Proof	—	—	—	£1850

The last issue of coins made in the Isle of Man had been in 1839 but in 1970 Spink & Son Ltd was commissioned to produce a modern coinage for the Isle of Man Government which was struck at the Royal Mint. From 1973 onwards the Pobjoy Mint took over the contract and has been a very prolific producer of definitive and commemorative issues. It is not proposed to give a complete listing of all these coins but the Crown and 25p, which from the collector's point of view are the most interesting in the series, have been selected. Additionally a special 50p coin is issued to celebrate Christmas each year.

The listings that follow are of the ordinary uncirculated cupro-nickel crown-size coins. The Island has also issued most of the coins listed in other metals, including silver, gold and platinum in non proof and proof form and in 1984 some were also issued in silver clad cupro-nickel in proof form.

DATE	UNC
1970 Manx Cat	£12
1972 Royal Silver Wedding	£10
1974 Centenary of Churchill's birth	£10
1975 Manx Cat	£12
1976 Bi-Centenary of American Independence	£12
1976 Centenary of the Horse Drawn Tram	£9
1977 Silver Jubilee	£9
1977 Silver Jubilee Appeal	£9
1978 25th Anniversary of the Coronation............................	£9
1979 300th Anniversary of Manx Coinage	£8
1979 Millennium of Tynwald (5 coins).................................	£19
1980 Winter Olympics	£10
1980 Derby Bicentennial	£10
1980 22nd Olympics (3 coins)	£16
1980 80th Birthday of Queen Mother..................................	£8
1981 Duke of Edinburgh Award Scheme (4 coins)...............	£14
1981 Year of Disabled (4 coins)..	£14
1981 Prince of Wales' Wedding (2 coins)............................	£12
1982 12th World Cup—Spain (4 coins)................................	£16
1982 Maritime Heritage (4 coins)	£16
1983 Manned Flight (4 coins)	£16
1984 23rd Olympics (4 coins)...	£19
1984 Quincentenary of College of Arms (4 coins)..............	£18
1984 Commonwealth Parliamentary Conference (4 coins)...	£18
1985 Queen Mother (6 coins)	£16
1986 13th World Cup—Mexico (6 coins)	£14
1986 Prince Andrew Wedding (2 coins)	£12
1987 200th Anniversary of the United States Constitution ...	£10

DATE	UNC
1987 America's Cup Races (5 coins)...	£16
1988 Bicentenary of Steam Navigation (6 coins)	£16
1988 Australia Bicentennial (6 coins)	£16
1988 Manx Cat	£10
1989 Royal Visit	£8
1989 Bicentenary of the Mutiny on the Bounty (4 coins)	£16
1989 Persian Cat...	£10
1989 Bicentenary of Washington's Inauguration (4 coins)	£14
1990 150th Anniversary of the Penny Black	£12
1990 World Cup—Italy (4 coins)...	£18
1990 25th Anniversary of Churchill's Death (2 coins)	£10
1990 Alley Cat	£8
1990 Queen Mother's 90th Birthday	£8
1991 Norwegian Forest Cat	£8
1991 Centenary of the American Numismatic Association.................	£9
1991 1992 America's Cup	£10
1991 10th Anniversary of Prince of Wales' Wedding (2 coins)............	£10
1992 Discovery of America (4 coins)...	£17
1992 Siamese Cat	£10
1992 1992 America's Cup	£8
1993 Maine Coon Cat	£8
1993 Preserve Planet Earth—Dinosaurs (2 coins)...........................	£12
1994 Preserve Planet Earth—Mammoth.....................................	£10
1994 Year of the Dog...	£10
1994 World Football Cup (6 coins)	£27
1994 Japanese Bobtail Cat	£8
1994 Normandy Landings (8 coins)..	£38
1994 Preserve Planet Earth—Endangered Animals (3 coins)..............	£19
1995 Man in Flight—Series i (8 coins)	£58
1995 Man in Flight—Series ii (8 coins)	£58
1995 Queen Mother's 95th Birthday	£10
1995 Year of the Pig	£10
1995 Turkish Cat	£10
1995 Preserve Planet Earth—Egret and Otter..............................	£14
1995 America's Cup	£10
1995 Aircraft of World War II (19 coins)......................................	£125
1995 Famous World Inventions—Series i (12 coins)	£110
1996 Year of the Rat	£10
1996 70th Birthday of HM the Queen	£16
1996 The Flower Fairies—Series i (4 coins)	£38
1996 Famous World Inventions—Series ii (6 coins)	£38
1996 Olympic Games (6 coins)	£30
1996 Preserve Planet Earth—Killer Whale and Razorbill	£14
1996 Burmese Cat	£14
1996 Robert Burns (4 coins)...	£25
1996 King Arthur & the Knights of the Round Table (5 coins)	£32
1996 European Football Championships (8 coins)...........................	£48
1996 Football Championships Winner	£14
1996 Explorers (2 coins)	£19
1997 Year of the Ox..	£15
1997 The Flower Fairies—Series ii (4 coins)................................	£24
1997 Royal Golden Wedding (2 coins)	£15
1997 Explorers—Eriksson and Nansen (2 coins)	£14
1997 Long-haired Smoke Cat	£12
1997 10th Anniversary of the "Cats on Coins" series (silver only)	£40
1997 90th Anniversary of the TT Races (4 coins)...........................	£30
1998 The Millennium (16 coins issued over 3 years)........................	—
1998 Year of the Tiger	£16
1998 FIFA World Cup (4 coins)...	£30
1998 Birman Cat	£16
1998 The Flower Fairies—Series iii (4 coins)...............................	£28
1998 18th Winter Olympics, Nagano (4 coins)...............................	£28
1998 Explorers—Vasco da Gama and Marco Polo (2 coins)	£20

DATE	UNC
1998 125th Anniversary of Steam Railway (8 coins)	£58
1998 International Year of the Oceans (4 coins)...................................	£30
1999 50th Birthday of HRH the Prince of Wales	£12
1999 Year of the Rabbit...	£12
1999 27th Olympics in Sydney (5 coins)	£38
1999 Rugby World Cup (6 coins)...	£38
1999 Wedding of HRH Prince Edward and Sophie Rhys-Jones.........	£12
1999 Queen Mother's 100th Birthday (4 coins)...................................	£30
1999 The Millennium (4 coins)..	£30
1999 Titanium Millennium crown..	£10
2000 Year of the Dragon	£10
2000 Scottish Fold cat	£10
2000 Millennium—own a piece of time	£10
2000 Explorers, Francisco Piarro and Wilem Brents (2 coins)	£14
2000 Life and times of the Queen Mother (4 coins)	£26
2000 Queen Mother's 100th Birthday	£10
2000 60th Anniversary of the Battle of Britain....................................	£10
2000 BT Global Challenge	£10
2000 18th Birthday of HRH Prince William	£10
2001 Year of the Snake	£10
2001 The Somali cat..	£10
2001 Life and times of the Queen Mother (2 coins)	£14
2001 Explorers, Martin Frobisher and Roald Amundsen (2 coins)......	£14
2001 75th Birthday of HM the Queen	£10
2001 Joey Dunlop	£11
2001 Harry Potter (6 coins)...	£75
2002 Year of the Horse...	£10
2002 The XIX Winter Olympiad, Salt Lake City (2 coins)....................	£18
2002 World Cup 2002 in Japan/Korea (4 coins)	£34
2002 The Bengal Cat	£12
2002 The Queen's Golden Jubilee—i (1 coin)	£14
2002 Introduction of the Euro..	£12
2002 The Queen's Golden Jubilee—ii (4 coins).................................	£55
2002 A Tribute to Diana Princess of Wales—5 years on	£25
2003 Year of the Goat...	£12
2003 The Balinese Cat	£14
2003 Anniversary of the "Star of India"	£14
2003 Lord of the Rings (5 coins)	£55
2004 Olympics (4 coins)..	£45
2004 100 Years of Powered Flight (2 coins)	£25
2005 Lord of the Rings: The Return of the King..................................	£25
2005 Manx Hero Lt. John Quilliam and the Battle of Trafalgar (2 coins)	£25
2005 The Himalayan Cat with kittens..	£15
2005 Bicentenary of the Battle of Trafalgar (6 coins)	£52
2005 60th Anniversary of D-Day (6 coins)...	£59
2005 60th Anniversary of Victory in Europe	£25
2005 200th Anniversary of the Battle of Trafalgar	£29
2005 400th Anniversary of the Gun Powder Plot (2 coins)	£28
2005 Bicentenary of the Battle of Trafalgar and Death of Nelson.......	£28
2005 Italy and the Isle of Man TT races (2 coins)	£28
2005 Harry Potter and the Goblet of Fire (4 coins)............................	£32
2006 100 Years of Norwegian Independence	£21
2006 80th Birthday of Her Majesty the Queen (4 coins)	£34
2006 Battles that Changed the World—Part II (6 coins)..............	£48
2006 150th Anniversary of the Victoria Cross (2 coins)......................	£26
2007 The Ragdoll Cat..	£10
2007 Fairy Tales—Sleeping Beauty, The Three Little Pigs (2 coins)....	£22
2007 The Graceful Swan..	£10

GUERNSEY

DATE	F	VF	EF	UNC

TEN SHILLINGS
1966...	—	£3	£7	£8
1966 Proof...	—	—	—	£12

THREEPENCE
1956...	50p	£2	£6	£6
1956 Proof...	—	—	—	£12
1959...	50p	£2	£6	£8
1966 Proof...	—	—	—	£10

EIGHT DOUBLES
1834...	£8	£8	£35	£115
1858 5 berries..	£4	£7	£35	£115
1858 4 berries..	£4	£7	£35	£115
1864 1 stalk	£4	£3	£25	£55
1864 3 stalks	£4	£3	£21	£50
1868...	£6	£7	£21	£50
1874...	£3	£4	£11	£38
1885H...	£3	£4	£10	£30
1889H...	£2	£3	£9	£26
1893H small date	£2	£3	£9	£26
1893H large date	£2	£3	£9	£26
1902H...	£2	£3	£9	£25
1903H...	£2	£3	£9	£25
1910...	£2	£3	£9	£26
1911H...	£2	£3	£8	£30
1914H...	50p	£2	£7	£20
1918H...	50p	£2	£6	£17
1920H...	50p	£2	£6	£17
1934H...	60p	£2	£6	£22
1934H Proof...	—	—	—	£100
1938H...	60p	£2	£6	£19
1945H...	50p	£1	£5	£12
1947H...	40p	£1	£5	£12
1949H...	40p	£1	£5	£12
1956...	30p	50p	£4	£12
1956...	30p	50p	£4	£12
1959...	30p	50p	£4	£12
1966 Proof...	—	—	—	£22

FOUR DOUBLES
1830...	£3	£8	£40	£85
1830 Mule with obv. St Helena 1/2 d	—	£650	—	—
1858...	£5	£10	£50	£85
1864 Single stalk	£1	£5	£15	£48
1864 3 stalks	31	£5	£17	£55
1868...	£2	£6	£19	£60
1874...	£1	£5	£19	£60
1885H...	£1	£5	£17	£35
1889H...	£1	£2	£11	£30
1893H...	£1	£2	£11	£30
1902H...	£1	£2	£8	£25
1903H...	£1	£2	£11	£25
1906H...	£1	£2	£8	£22
1908H...	£1	£2	£8	£22
1910H...	£1	£2	£8	£22
1911H...	£1	£2	£7	£20
1914H...	£1	£2	£11	£32
1918H...	£1	£2	£10	£30
1920H...	£1	£2	£8	£30
1945H...	£1	£2	£8	£28
1949H...	£1	£2	£10	£28
1956...	50p	£1	£5	£12
1966 Proof...	—	—	—	£12

DATE	F	VF	EF	UNC
TWO DOUBLES				
1858...	£5	£8	£45	£150
1868 Single stick	£5	£10	£50	£150
1868 3 stalks	£6	£12	£70	£155
1874...	£3	£8	£45	£110
1885H..	£2	£5	£15	£30
1889H..	£2	£3	£15	£30
1899H..	£2	£4	£19	£35
1902H..	£2	£3	£17	£30
1902H..	£2	£3	£17	£30
1906H..	£2	£3	£17	£30
1908H..	£2	£4	£17	£30
1911H..	£2	£4	£20	£35
1914H..	£2	£4	£20	£35
1917H..	£6	£16	£70	£155
1918H..	£2	£3	£12	£25
1920H..	£2	£3	£12	£25
1929H..	£1	£2	£10	£15
ONE DOUBLE				
1830...	£2	£3	£20	£40
1868...	£3	£9	£30	£80
1868/30	£4	£6	£25	£75
1885H..	£1	£2	£7	£18
1889H..	50p	£1	£5	£18
1893H..	50p	£1	£5	£18
1899H..	50p	£1	£5	£18
1902...	50p	£1	£5	£18
1903H..	50p	£1	£5	£18
1911H..	50p	£1	£7	£18
1911 (new shield)	50p	£1	£5	£18
1914H	50p	£1	£7	£18
1929H..	50p	£1	£5	£18
1933H..	50p	£1	£5	£18
1938H..	50p	£1	£5	£18

DECIMAL COINAGE

Ordinary circulating coinage from 1986 onwards is usually available in uncirculated condition at a small premium above face value thus it is not listed here. The coins listed are cupro-nickel unless otherwise stated.

	UNC
ONE HUNDRED POUNDS—Gold	
1994 50th Anniversary of Normandy Landings. Proof	£650
1995 Anniversary of the Liberation. Proof...	£650
FIFTY POUNDS—Gold	
1994 50th Anniversary of Normandy Landings. Proof	£300
1995 Anniversary of the Liberation. Proof...	£300
TWENTY-FIVE POUNDS—Gold	
1994 50th Anniversary of Normandy Landings......................................	£195
1994 — Proof	£210
1995 Anniversary of the Liberation. Proof..	£200
1996 European Football Championships. Proof	£200
1997 Royal Golden Wedding. Proof..	£250
1998 Royal Air Force. Proof	£195
2000 Queen Mother 100th Birthday. Proof	£225
2001 Queen Victoria centennial	£225
2001 HM the Queen's 75th Birthday	£220
2002 Princess Diana memorial...	£220
2002 Duke of Wellington	£225
TEN POUNDS	
1994 50th Anniversary of Normandy Landings. Gold proof....................	£125
1995 Anniversary of the Liberation. Gold proof	£125
2000 Century of Monarchy. Silver proof...	£125
2001 19th Century Monarchy. Silver proof...	£125
2002 18th Century Monarchy. Silver proof...	£125

DATE	UNC

FIVE POUNDS

1995 Queen Mother's 95th birthday	£20
1995 — Silver proof	£45
1995 — Small size gold	£120
1996 HM the Queen's 70th birthday	£15
1996 — Silver proof	£45
1996 European Football Championships	£25
1996 — Silver proof	£50
1997 Royal Golden Wedding	£18
1997 — Silver proof	£50
1997 — Small size gold. BU	£65
1997 Castles of the British Isles—Castle Cornet, Guernsey	£15
1997 — Silver proof	£55
1997 Castles of the British Isles—Caernarfon Castle. Silver proof	£55
1997 Castles of the British Isles—Leeds Castle. Silver proof	£55
1998 Royal Air Force.	£12
1998 Royal Air Force. Silver proof	£55
1999 Millennium. Brass	£18
1999 — Silver proof	£45
1999 Wedding of HRH Prince Edward and Sophie Rhys-Jones	£18
1999 — Silver proof	£60
1999 Queen Mother	£19
1999 — Silver proof	£60
1999 Winston Churchill	£10
1999 — Gold	£715
2000 Queen Mother's 100th Birthday	£8
2000 — Silver proof	£55
2000 — Small size gold. Proof	£55
2000 Centuries of the British Monarchy	£23
2000 — Silver proof	£55
2000 — Small size gold. Proof	£55
2001 The Reign of Queen Victoria	£15
2001 — Proof	£45
2001 — Silver proof	£45
2001 HM the Queen's 75th Birthday	£12
2001 — Silver proof	£45
2001 — Small size gold. Proof	£60
2001 19th Century Monarchy	£13
2001 — Silver proof	£45
2001 — Small size gold. Proof	£48
2002 Golden Jubilee (two types)	£8
2002 — Silver proof	£50
2002 Princess Diana Memorial	£9
2002 — Proof	£45
2002 — Gold proof	£625
2002 Century of Monarchy	£8
2002 — Silver proof	£45
2002 — Small size gold. Proof	£60
2002 Queen Mother Memoriam	£12
2002 — Proof	£18
2002 — Silver proof	£45
2002 — Small size gold. Proof	£55
2003 Duke of Wellington	£12
2003 — Silver proof	£35
2003 — Gold proof	£75
2005 200th Anniversary of the Battle of Trafalgar	—
2005 60th Anniversary of the Liberation of the Channel Islands	£25
2006 Great Britons—Sir Winston Churchill Silver. Issued as part of set.	£40
2006 80th Birthday of Her Majesty the Queen	£45
2007 History of the Royal Navy—Henry the VIII, The Golden Hind (2 coins)	£45

TWO POUNDS

1985 40th anniversary of Liberation	£8
1985 — Proof	£20
1985 — Silver proof	£45
1986 Commonwealth Games, in plastic case	£10
1986 — in special folder	£10

DATE	UNC
1986 — .500 Silver	£35
1986 — .925 Silver proof	£45
1987 900th anniv. of death of William the Conqueror, in folder	£12
1987 — Silver proof	£40
1987 — Gold proof	£990
1988 William II, in presentation folder	£12
1988 — Silver proof	£45
1989 Henry I, in presentation folder	£12
1989 — Silver proof	£45
1989 Royal Visit	£12
1989 — Silver proof	£45
1990 Queen Mother's 90th birthday	£12
1990 — Silver proof	£45
1991 Henry II, in presentation folder	£12
1991 — Silver proof	£45
1993 40th Anniversary of the Coronation	£12
1993 — Silver proof	£45
1994 Anniversary of the Normandy Landings	£12
1994 — Silver proof	£45
1995 50th Anniversary of Liberation	£12
1995 — Silver proof	£45
1995 — Silver Piedfort proof	£85
1997 Conserving Nature i	£8
1997 — Silver proof	£45
1998 Conserving Nature ii	£8

ONE POUND

1981	£8
1981 Gold proof	£100
1981 Gold piedfort	£275
1983 New specification, new reverse	£7
1985 New design (in folder)	£7
1995 Queen Mother's 95th Birthday. Silver proof	£40
1996 Queen's 70th Birthday. Silver proof	£45
1997 Royal Golden Wedding. Silver BU	£15
1997 — Silver proof	£45
1997 Castles of the British Isles—Tower of London. Silver proof only	£24
1998 Royal Air Force. Silver proof	£35
1999 Wedding of Prince Edward. Silver proof	£45
1999 Queen Mother. Silver proof	£45
1999 Winston Churchill. Silver proof	£45
2000 Millennium. Silver proof (gold plated)	£55
2000 Queen Mother's 100th Birthday. Silver proof	£35
2001 HM the Queen's 75th Birthday. Silver proof	£35

FIFTY PENCE

1969	£3
1970	£5
1971 Proof	£7
1981	£3
1982	£3
1985 New design	£3
2000 60th Anniversary of the Battle of Britain.	£3
2000 — Silver proof	£45
2000 — silver piedfort	£65
2000 — Gold proof	£300

TWENTY-FIVE PENCE

1972 Royal Silver Wedding	£10
1972 — Silver proof	£35
1977 Royal Silver Jubilee	£7
1977 — Silver proof	£35
1978 Royal Visit	£7
1978 — Silver proof	£35
1980 Queen Mother's 80th birthday	£7
1980 — Silver proof	£35
1981 Royal Wedding	£7
1981 — Silver proof	£35

JERSEY

DATE	F	VF	EF	UNC

FIVE SHILLINGS
1966	—	£2	£6	10
1966 Proof	—	£2	£8	£18

ONE QUARTER OF A SHILLING
1957	—	£1	£4	£8
1960 Proof	—	—	£4	£12
1964	—	—	£3	£8
1966	—	—	£3	£8

ONE TWELFTH OF A SHILLING
1877H	£1	£2	£15	£45
1877H Proof in nickel	—	—	—	£1100
1877 Proof only	—	—	—	£410
1877 Proof in nickel	—	—	—	£1100
1881	£2	£2	£12	£52
1888	£1	£2	£12	£40
1894	£1	£2	£12	£40
1909	£1	£2	£12	£30
1911	£1	£2	£6	£25
1913	£1	£2	£6	£25
1923 Spade shield	£1	£2	£6	£25
1923 Square shield	£1	£2	£6	£25
1926	£1	£2	£7	£35
1931	£1	£2	£4	£10
1933	£1	£2	£6	£10
1935	£1	£2	£6	£10
1937	£1	£2	£6	£10
1946	£1	£2	£6	£10
1947	—	£2	£6	£10
"1945" GVI	—	—	75p	£8
"1945" QE2	—	—	75p	£6
1957	—	—	75p	£6
1960 1660–1960 300th anniversary	—	—	60p	£6
1960 Mule	—	—	—	£112
1966 "1066–1966"	—	—	75p	£6

ONE THIRTEENTH OF A SHILLING
1841	£3	£7	£34	£160
1844	£3	£8	£34	£160
1851	£4	£12	£50	£165
1858	£3	£8	£38	£160
1861	£4	£12	£50	£165
1865 Proof only	—	—	—	£585
1866 with LCW	£1	£4	£33	£95
1866 without LCW Proof only	—	—	—	£310
1870	£3	£7	£34	£85
1871	£3	£7	£35	£85

ONE TWENTY-FOURTH OF A SHILLING
1877H	£2	£3	£9	£45
1877 Proof only	—	—	—	£225
1888	£2	£3	£9	£35
1894	£2	£3	£9	£35
1909	£2	£3	£9	£35
1911	£1	£2	£7	£30
1913	£1	£2	£7	£30

DATE	F	VF	EF	UNC
1923 Spade shield...	£1	£2	£8	£28
1923 Square shield..	£1	£2	£7	£30
1926..	£1	£2	£7	£19
1931..	£1	£2	£7	£19
1933..	£1	£2	£7	£19
1935..	£1	£2	£7	£19
1937..	50p	£1	£5	£14
1946..	50p	£1	£5	£16
1947..	50p	£1	£5	£14

ONE TWENTY-SIXTH OF A SHILLING

1841..	£3	£6	£27	£75
1844..	£3	£6	£22	£75
1851..	£2.50	£5	£20	£75
1858..	£3	£10	£42	£135
1861..	£2.50	£5	£20	£58
1866..	£2	£5	£22	£68
1870..	£2	£5	£17	£48
1871..	£2	£5	£17	£48

ONE FORTY-EIGHTH OF A SHILLING

1877H...	£5	£10	£50	£95
1877 Proof only	—	—	—	£315

ONE FIFTY-SECOND OF A SHILLING

1841..	£8	£20	£55	£155
1861 Proof only	—	—	—	£555

DECIMAL COINAGE

Ordinary circulating coinage from 1986 onwards is usually available in uncirculated condition at a small premium above face value thus it is not listed here.

ONE HUNDRED POUNDS—Gold
1995 50th Anniversary of Liberation. Gold proof £575

FIFTY POUNDS—Gold
1995 50th Anniversary of Liberation. Gold proof £475

TWENTY-FIVE POUNDS—Gold
1972 25th Royal Wedding anniversary. Gold £175
1972 — Gold proof... £225
1990 50th Anniversary of Battle of Britain. Gold proof £225
1995 50th Anniversary of Liberation. Gold proof £225
2002 Princess Diana memorial. Gold proof £275

TEN POUNDS—Gold
1972 25th Royal Wedding anniversary. Gold £55
1972 — Gold proof... £70
1990 50th Anniversary of the Battle of Britain. Gold proof £185
1995 50th Anniversary of Liberation. Gold proof £155

FIVE POUNDS
1972 25th Royal Wedding anniversary. Gold £40
1972 — Gold proof... £55
1990 50th Anniversary of the Battle of Britain. Silver Proof (5 ounces) £125
1997 Royal Golden Wedding... £25
1997 — Silver proof.. £60
2000 Millennium. Silver proof... £45
2002 Princess Diana memorial.. £15
2002 — Silver proof.. £35
2002 — Gold proof... £650
2005 200th Anniversary of the Battle of Trafalgar..................................... —
2006 60th Anniversary of the Liberation of the Channel Islands................ £25
2006 80th Birthday of Her Majesty the Queen (3-coin set)....................... —
2007 History of the Royal Navy—Sir Francis Drake (2 coins) .... —

(Reduced)

(Enlarged)

DATE	UNC

TWO POUNDS FIFTY PENCE
1972 Royal Silver Wedding	£18
1972 — Silver proof..	£25

TWO POUNDS
(note all modern Proof coins have frosted relief)
1972 Royal Silver Wedding	£18
1972 — Silver proof...	£30
1981 Royal Wedding, nickel silver (crown size).................	£13
1981 — in presentation pack	£18
1981 — Silver proof...	£28
1981 — Gold proof...	£360
1985 40th Anniversary of Liberation (crown size)	£13
1985 — in presentation pack	£13
1985 — Silver proof...	£33
1985 — Gold proof..	£1,000
1986 Commonwealth Games.......................................	£15
1986 — in presentation case....................................	£15
1986 — .500 silver..	£33
1986 — .925 silver proof..	£37
1987 World Wildlife Fund 25th Anniversary	£17
1987 — Silver proof...	£37
1989 Royal Visit	£17
1989 — Silver proof...	£38
1990 Queen Mother's 90th Birthday	£17
1990 — Silver proof...	£12
1990 — Gold proof..	£475
1990 50th Anniversary of the Battle of Britain, silver proof...	£47
1993 40th Anniversary of the Coronation.......................	£15
1993 — Silver proof...	£53
1995 50th Anniversary of Liberation	£17
1995 — Silver Proof...	£53
1996 HM the Queen's 70th Birthday	£16
1996 — Silver proof...	£45
1997 Bi-metal...	£18
1997 — Silver proof...	£43
1997 — new portrait..	£16

ONE POUND
1972 Royal Silver Wedding	£13
1972 — Silver proof...	£17
1981...	£13
1981 Silver proof..	£38
1981 Gold proof	£250
1983 New designs and specifications on presentation card (St Helier).....	£18
1983 — Silver proof...	£38
1983 — Gold proof...	£395
1984 Presentation wallet (St Saviour)...........................	£18
1984 — Silver proof...	£39
1984 — Gold proof..	£375
1984 Presentation wallet (St Brelade)	£17
1984 — Silver proof...	£39
1984 — Gold proof..	£395
1985 Presentation wallet (St Clement)	£21
1985 — Silver proof...	£38
1985 — Gold proof..	£395
1985 Presentation wallet (St Lawrence)	£20
1985 — Silver proof...	£32
1985 — Gold proof..	£375
1986 Presentation wallet (St Peter)	£14
1986 — Silver proof...	£32
1986 — Gold proof..	£375
1986 Presentation wallet (Grouville)	£15
1986 — Silver proof...	£32

DATE	UNC
1986 — Gold proof	£375
1987 Presentation wallet (St Martin)	£15
1987 — Silver proof	£32
1987 — Gold proof	£375
1987 Presentation wallet (St Ouen)	£10
1987 — Silver proof	£34
1987 — Gold proof	£375
1988 Presentation wallet (Trinity)	£11
1988 — Silver proof	£32
1988 — Gold proof	£375
1988 Presentation wallet (St John)	£12
1988 — Silver proof	£32
1988 — Gold proof	£375
1989 Presentation wallet (St Mary)	£12
1989 — Silver proof	£32
1989 — Gold proof	£375

1991 Ship Building in Jersey Series

1991 "Tickler" Silver proof	£46
1991 — Gold proof	£375
1991 "Percy Douglas" Silver proof	£40
1991 — Gold proof	£375
1992 "The Hebe" Silver proof	£34
1992 — Gold proof	£375
1992 "Coat of Arms" Silver proof	£34
1992 — Gold proof	£375
1993 "The Gemini" Silver proof	£32
1993 — Gold proof	£375
1993 "The Century" Silver proof	£32
1993 — Gold proof	£375
1994 "Resolute" Silver proof	£40
1994 — Gold proof	£375

FIFTY PENCE

1969	£8
1972 Royal Silver Wedding	£10
1972 — Silver proof	£10
1983 New design	£8
1985 40th Anniversary of Liberation	£10

TWENTY-FIVE PENCE

1977 Royal Jubilee	£7
1977 — Silver proof	£16

TWENTY PENCE

1982 Date on rocks on rev. (cased)	£6
1982 — Silver proof piedfort	£48
1983 New obv. with date, rev. no date on rocks	£4

SOVEREIGN—Gold sovereign size

1999 The Millennium	£110
1999 — Gold proof	£195

ALDERNEY

DATE	UNC

ONE HUNDRED POUNDS
1994 50th Anniversary of D-Day Landings. Gold proof £550

FIFTY POUNDS
1994 50th Anniversary of D–Day Landing. Gold proof............................ £310
2005 200th Anniversary of the Battle of Trafalgar .... —

TWENTY FIVE POUNDS
1993 40th Anniversary of Coronation. Gold proof £210
1994 50th Anniversary of D-Day Landings. Gold proof £210
1997 Royal Golden Wedding. Gold proof £210
1997 — Silver proof... £40
2000 60th Anniversary of the Battle of Britain. Gold proof £210
2002 Princess Diana memorial £245
2002 Duke of Wellington £245
2006 World Cup 2006 (4 Coins). Gold.. £725

TEN POUNDS
1994 50th Anniversary of D–Day Landing. Gold proof............................... £74
2004 Concorde.. £225
2005 60th Anniversary of the Liberation of the Channel Islands (65mm)... £115
2005 60th Anniversary of the Liberation of the Channel Islands............... £35
2007 80th Birthday of Her Majesty the Queen .... —

FIVE POUNDS
1995 Queen Mother £19
1995 — Silver proof.. £42
1995 — Silver piedfort... £75
1995 — Gold proof... £690
1996 HM the Queen's 70th Birthday £15
1996 — Silver proof.. £50
1996 — Silver piedfort... £72
1996 — Gold proof... £690
1999 Eclipse of the Sun £20
1999 — Silver proof with colour centre.. £39
1999 Winston Churchill. Gold proof £690

2000 60th Anniversary of the Battle of Britain.. £19
2000 — Silver proof.. £45
2002 Golden Jubilee. Silver proof £43
2002 50 Years of Reign. Silver proof £43
2002 Diana memorial £13
2002 — Silver proof.. £37
2002 — Gold proof... £645
2002 Duke of Wellington £17
2002 — Silver proof.. £42
2002 — Gold proof... £645
2004 Concorde.. —
2005 2004 European Football Championships .... —
2005 200th Anniversary of the Battle of Trafalgar .... —2006
2006 Diamond Set—80th Birthday of Her Majesty the Queen (3-coin set) —
2006 Gold plated portraits of Her Majesty the Queen .... —
2006 80th Birthday of Her Majesty the Queen (3-coin set) .... —
2007 History of the Royal Navy—*Mary Rose* (2 coins) .... —
2007 150th Anniversary of the Victoria Cross .... —
2007 Monarchs of England (12 coins).. —

DATE   UNC

TWO POUNDS

1989 Royal Visit	£15
1989 — Silver proof	£42
1989 — Silver piedfort	£75
1989 — Gold proof	£975
1990 Queen Mother's 90th Birthday	£15
1990 — Silver proof	£43
1990 — Silver piedfort	£77
1990 — Gold proof	£975
1992 40th Anniversary of Accession	£17
1992 — Silver proof	£42
1992 — Silver piedfort	£77
1992 — Gold proof	£975
1993 40th Anniversary of Coronation	£16
1993 — Silver proof	£43
1993 — Silver piedfort	£76
1994 50th Anniversary of D-Day Landings	£16
1994 — Silver proof	£47
1994 — Silver piedfort	£80
1995 50th Anniversary of Return of Islanders	£16
1995 — Silver proof	£43
1995 — Silver piedfort	£73
1995 — Gold proof	£795
1997 WWF Puffin	£18
1997 — Silver proof	£45
1997 Royal Golden Wedding	£18
1997 — Silver proof	£55
1999 Eclipse of the Sun. Silver	£17
1999 — Silver proof	£40
1999 — Gold proof	£895
2000 Millennium. Silver proof	£44

ONE POUND

1993 40th Anniversary of Coronation Silver proof	£43
1995 50th Anniversary of VE Day Silver proof	£38
1995 — Gold proof	£350

IRELAND

As in the English hammered section (q.v.) the prices given here are for the most common coins in the series. For a more specialised listing the reader is referred to *Coincraft's Standard Catalogue of Scotland, Ireland, Channel Islands & Isle of Man*, or other specialised publications. Collectors should be aware that with most of the coins of the Irish series there are many varieties struck at different mints. The coins listed are all silver unless mentioned otherwise. Another important factor to consider when collecting early Irish coins is that few examples exist in high grades.

	F	VF

HIBERNO-NORSE ISSUES (995–1155)
Penny, imitating English silver pennies,
many various types £175 £400

JOHN, Lord of Ireland (1185–99)
Halfpenny, profile		Extremely rare
Halfpenny, facing	£75	£180
Farthing	£285	£750

A typical Hiberno-Norse period example.

JOHN de COURCY, Lord of Ulster (1177–1205)
Halfpenny		Extremely rare
Farthing	£550	£2000

JOHN as King of England and Lord of Ireland (c. 1199–1216)
Penny	£55	£185
Halfpenny	£125	£300
Farthing	£550	£1500

John Lord of Ireland halfpenny.

HENRY III (1216–72)
Penny £55 £200

EDWARD I (1272–1307)
Penny	£55	£200
Halfpenny	£55	£200
Farthing	£115	£300

No Irish coins were struck for Edward II (1307–27).

Henry III penny.

EDWARD III (1327–77)
Halfpenny .... Extremely rare

No Irish coins were struck for Richard II (1377–99), Henry IV (1399–1413) or Henry V (1413–22).

HENRY VI (1422–61)
Penny .... Extremely rare

Edward III halfpenny.

	F	VF

EDWARD IV (1461–83)

	F	VF
"Anonymous crown" groat	£500	£9500
— penny	£825	—
"Titled crown" groat	£1200	—
— halfgroat...............................		Extremely rare
— penny		Extremely rare
Cross on rose/Sun groat	£1375	
Bust/Rose on sun double groat	£1750	£4750
— groat................................	£1925	—
— halfgroat...............................		Extremely rare
— penny		Extremely rare
Bust/Cross & pellets groat—First issue	£85	£275
— halfgroat...............................	£450	£1000
— penny	£75	£175
— halfpenny		Extremely rare
— Second (light) issue......................	£85	£275
— halfgroat...............................	£450	£900
— penny	£75	£175
— halfpenny		Extremely rare
Bust/Rose on cross groat.....................	£385	£875
— penny	£55	£125

Billon/Copper issues

	F	VF
Small crown/Cross farthing (1460–61) ..	£1200	—
— half farthing ("Patrick")......................	£875	—
Large crown/Cross farthing (1462)........		Extremely rare
Patricius/Salvator farthing (1463–65)	£275	£1500
— half farthing		Extremely rare
Shield/Rose on sun farthing	£145	£650

Edward IV groat. "Anonymous crown" issue.

Edward IV penny. "Anonymous crown" issue.

RICHARD III (1483–85)

	F	VF
Bust/Rose on cross groat.....................	£975	£3000
— halfgroat...............................		Unique
— penny		Unique
Bust/Cross and pellets penny	£875	£2000
Shield/Three-crowns groat...................	£500	£1850

HENRY VII (1485–1509)

Early issues (1483–90)

	F	VF
Shield/Three crowns groat	£125	£350
— halfgroat...............................	£225	£450
— penny	£500	£1500
— halfpenny		Extremely rare

Later issues (1488–90)

	F	VF
Shield/Three crowns groat	£85	£250
— halfgroat...............................	£175	£450
— penny	£425	£875
Facing bust groat (1496–1505).............	£100	£250
— halfgroat...............................	£875	—
— penny	£725	—

Richard III bust/rose on cross groat.

Henry VII "three crowns" half groat.

LAMBERT SIMNEL
(as EDWARD VI, Pretender, 1487)

	F	VF
Shield/Three crowns groat	£875	£3000

	F	VF

HENRY VIII (1509–47)

"Harp" groat	£75	£200
— halfgroat	£385	£1500

*The "Harp" coins have crowned initials either side of the reverse harp,
e.g. HR (Henricus Rex), HA (Henry and Anne Boleyn), HI (Henry and Jane
Seymour), HK (Henry and Katherine Howard).*

Posthumous (Portrait) issues

Sixpence	£125	£300
Threepence	£125	£375
Threehalfpence	£425	£1250
Threefarthings	£550	£1500

*Henry VIII "harp"
halfgroat.*

EDWARD VI (1547–53)

Shilling (base silver) 1552 (MDLII)	£750	£2500
Brass contemporary copy	£75	£300

MARY (1553–54)

Shilling 1553 (MDLIII)	£700	£2500
Shilling 1554 (MDLIIII)		Extremely rare
Groat		Extremely rare
Halfgroat		Extremely rare
Penny		Extremely rare

PHILIP & MARY (1554–58)

Mary Tudor shilling.

Shilling	£300	£1000
Groat	£85	£250
Penny		Extremely rare

ELIZABETH I (1558–1603)

Base silver portrait coinage

Shilling	£300	£1000
Groat	£150	£500

Fine silver, portrait coinage (1561)

Shilling	£225	£675
Groat	£275	£875

Third (base silver) shield coinage

Shilling	£175	£500
Sixpence	£125	£375

Copper

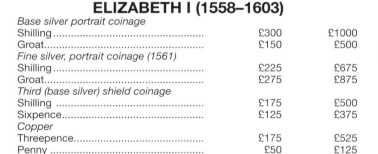

Threepence	£175	£525
Penny	£50	£125
Halfpenny	£85	£225

*Reverse of a "fine"
Elizabeth I shilling.*

JAMES I (1603–25)

Shilling	£85	£300
Sixpence	£65	£175

Coins struck under Royal Licence
from 1613

"Harrington" farthing (small size)	£45	£150
"Harrington" farthing (large size)	£40	£125
"Lennox" farthing	£40	£125

James I sixpence.

CHARLES I (1625–49)

During the reign of Charles I and the Great Rebellion many coins were struck under unusual circumstances, making the series a difficult but fascinating area for study. Many of the "coins" were simply made from odd-shaped pieces of plate struck with the weight or value.

Charles I "Maltravers" farthing.

	F	VF
Coins struck under Royal Licence from 1625		
"Richmond" farthing	£35	£100
"Maltravers" farthing	£45	£150
"Rose" farthing	£35	£125

Siege money of the Irish Rebellion, 1642–49

"Inchiquin" Money (1642)

Crown	£1750	£4000
Halfcrown	£1500	£3750
Shilling		Extremely rare
Ninepence		Extremely rare
Sixpence		Extremely rare
Groat		Extremely rare

"Dublin" Money (1643)

Crown	£725	£2500
Halfcrown	£500	£2000

Coinage of the Great Rebellion—a "Dublin Money" crown.

"Ormonde" Money (1643–44)

Crown	£425	£1000
Halfcrown	£275	£750
Shilling	£110	£350
Sixpence	£110	£350
Groat	£100	£250
Threepence	£95	£225
Twopence	£385	£900

"Ormonde" gold coinage (1646)

Double pistole. 2 known (both in museums)		Extremely rare
Pistole. 10 known (only 1 in private ownership		Extremely rare

"Ormonde" money threepence.

"Ormonde" Money (1649)

Crown		Extremely rare
Halfcrown	£950	£3000

Dublin Money 1649

Crown	£2250	£6000
Halfcrown	£1750	£3500

Issues of the Confederated Catholics

Kilkenny issues (1642–43)

Halfpenny	£225	£650
Farthing	£330	£875

Rebel Money (1643–44)

Crown	£1650	£3750
Halfcrown	£2200	£4000

Kilkenny halfpenny.

	F	VF
"Blacksmith's" Money (16??)		
Imitation of English Tower halfcrown.....	£550	£1825

Local Town issues of "Cities of Refuge"

Bandon

Farthing (copper)		Extremely rare

Cork

Shilling...		Extremely rare
Sixpence...	£660	£1550
Halfpenny (copper)		Extremely rare
Farthing (copper)	£440	—

Kinsale

Farthing (copper)	£350	—

"Cork" countermarked on a copper coin.

Youghal

Farthing (copper)	£400	£1250

CHARLES II (1660–85)

	Fair	F	VF	EF
"Armstrong" coinage				
Farthing (1660–61)................................	£55	£195	—	—
"St Patrick's" coinage				
Halfpenny	£185	£395	—	—
Farthing	£55	£140	£450	£1000
Legg's Regal coinage				
Halfpennies				
1680 large lettering...............................	£30	£75	£200	—
1681 large lettering...............................	—	£170	£525	—
1681 small lettering		Extremely rare		
1682 small lettering	—	£170	£525	—
1683 small lettering	£20	£30	£300	—
1684 small lettering	£30	£95	£500	—

"St Patrick" farthing of Charles II.

JAMES II (1685–88)

REGAL COINAGE

Halfpennies

1685..	£15	£65	£250	£550
1686..	£15	£50	£175	£450
1687..		Extremely rare		
1688..	£15	£65	£250	£875

	Fair	F	VF	EF

EMERGENCY COINAGE

GUN MONEY
Most of these coins were struck in gun metal but a few rare specimens are also known struck in gold and in silver

"Gun Money" crown.

Crowns

	Fair	F	VF	EF
1690 (many varieties).....................from	£35	£50	£300	—

Large halfcrowns
Dated July 1689–May 1690

Prices from	£25	£50	£150	—

Small halfcrowns
Dated April–October1690

Prices from	£25	£50	£150	—

Large shillings
Dated from July 1689–April 1690

Prices from	£25	£45	£100	£350

Small shillings
Dated from April–September 1690

Prices from	£15	£25	£100	£300

Sixpences
Dated from June 1689–October 1690

Prices from	£25	£50	£175	—

PEWTER MONEY (1689–90)

	Fair	F	VF	EF
Crown..	£495	£850	£2000	—
Groat...		Extremely rare		
Penny large bust...................................	£195	£550	—	—
— small bust	£140	£395	£1000	—
Halfpenny large bust	£110	£280	£600	—
— small bust	£95	£195	£550	—

"Gun Money" shilling (large size).

LIMERICK MONEY (1690–91)

	Fair	F	VF	EF
Halfpenny, reversed N in HIBERNIA......	£25	£65	£175	—
Farthing, reversed N in HIBERNIA.........	£25	£65	£175	—
— normal N	£35	£85	£225	—

WILLIAM & MARY (1688–94)

Halfpennies

	Fair	F	VF	EF
1692..	£10	£30	£85	£450
1693..	£10	£30	£75	£450
1694..	£15	£35	£95	£525

Reverse of a "Pewter Money" penny.

WILLIAM III (1694–1702)

	Fair	F	VF	EF
1696 Halfpenny draped bust.................	£25	£55	£175	—
1696 — crude undraped bust	£35	£225	£650	—

No Irish coins were struck during the reign of Queen Anne (1706–11).

DATE	F	VF	EF	UNC

GEORGE I (1714–27)

Farthings

1722 D.G. REX Harp to left (Pattern).............	£550	£1120	£2000	—
1723 D.G. REX Harp to right	£100	£195	£450	—
1723 DEI GRATIA REX Harp to right	£25	£55	£175	£450
1723 — Silver Proof	—	—	—	£1500
1724 DEI GRATIA REX Harp to right	£50	£110	£300	£650

Halfpennies

1722 Holding Harp left	£45	£110	£325	£675
1722 Holding Harp right	£35	£90	£300	£600
1723/2 Harp right	£35	£90	£275	£600
1723 Harp right	£20	£55	£175	£350
1723 Silver Proof...	—	—	—	£2500
1723 Obv. Rs altered from Bs	£25	£85	£225	—
1723 No stop after date	£20	£70	£225	£375
1724 Rev. legend divided	£30	£85	£250	—
1724 Rev. legend continuous.......................	£30	£95	£300	—

Farthing of George I.

GEORGE II (1727–60)

Farthings

1737..	£25	£50	£145	£325
1737 Proof..	—	—	—	£350
1737 Silver Proof	—	—	—	£650
1738..	£25	£55	£145	£350
1744..	£25	£55	£145	£350
1760	£20	£35	£85	£250

Halfpennies

1736..	£20	£50	£170	£350
1736 Proof..	—	—	—	£475
1736 Silver Proof	—	—	—	£875
1737..	£20	£40	£145	—
1738..	£25	£50	£170	—
1741..	£25	£50	£170	—
1742..	£25	£50	£170	—
1743..	£25	£50	£150	—
1744/3	£25	£50	£145	—
1744..	£25	£50	£260	—
1746..	£25	£50	£170	—
1747..	£25	£50	£170	—
1748..	£25	£50	£170	—
1749..	£25	£50	£170	—
1750..	£25	£50	£170	—
1751..	£25	£50	£170	—
1752..	£25	£50	£170	—
1753..	£25	£50	£170	—
1755..	£25	£85	£255	—
*1760	£20	£45	£145	—

Halfpenny of George II

GEORGE III (1760–1820)

All copper unless otherwise stated

Pennies

1805..	£15	£35	£150	£320
1805 Proof..	—	—	—	£450
1805 in Bronze Proof....................................	—	—	—	£450
1805 in Copper Gilt Proof.............................	—	—	—	£450
1805 in Silver Proof (restrike)........................	—	—	—	£1825
1822..	£15	£35	£150	£320

DATE	F	VF	EF	UNC
1822 Proof	—	—	—	£450
1823	£10	£20	£125	£300
1823 Proof	—	—	—	£450

Halfpennies

	F	VF	EF	UNC
1766	£20	£40	£125	—
1769	£20	£40	£125	—
1769 Longer bust	£30	£60	£150	£425
1774 Pattern only Proof	—	—	—	£1250
1775	£20	£40	£150	£325
1775 Proof	—	—	—	£475
1776	£40	£110	£325	—
1781	£30	£45	£125	£300
1782	£30	£45	£125	£300
1805	£15	£30	£95	£300
1805 Copper Proof	—	—	—	£300
1805 in Bronze	—	—	—	£200
1805 in Gilt Copper	—	—	—	£325
1805 in Silver (restrike)	—	—	—	£1250
1822	£15	£30	£95	£275
1822 Proof	—	—	—	£450
1823	£15	£30	£95	£275
1823 Proof	—	—	—	£465

1806 farthing

NB Prooflike Unirculated Pennies and Halfpennies of 1822/23 are often misdescribed as Proofs. The true Proofs are rare. Some are on heavier, thicker flans.

Farthings

	F	VF	EF	UNC
1806	£15	£25	£60	£115
1806 Copper Proof	—	—	—	£250
1806 Bronzed Copper Proof	—	—	—	£185
1806 Copper Gilt Proof	—	—	—	£250
1806 Silver Proof (restrike)	—	—	—	£725
1822 George IV (Pattern) Proof	—	—	—	£1250

TOKEN ISSUES BY THE BANK OF IRELAND

Five Pence in Silver

	F	VF	EF	UNC
1805	£20	£35	£60	£250
1806	£25	£55	£115	£275
1806/5	£40	£110	£345	£950

Ten Pence in Silver

	F	VF	EF	UNC
1805	£15	£30	£85	£175
1806	£15	£50	£115	£200
1813	£15	£30	£75	£155
1813 Proof	—	—	—	£350

Thirty Pence in Silver

	F	VF	EF	UNC
1808	£30	£85	£185	£450

Six Shillings

	F	VF	EF	UNC
1804 in Silver	£85	£170	£345	£1250
1804 Proof	—	—	—	£1250
1804 in Copper (restrike)	—	—	—	£575
1804 Copper Gilt	—	—	—	£1250
1804 in Gilt Silver	—	—	—	£2225

In this series fully struck specimens, with sharp hair curls, etc., are worth appreciably more than the prices quoted.

IRISH FREE STATE/EIRE

DATE	F	VF	EF	UNC

TEN SHILLINGS

	F	VF	EF	UNC
1966 Easter Rising	—	£10	£15	£20
1966 Cased Proof	—	—	—	£25
1966 special double case	—	—	—	£50

HALF CROWNS

	F	VF	EF	UNC
1928	£5	£10	£35	£55
1928 Proof	—	—	—	£60
1930	£10	£25	£110	£400
1931	£10	£30	£140	£430
1933	£10	£20	£140	£345
1934	£10	£10	£45	£200
1937	£50	£125	£500	£1250
1938				Unique
1939	£5	£15	£25	£75
1939 Proof	—	—	—	£545
1940	£5	£10	£25	£65
1941	£5	£15	£30	£70
1942	£5	£108	£30	£65
1943	£75	£175	£775	£2500
1951	£1	£2	£15	£35
1951 Proof	—	—	—	£400
1954	£1	£2	£8	£50
1954 Proof	—	—	—	£400
1955	£1	£2	£8	£30
1955	—	—	—	£520
1959	£1	£2	£10	£30
1961	£1	£2	£20	£40
1961 Obv as 1928, rev. as 1951	£25	£50	£250	—
1962	£1	£2	£5	£20
1963	£1	£2	£5	£15
1964	£1	£2	£5	£15
1966	£1	£2	£5	£15
1967	£1	£2	£5	£15

FLORINS

	F	VF	EF	UNC
1928	£2	£5	£20	£40
1928 Proof	—	—	—	£55
1930	£3	£10	£115	£350
1930 Proof				Unique
1931	£4	£17	£145	£350
1933	£3	£15	£115	£350
1934	£5	£95	£200	£550
1934 Proof	—	—	—	£2300
1935	£2	£10	£55	£150
1937	£5	£20	£115	£325
1939	£1	£5	£25	£50
1939 Proof	—	—	—	£575
1940	£2	£5	£25	£50
1941	£2	£5	£30	£55
1941 Proof	—	—	—	£650
1942	£5	£10	£25	£50
1943	£2250	£4500	£8000	£18000
1951	50p	£1	£10	£25
1951 Proof	—	—	—	£375
1954	50p	£1	£8	£25
1954 Proof	—	—	—	£300

DATE	F	VF	EF	UNC
1955...	—	£1	£5	£25
1955 Proof................................	—	—	—	£450
1959...	35p	£1	£5	£20
1961...	50p	£2	£10	£35
1962...	35p	£1	£5	£15
1963...	25p	£1	£5	£10
1964...	25p	£1	£5	£10
1965...	25p	£1	£5	£10
1966...	25p	£1	£5	£10
1968...	25p	£1	£5	£10

SHILLINGS

	F	VF	EF	UNC
1928...	£1	£5	£15	£30
1928 Proof................................	—	—	—	£50
1930...	£5	£20	£80	£345
1930 Proof................................	—	—	—	£750
1931...	£2	£15	£85	£345
1933...	£2	£15	£85	£345
1935...	£2	£10	£40	£115
1937...	£5	£50	£190	£860
1939...	£1	£5	£20	£40
1939 Proof................................	—	—	—	£575
1940...	£1	£5	£15	£35
1941...	£2	£5	£16	£40
1942...	£2	£5	£10	£30
1951...	50p	£1	£5	£15
1951 Proof................................	—	—	—	£350
1954...	50p	£1	£5	£15
1954 Proof................................	—	—	—	£400
1955...	50p	£1	£5	£15
1959...	50p	£1	£5	£20
1962...	25p	£1	£2	£10
1963...	25p	£1	£2	£5
1964...	25p	£1	£2	£5
1966...	25p	£1	£2	£5
1968...	25p	£1	£2	£5

SIXPENCES

	F	VF	EF	UNC
1928...	50p	£1	£10	£30
1928 Proof................................	—	—	—	£35
1934...	50p	£2	£15	£70
1935...	75p	£2	£20	£90
1939...	50p	£1	£5	£35
1939 Proof................................	—	—	—	£520
1940...	50p	£1	£5	£35
1942...	50p	£1	£8	£40
1945	£2	£10	£30	£80
1946...	£2	£5	£55	£325
1947...	£1	£2	£20	£60
1948...	50p	£2	£12	£40
1949...	50p	£1	£7	£30
1950...	£1	£2	£20	£75
1952...	50p	£1	£3	£15
1953...	50p	£1	£3	£15
1953 Proof................................	—	—	—	£90
1955...	50p	£1	£3	£15
1956...	50p	£1	£2	£12
1956 Proof................................	—	—	—	£125
1958...	£1	£2	£10	£50
1958 Proof................................	—	—	—	£300
1959...	25p	50p	£2	£10
1960...	25p	50p	£1	£10

DATE	F	VF	EF	UNC
1961	—	£1	£2	£15
1962	£1	£5	£25	£55
1963	50p	£2	£5	£10
1964	50p	£1	£3	£6
1966	50p	£1	£3	£6
1967	50p	£1	£1	£5
1968	50p	£1	£1	£5
1969	£1	£2	£5	£10

THREEPENCES

	F	VF	EF	UNC
1928	£1	£2	£8	£20
1928 Proof	—	—	—	£30
1933	£2	£10	£60	£295
1934	50p	£1	£8	£55
1935	£1	£3	£25	£170
1939	£2	£6	£50	£300
1939 Proof	—	—	—	£900
1940	£1	£2	£10	£45
1942	—	£1	£5	£35
1943	£1	£2	£10	£60
1946	—	75p	£5	£30
1946 Proof	—	—	—	£225
1948	£1	£2	£20	£60
1949	—	£1	£5	£25
1949 Proof	—	—	—	£195
1950	—	£1	£5	£15
1950 Proof	—	—	—	£185
1953	—	£1	£3	£10
1956	—	£1	£2	£5
1961	—	50p	£1	£3
1962	—	50p	£1	£5
1963	—	50p	£1	£5
1964	—	50p	£1	£3
1965	—	50p	£1	£2
1966	—	50p	£1	£2
1967	—	50p	£1	£2
1968	—	—	£1	£2

PENNIES

	F	VF	EF	UNC
1928	£1	£2	£10	£30
1928 Proof	—	—	—	£40
1931	£1	£3	£30	£90
1931 Proof	—	—	—	£875
1933	£1	£4	£40	£175
1935	50p	£1	£20	£55
1937	75p	£1	£30	£90
1937 Proof	—	—	—	£875
1938			2 known	
1940	£5	£25	£115	—
1941	50p	£1	£8	£20
1942	—	50p	£3	£12
1943	—	£1	£5	£20
1946	—	£1	£3	£12
1948	—	£1	£3	£12
1949	—	£1	£3	£12
1949 Proof	—	—	—	£325
1950	—	£1	£5	£20
1952	—	£1	£3	£6
1962	—	£1	£3	£8
1962 Proof	—	—	—	£125
1963	—	—	£1	£5
1963 Proof	—	—	—	£85

DATE	F	VF	EF	UNC
1964	—	—	£1	£5
1965	—	—	50p	£3
1966	—	—	50p	£3
1967	—	—	50p	£3
1968	—	—	50p	£3
1968 Proof	—	—	—	£200

HALFPENNIES

	F	VF	EF	UNC
1928	£1	£2	£10	£25
1928 Proof	—	—	—	£35
1933	£5	£15	£55	£425
1935	£2	£5	£25	£135
1937	£1	£3	£10	£45
1939	£2	£5	£30	£145
1939 Proof	—	—	—	£675
1940	£1	£3	£40	£150
1941	50p	£1	£5	£20
1942	50p	£1	£5	£20
1943	50p	£1	£6	£22
1946	£1	£2	£15	£60
1949	50p	£1	£5	£20
1953	—	£1	£2	£8
1953 Proof	—	—	—	£400
1964	—	—	50p	£2
1965	—	—	75p	£3
1966	—	—	50p	£2
1967	—	—	50p	£2

FARTHINGS

	F	VF	EF	UNC
1928	£2	£3	£8	£12
1928 Proof	—	—	—	£35
1930	£2	£3	£8	£18
1931	£3	£5	£12	£25
1931 Proof	—	—	—	£675
1932	£3	£5	£15	£35
1933	£2	£3	£10	£20
1935	£3	£5	£15	£25
1936	£3	£5	£15	£25
1937	£2	£3	£10	£20
1939	£2	£3	£5	£10
1939 Proof	—	—	—	£475
1940	£3	£4	£7	£15
1941	£2	£3	£5	£9
1943	£2	£3	£5	£9
1944	£2	£3	£5	£9
1946	£2	£3	£5	£9
1949	£3	£5	£7	£14
1949 Proof	—	—	—	£375
1953	£2	£3	£4	£5
1953 Proof	—	—	—	£250
1959	£2	£3	£4	£5
1966	£2	£3	£4	£5

For the 1928–50 copper issues it is worth noting that UNC means UNC with some lustre. BU examples with full lustre are extremely elusive and are worth much more than the quoted prices.

Decimal issues are not included in this publication but it should be noted that many dates are virtually impossible to find in uncirculated grade. An example is the 1986 set which was sold exclusively through souvenir shops and included the only specimens of the half pence for that year.

Official and semi-official commemorative
Medals

It is probably a strong love of history, rather than the strict disciplines of coin collecting that make collectors turn to commemorative medals. The link between the two is intertwined, and it is to be hoped that collectors will be encouraged to venture into the wider world of medallions, encouraged by this brief guide, supplied by courtesy of Daniel Fearon, acknowledged expert and author of the *Catalogue of British Commemorative Medals*.

DATE	VF	EF

JAMES I

1603 Coronation (possibly by
  C. Anthony), 29mm, Silver £375   £850

QUEEN ANNE

1603 Coronation, 29mm, AR.............................. £375   £850

CHARLES I

1626 Coronation (by N. Briot), 30mm, Silver....... £300   £650
1633 Scottish Coronation (by N. Briot), 28mm,
  Silver.. £175   £350
1649 Memorial (by J. Roettier). Struck after the
  Restoration, 50mm, Bronze £100   £250

James I Coronation, 1603

CHARLES II

1651 Scottish Coronation, in exile (from design
  by Sir J. Balfour), 32mm, Silver £375   £925

CROMWELL

1651 Lord Protector (by T. Simon), 38mm,
  Silver... £350   £800
— Cast examples £85   £200

CHARLES II

1661 Coronation (by T. Simon), 29mm
— Gold £800   £1500
— Silver... £100   £250
1685 Death (by N. Roettier), 39mm, Bronze £100   £200

Charles II Coronation, 1661

297

DATE	VF	EF

JAMES II
1685 Coronation (by J. Roettier), 34mm

— Gold	£1000	£2000
— Silver	£185	£375

MARY
1685 Coronation (by J. Roettier), 34mm

— Gold	£850	£1700
— Silver	£150	£350

WILLIAM & MARY
1689 Coronation (by J. Roettier), 32mm

— Gold	£850	£1750
— Silver	£125	£225
1689 Coronation,"Perseus" (by G. Bower), 38mm, Gold	£700	£1600

MARY
1694 Death (by N. Roettier), 39mm, Bronze £85 £200

WILLIAM III
1697 "The State of Britain" (by J. Croker), 69mm, Silver £350 £850

ANNE
1702 Accession, "Entirely English" (by J. Croker), 34mm

— Gold	£650	£1500
— Silver	£85	£175

1702 Coronation (by J. Croker), 36mm

— Gold	£550	£1500
— Silver	£85	£175

1707 Union with Scotland (by J. Croker, rev. by S. Bull), 34mm

— Gold	£500	£1000
— Silver	£75	£150

1713 Peace of Utrecht (by J. Croker—issued in gold to Members of Parliament), 34mm

— Gold	£450	£1200
— Silver	£75	£150

Queen Anne Peace of Utrecht, 1713

GEORGE I
1714 Coronation(by J. Croker), 34mm

— Gold	£750	£2000
— Silver	£85	£200
1727 Death (by J. Dassier), 31mm, Silver	£75	£150

GEORGE II
1727Coronation (by J. Croker), 34mm

— Gold	£650	£1750
— Silver	£85	£175

QUEEN CAROLINE
1727 Coronation (by J. Croker), 34mm

— Gold	£650	£1750
— Silver	£85	£175

1732 The Royal Family (by J. Croker), 70mm

— Silver	£175	£400
— Bronze..	£85	£175

George III, Coronation, 1761

DATE	VF	EF

GEORGE III
1761 Coronation (by L. Natter), 34mm

— Gold	£850	£2000
— Silver	£125	£275
— Bronze..	£55	£150

QUEEN CHARLOTTE
1761 Coronation (by L. Natter), 34mm

— Gold	£850	£2000
— Silver	£125	£275
— Bronze..	£55	£125
1810 Golden Jubilee, "Frogmore", 48mm, Silver	£85	£200
— Bronze..	£55	£125

GEORGE IV
1821 Coronation (by B. Pistrucci), 35mm

— Gold	£500	£950
— Silver	£55	£150
— Bronze..	£40	£75

WILLIAM IV
1831 Coronation (by W. Wyon; rev.shows
   Queen Adelaide), 33mm

— Gold	£395	£875
— Silver	£55	£120
— Bronze..	£45	£85

George IV Coronation, 1821

QUEEN VICTORIA
1838 Coronation (by B. Pistrucci), 37mm

— Gold	£395	£875
— Silver	£65	£150
— Bronze..	£35	£85

Queen Victoria Coronation, 1838

Queen Victoria Diamond Jubilee 1897

DATE	VF	EF
1887 Golden Jubilee (by J. E. Boehm, rev. by Lord Leighton)		
— Gold, 58mm	£850	£1500
— Silver, 78mm	£85	£200
— Bronze, 78mm	£45	£125
1897 Diamond Jubilee (by T. Brock),		
— Gold, 56mm	£750	£1000
— Silver, 56mm	£45	£85
— Bronze, 56mm	£20	£35
— Gold, 25mm	£125	£165
— Silver, 25mm	£25	£45

EDWARD VII
1902 Coronation (August 9) (by G. W. de Saulles)

	VF	EF
— Gold, 56mm	£750	£1000
— Silver, 56mm	£35	£75
— Bronze, 56mm	£20	£35
— Gold, 31mm	£135	£185
— Silver, 31mm	£20	£35

Some rare examples of the official medal show the date as June 26, the original date set for the Coronation which was postponed because the King developed appendicitis.

GEORGE V
1911 Coronation (by B. Mackennal)

	VF	EF
— Gold, 51mm	£750	£1000
— Silver, 51mm	£30	£75
— Bronze, 51mm	£15	£30
— Gold, 31mm	£145	£185
— Silver, 31mm	£15	£30

George V Silver Jubilee, 1935

1935 Silver Jubilee (by P. Metcalfe)

	VF	EF
— Gold, 58mm	£750	£1000
— Silver, 58mm	£25	£65
— Gold, 32mm	£125	£175
— Silver, 32mm	£20	£35

PRINCE EDWARD
1911 Investiture as Prince of Wales (by W. Goscombe John)

	VF	EF
— Gold, 31mm	£275	£500
— Silver, 31mm	£35	£55

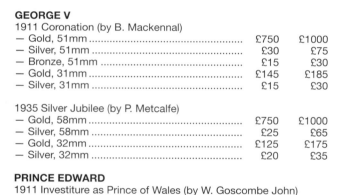

EDWARD VIII
1936 Abdication (by L. E. Pinches), 35mm

	VF	EF
— Gold	£375	£750
— Silver	£35	£65
— Bronze	£15	£35

GEORGE VI
1937 Coronation (by P. Metcalfe)

	VF	EF
— Gold, 58mm	£850	£1250
— Silver, 58mm	£35	£75
— Gold, 32mm	£145	£185
— Silver, 32mm	£15	£25
— Bronze, 32mm	£5	£12

Edward, Prince of Wales, 1911

DATE	VF	EF

ELIZABETH II
1953 Coronation (by Spink & Son)

	VF	EF
— Gold, 57mm	£750	£1000
— Silver, 57mm	£25	£75
— Bronze, 57mm	£15	£25
— Gold, 32mm	£175	£350
— Silver, 32mm	£15	£35
— Bronze, 32mm	£10	£15

1977 Silver Jubilee (by A. Machin)

	VF	EF
— Silver, 57mm	—	£55
— Silver, 44mm	—	£35

*The gold medals are priced for 18ct—they can also be found as 22ct and 9ct, and prices should be adjusted accordingly.

PRINCE CHARLES
1969 Investiture as Prince of Wales (by M. Rizello)

	VF	EF
— Silver, 57mm	—	£50
— Bronze gilt, 57mm...	—	£35
— Silver, 45mm	—	£35
— Gold, 32mm	—	£185
— Silver, 32mm	—	£35
— Bronze, 32mm	—	£15

QUEEN ELIZABETH THE QUEEN MOTHER
1980 80th Birthday (by L. Durbin)

	VF	EF
— Silver, 57mm	—	£50
— Silver, 38mm	—	£35
— Bronze, 38mm	—	£20

Edward VIII Abdication, 1936

N.B.—Official Medals usually command a premium when still in their original cases of issue.

COIN
grading

CONDITION is the secret to the value of virtually anything, whether it be antiques, jewellery, horses or second-hand cars—and coins are *certainly* no exception. When collecting coins it is vital to understand the recognised standard British system of grading, i.e. accurately assessing a coin's condition or state of wear. Grading is an art which can only be learned by experience and so often it remains one person's opinion against another's, therefore it is important for the beginner or inexperienced collector to seek assistance from a reputable dealer or knowledgeable numismatist when making major purchases.

The standard grades as used in the Price Guide are as follows:

UNC — **Uncirculated**
A coin that has never been in circulation, although it may show signs of contact with other coins during the minting process.

EF — **Extremely Fine**
A coin in this grade may appear uncirculated to the naked eye but on closer examination will show signs of minor friction on the highest surface.

VF — **Very Fine**
A coin that has had very little use, but shows signs of wear on the high surfaces.

F — **Fine**
A coin that has been in circulation and shows general signs of wear, but with all legends and date clearly visible.

Other grades used in the normal grading system are:

BU — **Brilliant Uncirculated**
As the name implies, a coin retaining its mint lustre.

Fair — A coin extensively worn but still quite recognisable and legends readable.

Poor — A coin very worn and only just recognisable.

Other abbreviations used in the Price Guide are:

Obv — **Obverse**

Rev — **Reverse**

Other abbreviations, mintmarks, etc. can be identified under the appropriate section of this Yearbook.

Directory section

ON the following pages will be found the most useful names and addresses needed by the coin collector.

At the time of going to press with this edition of the YEARBOOK the information is correct, as far as we have been able to ascertain. However, people move and establishments change, so it is always advisable to make contact with the person or organisation listed before travelling any distance, to ensure that the journey is not wasted.

Should any of the information in this section not be correct we would very much appreciate being advised in good time for the preparation of the next edition of the COIN YEARBOOK.

Dealers who display this symbol are Members of the

BRITISH NUMISMATIC TRADE ASSOCIATION

The primary purpose of the Association is to promote and safeguard the highest standards of professionalism in dealings between its Members and the public. In official consultations it is the recognised representative of commercial numismatics in Britain.

For free a Membership Directory please send a stamped addressed envelope to:
General Secretary, BNTA
PO Box 2, Rye, East Sussex TN31 7WE
Tel/Fax: 01797 229988
E-mail: bnta@lineone.net

www.bnta.net

The BNTA will be organising the following events:

COINEX 2007 28 & 29 September

at Earls Court Conference Centre, Warwick Road, London SW5 9TA

COINEX 2008 For details please apply to Secretary.

The BNTA is a member of the International Numismatic Commisson.

BNTA MEMBERSHIPS IN COUNTY ORDER

(Those members with a retail premises
are indicated with an*)

LONDON AREA
*A.H. Baldwin & Sons Ltd.
ATS Bullion Ltd
Beaver Coin Room
* Classical Numismatic
Group Inc / Seaby Coins
*Philip Cohen Numismatics
Andre de Clermont
Michael Dickinson
*Dix Noonan Webb
Christopher Eimer
Glendining's
Harrow Coin & Stamp Centre
*Knightsbridge Coins
Lubbock & Son Ltd.
C. J. Martin (Coins) Ltd.
Morton & Eden Ltd.
Moruzzi Ltd
*Colin Narbeth & Son Ltd.
Numismatica Ars Classica
*Pavlos S Pavlou
Simmons Gallery
*Spink & Son Ltd.
Surena Ancient Art &
Numismatic
BEDFORSHIRE
Simon Monks
BERKSHIRE
Frank Milward
BRISTOL
Saltford Coins
BUCKINGHAMSHIRE
Charles Riley
CORNWALL
Richard W Jeffery

DEVON
Glenn S Ogden
DORSET
*Dorset Coin Co. Ltd.
ESSEX
Time Line Originals
HAMPSHIRE
*SPM Jewellers
Studio Coins
*Victory Coins
West Essex Coin Investments
HERTFORDSHIRE
K B Coins
KENT
London Coins
*Peter Morris
LANCASHIRE
*Colin de Rouffignac
*Peter Ireland Ltd.
*R & L Coins
James Murphy
LINCOLNSHIRE
Grantham Coins
MONMOUTHSHIRE
Anthony M. Halse
NORFOLK
*Roderick Richardson
Chris Rudd
NORTHAMPTONSHIRE
*Giuseppe Miceli Coin &
Medal Centre
NORTHUMBERLAND
*Corbitt Stamps Ltd.
SHROPSHIRE
*Collectors Gallery

SUFFOLK
*Lockdale Coins Ltd
Mike R. Vosper Coins
SURREY
The Duncannon Partnership
KMCC Ltd
Graeme & Linda Monk
Mark Rasmussen
Numismatist
Nigel Tooley Ltd
SUSSEX
*Brighton Coin Co.
WEST MIDLANDS
*Birmingham Coins
David Craddock
*Format of Birmingham Ltd.
Mint Coins Ltd
WARWICKSHIRE
*Peter Viola
*Warwick & Warwick Ltd
WORCESTERSHIRE
J. Whitmore
YORKSHIRE
Airedale Coins
Paul Clayton
Paul Davies Ltd.
*J. Smith
Weighton Coin Wonders
WALES
Lloyd Bennett
*Cardiff Coins & Medals
*North Wales Coins Ltd.
Colin Rumney

Museums and Libraries

Listed below are the Museums and Libraries in the UK which have coins or items of numismatic interest on display or available to the general public.

A

Anthropological Museum, University of Aberdeen, Broad Street, **Aberdeen,** AB9 1AS (01224 272014).

Curtis Museum (1855), High Street, **Alton,** Hants (01420 2802). *General collection of British coins.*

Ashburton Museum, 1 West Street, **Ashburton,** Devon. *Ancient British and Roman antiquities including local coin finds.*

Ashwell Village Museum (1930), Swan Street, **Ashwell,** Baldock, Herts. *Roman coins from local finds, local trade tokens, Anglo-Gallic coins and jetons.*

Buckinghamshire County Museum (1862), Church Street, **Aylesbury,** Bucks (01296 88849). *Roman and medieval English coins found locally, 17th/18th century Buckinghamshire tokens, commemorative medals.*

B

Public Library and Museum (1948), Marlborough Road, **Banbury,** Oxon (01295 259855). *Wrexlin Hoard of Roman coins.*

Museum of North Devon (1931), The Square, **Barnstaple,** EX32 8LN (01271 46747). *General coin and medal collection, including local finds. Medals of the Royal Devonshire Yeomanry.*

Roman Baths Museum, Pump Room, **Bath,** Avon (01225 461111 ext 2785). *Comprehensive collection of Roman coins from local finds.*

Bagshaw Museum and Art Gallery (1911), Wilton Park, **Batley,** West Yorkshire (01924 472514). *Roman, Scottish, Irish, English hammered, British and foreign coins, local traders' tokens, political medalets, campaign medals and decorations.*

Bedford Museum (1961), Castle Lane, **Bedford** (01234 353323). *Collections of the Bedford Library and Scientific Institute, the Beds Archaeological Society and Bedford Modern School (Pritchard Memorial) Museum.*

Ulster Museum (1928), Botanic Gardens, **Belfast** BT9 5AB (01232 381251). *Irish, English and British coins and commemorative medals.*

Berwick Borough Museum (1867), The Clock Block, Berwick Barracks, Ravensdowne, **Berwick.** TD15 1DQ (01289 330044). *Roman, Scottish and medievial coins.*

Public Library, Art Gallery and Museum (1910), Champney Road, **Beverley,** Humberside (01482 882255). *Beverley trade tokens, Roman, English, British and foreign coins.*

Bignor Roman Villa (1811), **Bignor,** nr Pulborough, West Sussex (017987 202). *Roman coins found locally.*

City Museum and Art Gallery (1861), Chamberlain Square, **Birmingham** B3 3DH (0121 235 2834). *Coins, medals and tokens, with special emphasis on the products of the Soho, Heaton, Birmingham and Watt mints.*

Blackburn Museum, Museum Street, **Blackburn,** Lancs (01254 667130). *Incorporates the Hart (5,000 Greek, Roman and early English) and Hornby (500 English coins) collections, as well as the museum's own collection of British and Commonwealth coins.*

Museum Collection, Town Hall, **Bognor Regis,** West Sussex. *Roman, English and British coins and trade tokens.*

Museum and Art Gallery,(1893), Civic Centre, **Bolton,** Lancashire (01204 22311 ext 2191). *General collection of about 3000 British and foreign coins, and over 500 British medals. Numismatic library.*

Art Gallery and Museum, Central Library, Oriel Road, **Bootle,** Lancs. *Greek, Roman, English, British and some foreign coins, local trade tokens.*

Roman Town and Museum (1949) Main Street, **Boroughbridge,** N. Yorks. YO2 3PH (01423 322768). *Roman coins.*

The Museum (1929), The Guildhall, **Boston,** Lincs (01205 365954). *Small collection of English coins.*

Natural Science Society Museum (1903), 39 Christchurch Road, **Bournemouth,** Dorset (01202 553525). *Greek, Roman and English hammered coins (including the Hengistbury Hoard), local trade tokens.*

Bolling Hall Museum (1915), Bolling Hall Road, **Bradford,** West Yorkshire BD4 7LP (01274 723057). *Some 2,000 coins and tokens, mostly 18th–20th centuries.*

Cartwright Hall Museum and Art Gallery (1904), Lister Park, **Bradford,** West Yorkshire BD9 4NS (01274 493313). *Roman coins found locally.*

Museum and Art Gallery (1932), South Street, **Bridport,** Dorset (01308 22116). *Roman coins, mainly from excavations at Claudian Fort.*

The City Museum (1820), Queen's Road, **Bristol** BS8 1RL (0117 9 27256). *Ancient British, Roman (mainly from local hoards), English hammered coins, especially from the Bristol mint, and several hundred local trade tokens.*

District Library and Museum (1891), Terrace Road, **Buxton,** Derbyshire SK17 6DU (01298 24658). *English and British coins, tokens and commemorative medals. Numismatic library.*

C

Segontium Museum (1928), Beddgelert Road, **Caernarfon,** Gwynedd (01286 675625) *Roman coins and artifacts excavated from the fort.*

Fitzwilliam Museum (1816), Department of Coins and Medals, Trumpington Street, **Cambridge** (01223 332900). *Ancient, English, medieval European, oriental coins, medals, plaques, seals and cameos.*

National Museum & Galleries of Wales, Cathays Park, **Cardiff** (029 20397951). *Greek, Celtic, Roman and British coins and tokens with the emphasis on Welsh interest. Also military, civilian and commemorative medals.*

Guildhall Museum (1979), Greenmarket, **Carlisle,** Cumbria (01228 819925). *General collection of coins and medals.*

Tullie House (1877), Castle Street, **Carlisle,** Cumbria (01228 34781). *Roman, medieval and later coins from local finds, including medieval counterfeiter's coin-moulds.*

Gough's Caves Museum (1934), The Cliffs, **Cheddar,** Somerset (01934 343). *Roman coins.*

Chelmsford and Essex Museum (1835), Oaklands Park, Moulsham Street, **Chelmsford,** Essex CM2 9AQ (01245 615100). *Ancient British, Roman, medieval and later coins mainly from local finds, local medals.*

Town Gate Museum (1949), **Chepstow,** Gwent. *Local coins and trade tokens.*

Grosvenor Museum (1886), Grosvenor Street, **Chester** (01244 21616). *Roman coins from the fortress site, Anglo-Saxon, English medieval and post-medieval coins of the Chester and Rhuddlan mints, trade tokens of Chester and Cheshire, English and British milled coins.*

Public Library (1879), Corporation Street, **Chesterfield,** Derbyshire (01246 2047). *Roman coins from local finds, Derbyshire trade tokens, medals, seals and railway passes. Numismatic library. Numismatic library and publications.*

Red House Museum (1919), Quay Road, **Christchurch,** Dorset (01202 482860). *Coins of archaeological significance from Hampshire and Dorset, notably the South Hants Hoard, ancient British, Armorican, Gallo-Belgic, Celtic and Roman coins, local trade tokens and medals.*

Corinium Museum (1856), Park Street, **Cirencester,** Glos (01285 655611). *Roman coins from archaeological excavations.*

Colchester and Essex Museum (1860), The Castle, **Colchester,** Essex (01206 712931/2). *Ancient British and Roman coins from local finds, medieval coins (especially the Colchester Hoard), later English and Essex trade tokens, commemorative medals.*

D

Public Library, Museum and Art Gallery (1921), Crown Street, **Darlington,** Co Durham (01325 463795). *General collection of coins, medals and tokens.*

Borough Museum (1908), Central Park, **Dartford,** Kent (01322 343555). *Roman, medieval and later English hammered coins, trade tokens and commemorative medals.*

Dartmouth Museum (1953), The Butterknowle, **Dartmouth,** Devon (01803 832923). *Coins and medals of a historical and maritime nature.*

Museum and Art Gallery (1878), The Strand, **Derby** (01332 255586). *Roman coins, English silver and copper regal coins, Derbyshire tradesmen's tokens, British campaign medals and decorations of the Derbyshire Yeomanry and the 9/12 Royal Lancers.*

Museum and Art Gallery (1909), Chequer Road, **Doncaster,** South Yorkshire (01302 734293). *General collection of English and foreign silver and bronze coins. Representative collection of Roman imperial silver and bronze coins, including a number from local hoards. English trade tokens, principally of local issues, medals.*

Dorset County Museum(1846), **Dorchester,** Dorset (01305 262735). *British, Roman, medieval and later coins of local interest.*

Central Museum (1884), Central Library, St James's Road, **Dudley,** West Midlands (01384 453576). *Small general collection of coins, medals and tokens.*

Burgh Museum (1835), The Observatory, Corberry Hill, **Dumfries** (01387 53374). *Greek, Roman, Anglo-Saxon, medieval English and Scottish coins, especially from local hoards. Numismatic library.*

Dundee Art Galleries and Museums (1873). Albert Square, **Dundee** DD1 1DA (01382 23141). *Coins and medals of local interest.*

The Cathedral Treasury (995 AD), The College, **Durham** (0191-384 4854). *Greek and Roman coins bequeathed by Canon Sir George Wheeler (1724), general collection of medals from the Renaissance to modern times, medieval English coins, especially those struck at the Durham ecclesiastical mint.*

Durham Heritage Centre, St Mary le Bow, North Bailey, **Durham** (0191-384 2214). *Roman, medieval and later coins, mainly from local finds.*

E

Royal Museum of Scotland (1781), Queen Street, **Edinburgh** EH1 (0131 225 7534). *Roman, Anglo-Saxon, Englsh and Scottish coins, trade tokens, commemorative medals and communion tokens. Numismatic library. Publications.*

Royal Albert Memorial Museum (1868), Queen St, **Exeter** EX4 3RX (01392 265858). *Roman and medieval. Coins of the Exeter Mint.*

G

Hunterian Museum (1807), Glasgow University, University Avenue, **Glasgow** G12 8QQ (041 339 8855). *Greek, Roman, Byzantine, Scottish, English and Irish coins, Papal and other European medals, Indian and Oriental coins, trade and communion tokens.*

Art Gallery and Museum (1888), Kelvingrove, **Glasgow** G3 (0141 357 3929). *General collection of coins, trade tokens, communion tokens, commemorative and military medals.*

Museum of Transport (1974), Kelvin Hall, Bunhouse Road, **Glasgow** G3 (0141 357 3929). *Transport tokens and passes, commemorative medals, badges and insignia of railway companies and shipping lines.*

City Museum and Art Gallery (1859), Brunswick Road, **Gloucester** (01452 524131). *Ancient British, Roman, Anglo-Saxon (from local finds), early medieval (from local mints), Gloucestershire trade tokens.*

Guernsey Museum and Art Gallery, St Peter Port, **Guernsey** (01481 726518). *Armorican, Roman, medieval and later coins, including the coins, medals, tokens and paper money of Guernsey.*

Guildford Museum (1898), Castle Arch, **Guildford**, Surrey GU1 3SX (01483 444750). *Roman and medieval coins and later medals.*

H

Gray Museum and Art Gallery, Clarence Road, **Hartlepool**, Cleveland (01429 268916). *General collection, including coins from local finds.*

Public Museum and Art Gallery (1890), John's Place, Cambridge Road, **Hastings,** East Sussex (01424 721952). *General collection of English and British coins, collection of Anglo-Saxon coins from Sussex mints.*

City Museum (1874), Broad Street, **Hereford** (01432 268121 ext 207). *Coins from the Hereford mint and local finds, Herefordshire trade tokens, general collection of later coins and medals.*

Hertford Museum (1902), 18 Bull Plain, **Hertford** (01992 582686). *British, Roman, medieval and later English coins and medals.*

Honiton and Allhallows Public Museum (1946), High Street, **Honiton,** Devon (01404 44966). *Small general collection, including coins from local finds.*

Museum and Art Gallery (1891), 19 New Church Road, **Hove,** East Sussex (01273 779410). *English coins, Sussex trade tokens and hop tallies, campaign medals, orders and decorations, commemorative medals.*

Tolson Memorial Museum (1920), Ravensknowle Park, **Huddersfield,** West Yorkshire (01484 541455). *Representative collection of British coins and tokens, Roman and medieval coins, mainly from local finds.*

Hull and East Riding Museum (1928), 36 High Street, **Hull** (01482 593902). *Celtic, Roman and medieval coins and artifacts from local finds. Some later coins including tradesmen's tokens.*

I

The Manx Museum, Douglas, **Isle of Man** (01624 675522). *Roman, Celtic, Hiberno-Norse, Viking, medieval English and Scottish coins, mainly from local finds, Manx traders' tokens from the 17th to 19th centuries, Manx coins from 1709 to the present day.*

J

Jersey Museum, Weighbridge, St Helier, **Jersey** (01534 30511). *Armorican, Gallo-Belgic, Roman, medieval English and French coins, coins, paper money and tokens of Jersey.*

K

Dick Institute Museum and Art Gallery (1893), Elmbank Avenue, **Kilmarnock,** Ayrshire (01563 26401). *General collection of coins and medals, and the Hunter-Selkirk collection of communion tokens.*

L

City Museum (1923), Old Town Hall, Market Square, **Lancaster** (01524 64637). *Roman, Anglo-Saxon, medieval English coins, provincial trade tokens, medals of the King's Own Royal Lancashire Regiment.*

City Museum (1820), Municipal Buildings, The Headrow, **Leeds,** West Yorkshire (01532 478279). *Greek, Roman, Anglo-Saxon, English medieval, Scottish, Irish, British, Commonwealth and foreign coins. Several Roman and Saxon hoards. The Backhouse collection of Yorkshire banknotes, the Thornton collection of Yorkshire tokens, British and foreign commemorative medals.*

Leicester Museum and Art Gallery (1849), New Walk, **Leicester** (01533 554100). *Roman, medieval and later coins, mainly from local finds, tokens, commemorative medals, campaign medals and decorations.*

Pennington Hall Museum and Art Gallery, **Leigh,** Lancashire. *General collection of Roman, English and British coins and medals.*

Museum and Art Gallery (1914), Broadway, **Letchworth,** Herts (01462 65647). *Ancient British coins minted at Camulodunum, Roman, medieval and English coins, Hertfordshire trade tokens, commemorative and campaign medals.*

City Library, Art Gallery and Museum (1859), Bird Street, **Lichfield,** Staffs (01543 2177). *Roman, medieval and later English coins, Staffordshire trade tokens and commemorative medals.*

Liverpool Museum(1851), William Brown Street, **Liverpool** L3 8EN (0151 207 0001). *General collection of Roman, medievaland later British coins, tokens.*

Bank of England Museum, Threadneedle Street, **London** EC2 (020-7601 5545). *Exhibits relating to gold bullion, coins, tokens and medals, the design and manufacture of banknotes, and a comprehensive collection of bank notes dating from the 17th century to the present day.*

British Museum(1752), HSBC Coin Gallery, Great Russell Street, **London** WC1 (020-7636 1555). *Almost a million coins, medals, tokens and badges of all period from Lydia, 7th century BC to the present time. Extensive library of books and periodicals.*

British Numismatic Society (1903), Warburg Institute, Woburn Square, **London** WC1. *Library containing over 5,000 volumes, including sale catalogues, periodicals and pamphlets. Open to members only.*

Cuming Museum (1906), Walworth Road, **London** SE17 (020-7703 3324/5529). *Some 8,000 items, including Greek, Roman, medieval English and modern British coins, English tokens and commemorative medals.*

Gunnersbury Park Museum (1927), Acton, **London** W3. *Ancient British, Greek, Roman, medieval English, British and some foreign coins, tradesmen's tokens and commemorative medals, including local finds. Small numismatic library.*

Horniman Museum and Library (1890), London Road, Forest Hill, **London** SE23 (020-7699 2339). *General collection, primitive currency, some tokens.*

Imperial War Museum, Lambeth Road, **London** SE1 6HZ (020-7416 5000). *Emergency coinage of two world wars, occupation and invasion money, extensive collection of German Notgeld, commemorative, propaganda and military medals, badges and insignia.*

Sir John Soane's Museum (1833), 13 Lincoln's Inn Fields, **London** WC2 (020-7405 2107). *Napoleonic medals and medallic series of the late 18th and early 19th centuries.*

National Maritime Museum, Romney Road, Greenwich, **London** SE10 (020-8858 4422). *Commemorative medals with a nautical or maritime theme, naval medals and decorations.*

Victoria and Albert Museum (1852), South Kensington, **London** SW7 (020-7938 8441). *Byzantine gold and medieval Hispano-Mauresque coins (Department of Metalwork), large collection of Renaissance and later medals (Department of Architecture and Sculpture). Library of numismatic books.*

Ludlow Museum (1833). The Assembly Rooms. Castle Square, **Ludlow** (01584 873857). *Roman and medieval coins from local finds.*

Luton Museum and Art Gallery (1927), Wardown Park, **Luton**, Beds (01582 36941). *Coins, tokens and medals.*

M

Museum and Art Gallery (1858), **Maidstone**, Kent (01622 754497). *Ancient British, Roman, Anglo-Saxon and medieval coins found in Kent, modern British coins, Kent trade tokens, banknotes, hop tallies and tokens, primitive currency, collections of Kent Numismatic Society.*

The Manchester Museum (1868), The University, **Manchester** M13 (0161-275 2634). *Very fine collections of Greek and Roman coins, comprehensive collections of English, European and Oriental coins, over 30,000 in all.*

Margate Museum (1923), The Old Town Hall, Market Place, **Margate**, Kent (01843 225511 ext 2520). *Small collection of coins, including Roman from local finds.*

Montrose Museum and Art Gallery (1836). Panmure Place, **Montrose**, Angus DD10 8HE (01674 73232). *Scottish and British coins.*

N

Newark-on-Trent Museum (1912), Appleton Gate, **Newark**, Notts (01636 702358). *Siege pieces, trade tokens and coins from local finds and hoards.*

Newbury District Museum, The Wharf, **Newbury**, Berkshire (01635 30511). *Ancient British, Roman and medieval coins and artifacts, later coins and tokens.*

The Greek Museum, Percy Building, **Newcastle-upon-Tyne** (0191 2226000 ext 7966). *Ancient coins.*

O

Heberden Coin Room, Ashmolean Museum (1683), **Oxford** (01865 278000). *Extensive collections of all periods, notably Greek, Roman, English and Oriental coins, Renaissance portrait and later medals, tokens and paper money. Large library. Numerous publications.*

P

Peterborough Museum (1881), Priestgate, **Peterborough**, Cambs (01733 340 3329). *Roman (mainly from local hoards and finds), Anglo-Saxon, medieval English, British and modern European coins, English and British commemorative medals and tokens.*

City Museum and Art Gallery (1897), Drake Circus, **Plymouth**, Devon (01752 264878). *General collections of British and Commonwealth coins and tokens, Devon trade tokens and Plymouth tradesmen's checks, Ancient British and Roman coins from local sites.*

Waterfront Museum, 4 High Street, **Poole**, Dorset (01202 683138). *General collection of British and foreign coins, medals and tokens (view by appointment).*

City Museum (1972), Museum Road, Old **Portsmouth** PO1 (023 80827261). *Roman, medieval and later coins mainly from local finds and archaeological excavation, British coins, trade tokens of Hampshire, commemorative medals.*

Harris Museum and Art Gallery (1893), Market Square, **Preston**, Lancashire (01772 58248). *English and British coins, tokens and medals.*

R

The Museum of Reading (1883), Blagrave Street, **Reading**, Berks (0118 939 9800). *British, Roman and medieval English coins, many from local finds, tradesmen's tokens and commemorative medals.*

Rochdale Museum (1905), Sparrow Hill, **Rochdale**, Lancs (01706 41085). *Roman and medieval coins from local finds, Rochdale trade tokens, miscellaneous British and foreign coins and medals.*

Municipal Museum and Art Gallery (1893), Clifton Park, **Rotherham** (01709 382121). *Roman coins from Templeborough Forts, medieval English coins from local hoards and a general collection of British coins.*

S

Saffron Walden Museum (1832) (1939), Museum Street, **Saffron** Walden, Essex (01799 522494). *Ancient British, Roman, medieval and later coins, mainly from local finds and archaeological excavation, trade tokens and commemorative medals.*

Verulamium Museum, St Michael's, **St Albans**, Herts (01727 819339). *Coins and artifacts excavated from the Roman town.*

Salisbury and South Wiltshire Museum (1861), The Cathedral Close, **Salisbury,** Wilts (01722 332151). *Collection of coins minted or found locally, including finds of Iron Age, Roman, Saxon and medieval coins, as well as 18th and 19th century tradesmen's tokens.*

Richborough Castle Museum (1930), **Sandwich,** Kent (0304 612013). *Roman coins of 1st–5th centuries from excavations of the Richborough site.*

Scarborough Museum (1829), The Rotunda, Vernon Road, **Scarborough**, North Yorkshire (01723 374839). *Over 4,000 Roman coins, 1,500 English and 600 coins from local finds, siege pieces and trade tokens.*

Shaftesbury and Dorset Local History Museum (1946), 1 Gold Hill, **Shaftesbury**, Dorset (01747 52157). *Hoard of Saxon coins.*

City Museum (1875), Weston Park, **Sheffield** (0114 2 768588). *Over 5,000 coins of all periods, but mainly English and modern British. European coins, imperial Roman (including three hoards of about 500 coins each), Yorkshire trade tokens, British historical medals, campaign medals. Library.*

Rowley's House Museum, Barker Street, **Shrewsbury**, Salop (01743 361196). *Coins minted at Shrewsbury 925-1180, Civil War coinage of 1642, Shropshire tradesmen's tokens, English coins and medals.*

Museum of Archaeology (1951), God's House Tower, Town Quay, **Southampton**, Hants (023 8022 0007). *Main emphasis lies in Ancient British, Roman and medieval English coins from local archaeological excavations. General collection of later coins and medals.*

Atkinson Art Gallery (1878), Lord Street, **Southport,** Lancs (01704 533133). *Roman coins.*

Botanic Gardens Museum, Churchtown, **Southport,** Lancs (01704 87547). *English and British coins and medals, military medals and decorations.*

Southwold Museum (1933), St Bartholomew's Green, **Southwold**, Suffolk (01502 722375). *General collection of coins, specialised Suffolk trade tokens.*

Stamford Museum (1961), Broad Street, **Stamford**, Lincs (01780 66317). *General collection of coins, medals and tokens, including a selection from the Stamford mint.*

Municipal Museum (1860), Vernon Park, Turncroft Lane, **Stockport**, Cheshire (0161 474 4460) *Miscellaneous general collection of coins, tokens and medals.*

Stroud Museum (1899), Lansdown, **Stroud**, Glos (01453 376394). *Ancient British, Roman, Saxon, Norman, later medieval English, British coins and Gloucestershire trade tokens.*

Museum and Art Gallery (1846), Borough Road, **Sunderland,** Tyne & Wear (0191 514 1235). *Roman imperial, medieval and later English, including examples of the pennies minted at Durham, modern British and foreign coins, 17th-19th century tradesmen's tokens, local medallions and campaign medals.*

Swansea Museum (1835), Victoria Road, **Swansea**, W. Glamorgan, SA1 1SN (0792 653765). *Coins and medals of local interest.*

T

Tamworth Castle and Museum (1899), The Holloway, **Tamworth**, Staffs (01827 63563). *Anglo-Saxon coins, medieval English including coins of the Tamworth mint, later English and British coins, tokens, commemorative medallions and medals.*

Somerset County Museum, Taunton Castle, **Taunton**, Somerset (01823 255510/320200). *Celtic, Roman, Anglo-Saxon, early Medieval, tokens, medallions and banknotes. Strong emphasis on locally-found items.*

Thurrock Local History Museum (1956), Civic Square, **Tilbury**, Essex (01375 390000 ext 2414). *Roman coins.*

Royal Cornwall Museum (1818), River Street, **Truro,** Cornwall (01872 72205). *Coins, tokens and medals pertaining principally to the county of Cornwall.*

W

Wakefield Museum (1919), Wood Street, **Wakefield,** West Yorkshire (01924 295351). *Roman and medieval English silver and copper coins.*

Epping Forest District Museum, 39/41 Sun Street, **Waltham Abbey**, Essex EN 9. *Ancient British, Roman and medieval coins, Essex tradesmen's tokensof local interest.*

Warrington Museum and Art Gallery (1848). Bold Street, **Warrington**, Cheshire, WA1 1JG (01925 30550). *Coins, medals and tokens.*

Worcester City Museum (1833), Foregate Street, **Worcester** (01905 25371). *Roman, medieval and later coins and tokens. Coins of the Worcester mint.*

Wells Museum (18903), 8 Cathedral Green, **Wells,** Somerset (01749 3477). *Ancient and modern British and world coins, local trade tokens and medals.*

Municipal Museum and Art Gallery (1878), Station Road, **Wigan**, Lancashire. *British, Commonwealth and foreign coins from about 1660 to the present. Roman coins from local sites, commemorative medals.*

City Museum (1851), The Square, **Winchester**, Hants (01962 848269). *Roman and medieval coins chiefly from local hoards and finds. Hampshire tradesmen's tokens and commemorative medals. Small reference library.*

Wisbech and Fenland Museum (1835), Museum Square, **Wisbech,** Cambridgeshire (01945 583817), *British Roman, medieval and later coins, medals and tokens.*

Y

The Museum of South Somerset (1928), Hendford, **Yeovil**, Somerset (01935 24774). *Roman coins from local sites, medieval English, modern British coins and medals and a fine collection of tokens (particularly 17th century Somerset).*

Castle Museum (1938), **York** (01904 653611). *English and British coins, campaign medals, orders and decorations, comemorative medals.*

Jorvik Viking Centre (1984), Coppergate, **York** (01904 643211). *Coins and artefacts pertaining to the Viking occupation of York.*

The Yorkshire Museum (1823), **York** (01904 629745). *Roman imperial, medieval English and later coins, about 12,000 in all.*

Club
directory

Details given here are the names of Numismatic Clubs and Societies, their date of foundation, and their usual venues, days and times of meetings. Meetings are monthly unless otherwise stated. Finally, the telephone number of the club secretary is given; the names and addresses of club secretaries are withheld for security reasons, but full details may be obtained by writing to the Secretary of the British Association of Numismatic Societies, Phyllis Stoddart, Honorary Curatorial Assistant, Deptartment of Numismatics, Manchester Museum, Oxford Road, Manchester M13 9PL or visiting the website at www.coinclubs.freeserve.co.uk.

Banbury & District NS (1967). St John's Social Club, St John's Church, Oxford Road, Banbury 2nd Mon (exc Jul & Aug), 19.45. (01295 275128).

Bath & Bristol Numismatic Society (1950). Fry's Club, Keynsham, Bristol. 2nd Thu, 19.30. (01275 851212).

Bedford Numismatic Society (1966).

(01234 228833 / 358369).

Bexley Coin Club (1968). St Martin's Church Hall, Erith Road, Barnehurst, Bexleyheath, Kent. 1st Mon (exc Jan & Aug), 19.30. (020 8303 0510).

Birmingham Numismatic Society (1964). Friend's Meeting House, Linden Road, Bournville, Birmingham 30. 2nd Wed, 19.45. (0121 308 1616).

Matthew Boulton Society (1994). PO Box 395, Birmingham B31 2TB (0121 781 6558 fax 0121 781 6574).

Bradford & District Numismatic Society (1967). East Bowling Unity Club, Leicester Street, Bradford, West Yorkshire. 3rd Mon, 19.00. (01532 677151).

British Cheque Collectors' Society (1980). John Purser, 71 Mile Lane, Cheylesmore, Coventry, West Midlands CV3 5GB.

British Numismatic Society (1903). Warburg Institute, Woburn Square, London WC1H 0AB. Monthly (exc Aug & Dec), 18.00. (01223 332918)

Cambridgeshire Numismatic Society (1946). Friends' Meeting House, 12 Jesus Lane (entrance in Park Street), Cambridge, CB5 8BA. 3rd Mon, Sept–June, 19.30. (01480 210992).

Chester & North Wales Coin & Banknote Society (1996). Liver Hotel, 110 Brook Street, Chester. 4th Tue, 20.00. (0151 478 4293)

Cheltenham Numismatic Society, The Reddings & District Community Association, North Road, The Reddings, Cheltenham. 3rd Mon, 19.45 (01242 673263)

Coin Correspondence Club (1988). Postal only. A.H. Chubb, 49 White Hart Lane, Barnes, London SW13 0PP. (0181-878 0472).

Cornwall Collectors' Club (1990). The Swan Inn, 40 Bosvigo Road, Truro. 1st Wed, 20.00. (01872 73376).

Crawley Coin Club (1969). Furnace Green Community Centre, Ashburnham Road, Furnace Green, Crawley, West Sussex. 1st Tue, 20.00. (01293 548671).

Crewe & District Coin & Medal Club (1968). Memorial Hall, Church Lane, Wistaston, Crewe, 2nd Tue (exc Jan & July), 19.30. (01270 569836).

Darlington & District Numismatic Society (1968). Darlington Arts Centre, Vane Terrace, Darlington, Co Durhm. 3rd Wed, 19.30. (01609 772976).

Derbyshire Numismatic Society (1964). The Friends' Meeting House, St Helens Street, Derby. 3rd Mon (exc August), 19.45. (01283 211623).

Devon & Exeter Numismatic Society (1965). Courtenay Room, The St. James Centre, Stadium Way, Exeter, Devon. 3rd Tue, 19.30. (01392 469111).

Edinburgh Numismatic Society (1996). Department of History and Applied Arts, Royal Museum of Scotland, Chambers Street, Edinburgh EH1 1JF. 3rd Mon, 19.30. (0131 225 7534).

Enfield & District Numismatic Society (1969). Millfield House Arts Centre, Silver Street, Edmonton, London N18 1PJ. 3rd Mon, 20.00. (0181-340 0767).

Essex Numismatic Society (1966). Chelmsford Museum, Moulsham Street, Chelmsford, Essex. 4th Fri (exc Dec), 20.00. (01277 656627).

Glasgow & West of Scotland Numismatic Society (1947). Woodside Halls, 26 Glenfarg Street, Glasgow, G3. 2nd Thu, Oct-May, 19.30. (0141 633 2564).

Harrow & North West Middlesex Numismatic Society (1968). Telephone for details of venue. 2nd and 4th Mon, 19.30. (020 8952 8765).

Havering Numismatic Society (1967). Fairkytes Arts Centre, Billet Lane, Hornchurch, Essex. 1st Tue, 19.30. (01708 704201).

Horncastle & District Coin Club (1963). Bull Hotel, Bull Ring, Horncastle, Lincs. 2nd Thu (exc Aug), 19.30. (01754 2706).

Huddersfield Numismatic Society (1947). Huddersfield Library, Princess Alexandra Walk, Huddersfield, West Yorkshire. 1st Mon (exc Jul & Aug), 19.30. (01484 866814).

Hull & District Numismatic Society (1967). The Young People's Institute, George Street, Hull. Monthly (exc Aug & Dec), 19.30. (01482 441933).

International Bank Note Society (1961). Victory Services Club, 63–79 Seymour Street, London W1. Website: www.ibns.org.uk. Last Thu (exc Dec), 18.00. (020-8969 9493).

International Bank Note Society, Scottish Chapter (1995). West End Hotel, Palmerston Place, Edinburgh. Last Sat (exc Dec), 14.30.

Ireland, Numismatic Society of (Northern Branch). Denman International, Clandeboye Road, Bangor or Shaws Bridge Sports Association,123 Milltown Road, Belfast. 1st Fri (exc Jan) 19.30. (028 9146 6743)

Ireland, Numismatic Society of. (Southern Branch). Ely House, 8 Ely Place, Dublin. Third Fri, 20.00. (0035 3 283 2027).

Ipswich Numismatic Society (1966). Ipswich Citizens Advice Bureau, 19 Tower Street, Ipswich, Suffolk. Monthly meetings, 19.30. (01473 728653).

Kent Towns Numismatic Society (1913). (Mr. R. Josland, 01634 721187).

Kingston Numismatic Society (1966). King Athelstan's School, Villiers Road, Kingston-upon-Thames, Surrey. 3rd Thu (exc Dec & Jan), 19.30. (020-8397 6944).

Lancashire & Cheshire Numismatic Society (1933). Reception Room, 2nd Floor, Manchester Central Library, St Peter's Square, Manchester. Monthly, Sep-June, Sat (14.00). Manchester Museum (May & Dec only). (0161 275 2661).

Lincolnshire Numismatic Society (1932). Grimsby Bridge Club, Bargate, Grimsby, South Humberside. 4th Wed (exc Aug), 19.30.

London Numismatic Club (1947). Warburg Institute, Woburn Square, London WC1H 0AB. First Tuesday of month (except January and August), 1830. (01223 332918).

Loughborough Coin & Search Society (1964). Wallace Humphry Room, Shelthorpe Community Centre, Loughborough, Leics. 1st Thu, 19.30. (01509 261352).

Mid Lanark Coin Circle (1969). Hospitality Room, The Civic Centre, Motherwell, Lanarkshire. 4th Thu, Sep–Apr (exc Dec), 19.30. (0141-552 2083).

Morecambe & Lancaster Numismatic Society. Monthly, 19.30. (01524 411036).

Newbury Coin & Medal Club (1971). Monthly, 20.00. (01635 41233).

Northampton Numismatic Society (1969). Old Scouts RFC, Rushmere Road, Northampton. 1st Thurs, 20.00.

Norwich Numismatic Society (1967). Assembly House, Theatre Street, Norwich, Norfolk. 3rd Mon, 19.30. (01603 419430).

Nottinghamshire Numismatic Society (1948). The Cecil Roberts Room, County Library, Angel Row, Nottingham NG1 6HP. 2nd Tue (Sep-Apr), 18.45. (0115 9257674).

Nuneaton & District Coin Club (1968). United Reformed Church Room, Coton Road, opposite Council House, Nuneaton, Warwickshire. 2nd Tue, 19.30. (01203 371556).

Orders & Medals Research Society (1942). National Army Museum, Royal Hospital Road, Chelsea, London SW3. Monthly, 14.30 (020-8680 2701).

Ormskirk & West Lancashire Numismatic Society (1970).The Eagle & Child, Maltkiln Lane, Bispham Green L40 1SN. 1st Thu, 20.15. (01704 531266).

Peterborough & District Numismatic Society (1967). Belsize Community Centre, Celta Road Peter-borough, Cambs. 4th Tue (exc July & Aug), 19.30. (01733 562768 or 567763).

Plymouth Numismatics Society (1970). Mutley Conservative Club, Mutley Plain, Plymouth, Devon. 2nd Wed (exc Dec), 19.30. (01752 362859).

Preston & District Numismatic Society (1965). Eldon Hotel, Eldon Street, Preston, Lancs. 1st and 3rd Tue, 20.00. (012572 66869).

Reading Coin Club (1964). Abbey Baptist Church, Abbey Square, Reading. 1st Mon, 20.00. (0118 986 0053).

Romsey Numismatic Society (1969). Romsey WM Conservative Club, Market Place, Romsey, Hants SO5 8NA. 4th Fri (exc Dec), 19.30. (01703 253921).

Rotherham & District Coin Club (1982). Rotherham Art Centre, Rotherham, South Yorkshire. 1st Wed, 19.00. (01709 528179).

Royal Mint Coin Club, PO Box 500, Cardiff CF1 1HA (01443 222111).

Royal Numismatic Society (1836). Warburg Institute, Woburn Square, London, WC1H 0AB.(some meetings held at British Museum). Third Thursday of monthly (Oct–June), 18.00. Joe Cribb, Coins and Medals, British Museum, London WC1B 3DG (020-7323 8175).

Rye Coin Club (1955). Rye Further Education Centre, Lion Street, Rye, East Sussex. 2nd Thu (Oct-Dec, Feb-May), 19.30. (01424 422974).

St Albans & Hertfordshire Numismatic Society (1948). St Michael's Parish Centre, Museum Entrance, Verulamium Park, St Albans, Herts AL3 4SL. 2nd Tue (exc Aug), 19.30. (01727 824434).

Sheffield Numismatic Society. Telephone for venue. 2nd Wed, 19.00. (0114 2817129)

South East Hants Numismatic Society. Havant Conservative Club, Havant. Second Fri. Contact: Tony Matthews, (01292 389419)

South Manchester Numismatic Society (1967). Nursery Inn, Green Lane, Heaton Mersey, Stockport. 1st & 3rd Mondays of each month (excl. Public hols), 20.15. (0161-476 3184).

South Wales & Monmouthshire Numismatic Society (1958). 1st Mon (except Bank Holidays when 2nd Mon, 19.30. (For location tel: 029 20561564).

Thurrock Numismatic Society (1970). Stanley Lazell Hall, Dell Road, Grays, Essex. 3rd Wed, 19.00.

Tyneside Numismatic Society (1954). RAFA Club, Eric Nelson House, 16 Berwick Road, Gateshead, Tyne & Wear. 2nd Wed, 19.30. (01661 825824).

Wessex NS (1948). Edward Wright RoomHotel Bristowe, Grange Road, Southbourne, Bournemouth, Dorset. 2nd Thurs (exc Aug), 20.00. (020 7731 1702).

Wiltshire Numismatic Society (1965). The Village Hall, Poulshot, Nr. Devizes, Wiltshire. 3rd Mon, Mar-Dec, 20.00. (01380 828453).

Worthing & District Numismatic Society (1967). Berkeley Hotel, Marine Parade, Worthing, West Sussex BN11 3QQ. 3rd Thu, 20.00. (01634 260114).

Yorkshire Numismatic Society (1909). Swarthmore Institute, Woodhouse Square, Leeds. 1st Sat (exc Jan, Aug & Dec) (0113 3910848).

Society activities are featured every month in the "Diary Section" of COIN NEWS—available from all good newsagents or on subscription. Telephone 01404 44166 for more details or log onto www.tokenpublishing.com

---

IMPORTANT NOTICE
Club Secretaries:

If your details as listed are incorrect please let us know in time for the next edition of the COIN YEARBOOK. Amendments can be sent via post or email jen@tokenpublishing.com

---

IMPORTANT ORGANISATIONS

ADA
The Antiquities Dealers Association

Secretary: Susan Hadida, Duke's Court, 32 Duke Street, London SW1Y 6DU

ANA
The American Numismatic Association

818 North Cascade Avenue, Colorado Springs, CO 80903-3279, USA

BNTA
The British Numismatic Trade Association

Secretary: Mrs R. Cooke, General Secretary, BNTA, PO Box 2, Rye, East Sussex TN31 7WE

IAPN
International Association of Professional Numismatists

Secretary: Jean-Luc Van der Schueren, 14 Rue de la Bourse, B–1000, Brussels.

IBNS
International Bank Note Society

Membership Secretary:
Clive Rice, 25 Copse Side, Binscombe, Godalming, Surrey, GU7 3RU

RNS
Royal Numismatic Society
Dept of Coins & Medals, British Museum, London WC1B 3DG.

BAMS
British Art Medal Society
Philip Attwood, Dept of Coins & Medals, British Museum, London WC1B 3DG.

BNS
British Numismatic Society
Dr K. Clancy, The Royal Mint, Llantrisant, Pontyclun, Mid Glamorgan CF72 8YT

The new
MEDAL
YEARBOOK
2008

is now available from
Token Publishing Ltd

The 2008 edition, published in September 2007
features definitive descriptions of, and prices for, British and Empire Orders,
Medals and Decorations. From Gallantry awards to Campaign medals and from Long
Service to Life-saving, all are covered and illustrated in full colour. This publication is a
must for all medal collectors and military enthusiasts.

Order your copy on line:

www.tokenpublishing.com

YES! I would like to order the Medal Yearbook 2008 for £19.95+£4.00p&p (UK/Europe/World Surface) ❏
YES! I would like to order the Medal Yearbook 2008 for £19.95+£8.00p&p (Airmail) ❏

Your Personal Details

Name ....
Address ....
....
....
....
Postcode...
Telephone ....
Signature ....

Your Payment Details

We accept: *Visa • Mastercard • JCB • Switch*

Card no: ☐☐☐☐☐☐☐☐☐☐☐☐☐☐☐☐☐☐☐

Expiry date:____/____Valid from:____/____

Issue no. (Switch) _____

Authorisation Code*_____

Total incl p&p_____

By cheque: Please make payable to Token Publishing Ltd
(*Last 3 digits from signature strip)

Please send to: Token Publishing Ltd, Orchard House, Duchy Road,
Heathpark, Honiton, Devon. EX14 1YD
Tel: 01404 44166   Fax: 01404 44788
E-mail: info@tokenpublishing.com   www.tokenpublishing.com

Token PUBLISHING

Directory of Auctioneers

Listed here are the major auction houses which handle coins, medals, banknotes and other items of numismatic interest. Many of them hold regular public auctions, whilst others handle numismatic material infrequently. A number of coin companies also hold regular Postal Auctions—these are marked with a P.

Baldwin's Auctions Ltd
11 Adelphi Terrace, London WC2N 6BJ (020 7930 6879 fax 020 7930 9450, auctions@ baldwin.sh, www.baldwin.sh)

Banking Memorabilia
PO Box 14, Carlisle CA3 8DZ (016974 76465).

Bloomsbury Auctions
24 Maddox Street, London, W1S 1PP (0207 495 9494, info@bloomsburyauctions.com, www. bloomsburyauctions.com)

Bonhams (incorporating Glendinings)
Montpelier Street, Knightsbridge, London SW7 1HH (020 7393 3914, www.bonhams.com).

A. F. Brock & Company
269 London Road, Hazel Grove, Stockport, Cheshire SK7 4PL (0161 456 5050 fax 0161 456 5112, www.afbrock.co.uk, info@afbrock.co.uk).

Christie, Manson & Wood Ltd
8 King Street, St James's, London SW1Y 6QT (020 7839 9060).

Christie's Scotland Ltd
164–166 Bath Street, Glasgow G2 4TG (0141 332 8134 fax 0141 332 5759).

Classical Numismatic Group Inc (Seaby Coins)
14 Old Bond Street, London W1X 4JL (020 7495 1888 fax 020-7499 5916, cng@historicalcoins.com, www.historicalcoins.com). **P**

Corbitts
5 Moseley Sreet, Newcastle upon Tyne NE1 1YE (0191-232 7268, fax 0191-261 4130).

Croydon Coin Auctions
272 Melfort Road, Thornton Heath, Surrey CR7 7RR (020 8656 4583, www.croydoncoinauctions.co.uk)

Dix Noonan Webb
16 Bolton Street, Piccadilly, London. (020 7016 1700, www.dnw.co.uk, auctions@dnw.co.uk).

Dublin Coin Auction
5 St. Assam's Park, Raheny, Dublin 5 (00 353 868 714 880)

E2bid.com
PO Box 50, Sevenoaks TN14 6WD. On-line auction.

Edinburgh Coin Shop
11 West Crosscauseway, Edinburgh EH8 9JW (0131 668 2928 fax 0131 668 2926). **P**

Jean Elsen & ses Fils s.a.
Avenue de Tervueren 65, B–1040, Brussels (0032 2 7346356, www.elsen.eu)

Fellows & Sons
Augusta House, 19 Augusta Street, Hockley, Birmingham B18 6JA (0121-212 2131). www.fellows.co.uk

B. Frank & Son
3 South Avenue, Ryton, Tyne & Wear NE40 3LD (0191 413 8749 fax 0191 413 2957, bfrankandson@aol.com).

T. Gillingham
42 Highbury Park, Warminster, Wilts BA12 9JF (01985 216486).

Gillio Coins International
1013 State Street, Santa Barbara, CA 93101, USA (805 9631345—London contact Eric Green 020-7586 3964).

Goldberg Coins & Collectibles
350 South Beverly Drive, Ste. 350, Beverly Hills CA 90212 (001 310.432.6688, fax: 001 310.551.2626, www.goldbergcoins.com)

Graves, Son & Pilcher Fine Arts
71 Church Road, Hove, East Sussex BN3 2GL (01273 735266, fax 01273 723813).

Heritage World Coin Auctions
3500 Maple Avenue, 17th Floor, Dallas, Texas 75219–3941, USA (001 214 528 3500, fax 001 214 443 8425, www.heritagecoins.com)

Kleeford Coin Auctions
19 Craythorns Crescent, Dishforth, Thirsk YO7 3LY (tel/fax 01845 577977). *P*

Fritz Rudok Künker
Gutenbergstrasse 23, 49076, Osnabrück, Germany (0049 541 962020, fax: 0049 541 96 20222, www.kuenker.com)

Lakeland Coin Auctions
The Riverside Hotel, Penrith, Cumbria (venue).
(01946 832693, www.lakelandcoinauctions.
co.uk).

W. H. Lane & Son
65 Morrab Road, Penzance, Cornwall TR18 2QT
(01736 61447 fax 01736 50097).

Lawrence Fine Art Auctioneers
South Street, Crewkerne, Somerset TA18 8AB
(01460 73041).

Lockdale Coins
Shops at: 37 Upper Orwell Street, Ipswich IP4
1BR.(01473 218588, www.lockdales.com).

London Coins
4–6 Upper Street South, New Ash Green, Kent
DA3 8JJ (01474 871464 , info@londoncoins.co.uk
www.londoncoins.co.uk)

Morton & Eden Ltd
45 Maddox Street, London W1S 2PE (020 7493
5344 fax 020 7495 6325, info@mortonand
eden.com, www.mortonandeden.com)

Neales
192–194 Mansfield Road, Nottingham NG1 3HU
(0115 9624141 fax 0115 9856890).

Numismatica Ars Classica NAC AG
3rd Floor, Genavco House, 17 Waterloo Place,
London SW1Y 4AR (020 783 97270,
info@arsclassicacoins.com).

Ponterio & Associates Inc
1818, Robinson Ave, San Diego, CA 92103, USA.
(Fax: 001 619 299 6952, www.ponterio.com).

R & W Coin Auctions
307 Bretch Hill, Banbury, Oxon OX16 0JD
(01295 275128).

Simmons Gallery
PO Box 104, Leytonstone, London. (Tel: 0207
8989 8097. www.simmonsgallery.co.uk
info@simmonsgallery.co.uk) **P**

Spink & Son Ltd
69 Southampton Row, Bloomsbury, London.
WC1B 4ET (020 7563 4000, fax 020 7563 4066,
www.spink.com, info@spink.com).

Stacks
123 West 57th Sreet, New York NY 10019 USA.
(001 866 811 1804, www.stacks.com).

St James's Auctions
43 Duke Street, St James's, London, SW1Y 6DD
(020 7930 7597/7888/8215, www.sixbid.com.

Sussex Auction Galleries
59 Perrymount Road, Haywards Heath, West
Sussex RH16 3DS (01444 414935 fax 01444
450402).

Tennants Auctioneers
The Auction Centre, Leyburn, North Yorkshire
DL8 5SG (01969 623780) www.tennants.co.uk.

Warwick & Warwick
Chalon House, Scarbank, Millers Road, Warwick
CV34 5DB (01926 499031 fax 01926 491906,
richard.beale@warwickandwarwick.com,
www.warwickandwarwick.com

Fairs

Listed below are the names of the fair organisers, their venue details where known along with contact telephone numbers. Please call the organisers direct for information on dates etc.

Aberdeen
Jarvis Amatola Hotel, Great Western Road, also venues in **Glenrothes** and **Glasgow.** *Cornucopia Collectors Fairs. (01382 224946)*

Birmingham
National Motor Cycle Museum, Bickenhill, Birmingham. *Midland Stamp & Coin Fair. (01743 246963, www.midlandfair.co.uk)*

Birmingham
Collingwood Centre, Collingwood Drive, Great Barr, Birmingham. *Dave Burnett Fairs. (0776 5792998)*

Bristol
Patchway High School,Hempton Lane, Almondsbury, Bristol. *Avemart Fairs. (0117 923 6178, avemart@btopenworld.com).*

Dublin
Serpentine Hall, RDS, Ballsbridge, Dublin 4. *Mike Kelly (00353 86 87 14 880)*

East Grinstead
Large Parish Hall, De La Warr Road, East Grinstead. *John Terry Fairs. (01342 326317)*

Exeter
The America Hall, De La Rue Way, Pinhoe, Exeter. *Phoenix Fairs. (01761 414304)*

Leeds-Morley
Cedar Court Hotel, Denby Dale Road, Calder Grove, Wakefield WF4 3QZ. *N. C. S. Promotions. (01552 684681).*

Lichfield
Civic Hall, Castle Dyke, City Centre. *C. S. Fairs. (01562 710424)*

London
Holiday Inn, Coram St., Bloomsbury, London WC1. *London Coin Fair. (020 8989 8097)*

London
Victory Services Club, off Marble Arch, 63 Seymour Street, off Edgeware Road, London W2. *West Promotions. (020 8641 3224).*

London
Jury's Hotel, 16-22 Great Russell Street, London WC1 3NN. *Linda Monk Fairs. (020 8656 4583)*

Plymouth
Lower Guildhall. *Bruce Stamps. (01749 813324)*

Sutton Coldfield
Fellowship Hall, South Parade. *C. S. Fairs. (01562 710424)*

Newcastle upon Tyne
The Royal Station Hotel. *B. Frank & Son. (0191 413 8749*

West Bromwich
Town Hall, High Street. *C. S. Fairs. (01562 710424)*

York
The Grandstand, York Racecourse. *York Coin Fair (01793 513431, 020 8946 4489 or 01425 656459)*

Important annual events

The B.N.T.A. (Coinex)
Tel: 01797 229 988 for details

**The I.B.N.S.
(World Paper Money Fair)**
Email: mike@ogrady.clara.co.uk
for details

Fair organisers—fair details are listed here free of charge. If you would like your fair featured in this section please email your details to jen@tokenpublishing.com

Directory of Dealers

The dealers listed below have comprehensive stocks of coins and medals, unless otherwise stated. Specialities, where known, are noted. Many of those listed are postal dealers only, so to avoid disappointment always make contact by telephone or mail in the first instance, particularly before travelling any distance.

Abbreviations:
ADA—Antiquities Dealers Association
ANA—American Numismatic Association
BADA—British Antique Dealers Association
BNTA—British Numismatic Trade Association
IAPN—International Association of Professional Numismatists
IBNS—International Bank Note Society
P—Postal only
L—Publishes regular lists

ABC Coins & Tokens
PO Box 52, Alnwick, Northumberland NE66 1YE (01665 603851, email: d-stuart@d-stuart.demon. co.uk, www.abccoinsandtokens.com)

A. Ackroyd (IBNS)
62 Albert Road, Parkstone, Poole, Dorset BH12 2DB (tel/fax 01202 739039, website www.AAnotes.com). *P. L. Banknotes and cheques*

Afribilia Ltd
16 Bury Place, London WC1A 2JL (020 7404 7134, fax: 020 7404 7138, email: info@afribilia.com, www.afribilia.com). *Medals, coins, banknotes etc*

Airedale Coins (ANA, BNTA)
PO Box 7, Bingley, West Yorkshire, BD16 1XU (01535 272754 fax 01535 275727, website www.airedalecoins.com, email info@airedalecoins.com). *P. L. British and modern coins of the world.*

David Allen Coins and Collectables
PO Box 125, Pinner, Middlesex HA5 2TX (020 866 6796). *P. L. British and world coins, tokens,*

Joan Allen Electronics Ltd
190 Main Road, Biggin Hill, Kent TN16 3BB (01959 71255). Mon-Sat 09.00–17.00. *Metal detectors.*

Allgold of Sevenoaks
P.O Box 50, Sevenoaks, TN14 6WD (0844 5447952, email: sales@allgoldcoins.co.uk, website: www.allgoldcoins.co.uk) *Quality Sovereigns.*

Ancient & Gothic
PO Box 5390, Bournemouth, BH7 6XR (01202 431721). *P. L. Greek, Roman, Celtic & Biblical coins. British, European and Medieval coins to about 1850.*

Ancient World
16 High Petergate, York, YO1 2EH (01904 624062) 10.30–17.00 weekdays. *Greek, Roman, Celtic and medieval coins, also antiquities.*

ATS Bullion (BNTA)
2, Savoy Court, Strand. London WC2R 0EZ (020 7240 4040, email bullion@atslimited.fsnet.co.uk.). *Bullion and modern coins*

Keith Austin (IBNS)
PO Box 89, Carlisle, Cumbria CA3 0GH (01228 819149, fax 01228 521176, email:kaustin@kabc.freeserve.co.uk). L. *Banknotes.*

Mark Bailey
120 Sterte Court, Sterte Close, Poole, Dorset BH15 2AY (01202 674936). *P. L. Ancient, modern, world coins and antiquities.*

A. H. Baldwin & Sons Ltd (ANA, BADA, BNTA, IAPN)
11 Adelphi Terrace, London WC2N 6BJ. 09.00–17.00 weekdays. (email coins@baldwin.sh) *Coins, tokens, commemorative medals, war medals and decorations, numismatic books.*

Banking Memorabilia (IBNS)
PO Box 14, Carlisle, Cumbria (016974 76465). 09.00– 18.00 (not Sun). *Cheques, banknotes, related ephemera.*

Banknotes of Auld Scotland
Sconser, Isle of Skye IV48 8TD. (01478 650459, website www.scottish-banknotes.com, email: johnaunc@aol.com).

Gene Barmak
PO Box 320, Prestwich, Manchester M25 2WY. (0161 773 0405). *Modern world silver.*

G. Barrington Smith
Cross Street, Oadby, Leicestershire LE2 4DD (01533 712114). 08.30–17.15 weekdays. *Albums, catalogues and accessories.*

Bath Stamp and Coin Shop
Pulteney Bridge, Bath, Avon BA2 4AY (01225 463073). Mon-Sat 09.30–17.30. *British*

Michael Beaumont
PO Box 8, Carlton, Notts NG4 4QZ (0115 9878361). *P. Coins, medals and tokens of the world.*

Beaver Coin Room (BNTA)
57 Philbeach Gardens, LondonSW5 9ED (020 7373 4553). *P. European coins and medals.*

R. P. & P. J. Beckett
Maesyderw, Capel Dewi, Llandyssul, Dyfed SA44 4PJ. (Fax only 01559 395631, email orders@rppjbeckett.com) *P. coin sets and banknotes.*

Lloyd Bennett (BNTA)
PO Box 2, Monmouth, Gwent NP5 3YE (01600
890634). Abergavenny Market (Tue), Monmouth
Market (Fri–Sat) 09.00–16.00. *English hammered,
milled and coins of the world.*

Berkshire Coin Centre
35 Castle Street, Reading, Berkshire RG1 7SB
(01734 575593). 10.00–16.00 weekdays, half-day
Sat. *British and world coins.*

Beron Coins
64 Rosewood Close, Glascote, Tamworth, Staffs
B77 3PD (01827 54541). *P. L. British & world coins.*

Stephen J. Betts
4 Victoria Street, Narborough, Leics LE9 5DP (0116
2864434). *P. L. Medieval and modern coins, counters,
jetons and tokens, countermarks and medals.*

Bigbury Mint
River Park, Ermington Mill, Ivybridge, Devon
PL21 9NT (01548 830717. *Specialists in reproduction
hammered coins*

Birchin Lane Gold Coin Company
6 Castle Court, St Michael's Alley (off Cornhill),
London EC3V 9DS (020 7621 0370 and 020 7263
3981). Mon-Fri 10.00–16.30. *Gold and bullion coins.*

Barry Boswell
24 Townsend Lane, Upper Boddington, Daventry,
Northants NN11 6DR (01327 261877, fax 01327
261391, email Barry.Boswell@btinternet.com). *P. L.
British and world banknotes.*

James & C. Brett
17 Dale Road, Lewes, East Sussex BN7 1LH. *P. L.
British and world coins.*

J. Bridgeman Coins
129a Blackburn Road, Accrington, Lancs (01254
384757). 09.30–17.00 (closed Wednesday). *British &
World coins.*

Brighton Coin Company (ANA, BNTA)
The Hove Coin Shop, Church Road, Hove, (01278
737537) Mon-Fri 9.45–17.30, Sat 9.45–15.30 (closed
alternate Wednesdays and Saturdays). *World coins.*

Britannia Jewellery Co
234 Yorkshire Street, Rochdale, Lancs OL16 2DP
(01706 341046/55507. Mon-Sat 10.00–17.00.

BRM Coins
3 Minshull Street, Knutsford, Cheshire WA16 6HG
(01565) 651480 and 0606 74522). Mon-Fri 11.00–
15.00, Sat 11.00–1.00 or by appt. *British coins.*

Peter F. Broadbelt
10 Dragon Road, Harrogate, North Yorkshire HG1
5DF (01423 562037). Mon-Sat 11–18.00. *Specialist in
Foreign coins.*

A. F. Brock & Company
269 London Road, Hazel Grove, Stockport,
Cheshire SK7 4PL (0161 456 5050/5112, email
info@afbrock.co.uk, www.afbrock.co.uk). *Auctioneers and valuers.*

E. J. & C. A. Brooks (BNTA, IBNS)
44 Kiln Road, Thundersley, Essex SS7 1TB (01268
753835). Any time up to 23.00. *L. British*

Iain Burn
2 Compton Gardens, 53 Park Road, Camberley,
Surrey GU15 2SP (01276 23304). *Bank of England &
Treasury notes*

BBM Coins
8–9 Lion Street, Kidderminster, Hereford &
Worcester, DY10 1PT (01562 744118). Wed-Sat
10.00–17.00. *World coins.*

Cambridge Stamp Centre Ltd
9 Sussex Street, Cambridge CB4 4HU (01223
63980). Mon-Sat 09.00–17.30. *British coins.*

Castle Curios
165 Wellgate, Rotherham, South Yorkshire S60
4DT. Wed-Sat 11.00–17.00. *English coins.*

Castle Galleries
81 Castle Street, Salisbury, Wiltshire SP1 3SP
(01722 333734). Tue, Thu Fri 09.00–17.00, Sat
09.30–16.00. *British coins, medals and tokens.*

Cathedral Coins
23 Kirkgate, Ripon, North Yorkshire HG4 1PB
(01765 701400). Mon-Sat 10.00–17.00.

David L. Cavanagh
49 Cockburn Street, Edinburgh EH1 1PB (0131 226
3391). Mon-Sat 10.30–17.00. *British coins.*

Cavendish Coins
14 Longfields, Ongar, Essex CM5 9BZ. *P. Modern
crown-sized coins.*

Central Bank of Ireland
Currency Centre, Sandyford Road, Dublin 16,
Ireland. *New coin and banknote issues of Ireland.*

Lance Chaplin
17 Wanstead Lane, Ilford, Essex IG1 3SB (020 8554
7154). *P. L. Roman, Greek, Celtic, hammered coins
and antiquities.*

Chard (BNTA)
521 Lytham Road, Blackpool, Lancs FY4 1RJ (01253
343081). Mon-Sat 09.00–17.00. www.chards.co.uk.
British, Commonwealth and European coins.

Chelsea Coins Ltd (BNTA)
PO Box 2, Fulham Road, London SW10 9PQ. (020
8870 5501 Fax 020 8875 1459). *P. World coins.*

Nigel A. Clark
28 Ulundi Road, Blackheath, London SE3 7UG (020
8858 4020). *P. L. Tokens (Mainly 17th century) and
British Farthings.*

Classical Numismatic Group
14 Old Bond Street, London W1X 4JL. (020 7495
1888 Fax 020 7499 5916, website www.cngcoins.
com, email cng@cngcoins.com). *P. Ancient and world
coins. Publishers of the Classical Numismatic Review.*

Paul Clayton (BNTA)
PO Box 21, Wetherby, West Yorkshire LS22 5JY.
(01937 72441). *Modern gold coins.*

André de Clermont (BNTA)
PO Box 3615, London, SW10 0YD. (020 7351 5727,
Fax 020 7352 8127). *World coins, especially Islamic &
Oriental coins, Latin America.*

M. Coeshaw
PO Box 115, Leicester LE3 8JJ (0116 287 3808). *P.
Coins, banknotes, coin albums and cases*

Philip Cohen Numismatics (ANA, BNTA)
20 Cecil Court, Charing Cross Road, London
WC2N 4HE (020 7379 0615). Mon-Sat 10.30–17.30
(half-days Mon and Sat).

Coin & Collectors Centre
PO Box 22, Pontefract, West Yorkshire WF8
1YT (01977 704112, website www.coincentre.co.uk,
email sales@coincentre.co.uk). *P. British coins.*

Coincraft (ANA, IBNS)
44/45 Great Russell Street, London WC1B 3LU
(020 7636 1188 and 020 7637 8785 fax 020 7323 2860,
Website www.coincraft.com. Email
info@coincraft.com). Mon-Fri 09.30–17.00, Sat
10.00–14.30. *L (newspaper format). Coins and
banknotes.*

Coinote Services Ltd
74–74a Elwick Road, Hartlepool TS26 9AP (01429 890894). *P. L. Coins and banknotes 1615 to date. Accessories and books.*

Coins of Beeston
PO Box 19, Beeston, Notts BG9 2NE. *P. L. Tokens, medals and paranumismatics.*

Coins of Canterbury
PO Box 47, Faversham, Kent ME13 7HX (01795 531980). *P. English coins.*

Collecta Coins Limited
PO Box 101, Northampton NN1 3LT (01604 766607/27076). Mon-Sat 09.00–21.00. *World coins.*

Collectors' Corner
Watford Market (off High Street), Watford, Herts (020 8904 0552). Tue, Fri, Sat 09.00-17.00. *World coins.*

Collectors Gallery (BNTA, IBNS)
22 The Parade, St Mary's Place, Shrewsbury SY1 1DL (01743 272140 fax 01743 366041). Mon-Fri 09.00–18.00, half-day Sat. www.collectors-gallery.co.uk. *Coins and banknotes, accessories and related books. Agents for the Abafil range of coin cases.*

Collectors' World
188 Wollaton Road, Wollaton, Nottingham NG8 1HJ. (01159 280347). *Coins, Tokens, Banknotes, Accessories.*

Constantia CB
15 Church Road, Northwood, Middlesex HA6 1AR. *P. Roman and medieval hammered coins.*

Colin Cooke
P.O. Box 602, Altrincham, WA14 5UN. (0161 927 9524 fax 0161 927 9540, website: www.colincooke.com, email coins@colincooke.com). *L. British coins.*

Colonial Coins & Medals
218 Adelaide Street, Brisbane, QLD 4001 (email: coinshop@bigpond.net.au). *Auctions of World coins*

Corbitts (BNTA)
5 Mosley Street, Newcastle Upon Tyne NE1 1YE (0191 232 7268 fax: 0191 261 4130). *Dealers and auctioneers of all coins and medals.*

G. D. Courtenay
58 New Peachey Lane, Uxbridge, Middlesex UB8 3SX. *P. L. Coins, medals, tokens and banknotes.*

David Craddock
PO Box 3785, Camp Hill, Birmingham B11 2NF. (0121 733 2259) *L. Crown to farthings. Copper and bronze specialist. Some foreign.*

Mark Davidson
PO Box 197, South Croydon, Surrey CR3 0ZD (020 8651 3890). *Ancient, hammered coinage.*

Linda Monk Fairs
PO Box 201, Croydon, Surrey CR9 7AQ (020 8656 4583). *Organiser of monthly fairs at the Jury's Hotel, 16–22 Great Russell Street, London, WC1 3NN.*

Paul Davies Ltd (ANA, BNTA, IAPN)
PO Box 17, Ilkley, West Yorkshire LS29 8TZ (01943 603116 fax 01943 816326). *P. World coins.*

Ian Davison
PO Box 256, Durham DH1 2GW (0191 3750808). *L. English hammered and milled coins 1066–1910.*

Patrick Deane
PO Box 800, Orpington, Kent BR6 7XE (01959 533737, fax: 01959 533388). *British coins, tokens.*

Decus Coins
The Haven, Brockweir, Chepstow, Gwent NP6 7NN (01291 689216). *P.*

Dei Gratia
PO Box 3568, Buckingham MK18 4ZS (01280 848000). *P. L. Pre-Roman to modern coins, antiquities, banknotes.*

Clive Dennett (BNTA)
66 St Benedicts Street, Norwich, Norfolk NR2 4AR (01603 624315). Mon-Fri 09.00–17.30, Sat 09.00–16.00 (closed 1.00–2.00 & Thu). *L. Paper money.*

C. J. Denton (ANA, BNTA, FRNS)
PO Box 25, Orpington, Kent BR6 8PU (01689 873690). *P. Irish coins.*

Detecnicks
3 Orchard Crescent, Arundel Road, Fontwell. West Sussex BN18 0SA (01243 545060 fax 01243 545922) *Retail shop. Wide range of detectors and accessories.*

Michael Dickinson (ANA, BNTA)
Ramsay House, 825 High Road Finchley, London N12 8UB (0181 441 7175). *P. British and world coins.*

Dorset Coin Co Ltd (BNTA)
193 Ashley Road, Parkstone, Poole, Dorset BH14 9DL (01202 739606, fax 01202 739230). *P. L. Separate coin and banknote lists.*

Dyas Coins & Medals
30 Shaftmoor Lane, Acocks Green, Birmingham B27 7RS (0121 707 2808). Fri 10.30–18.30, Sun 10.30–13.00. *World coins and medals.*

Eagle Coins
Winterhaven, Mourneabbey, Mallow, Co. Cork, Ireland (010 35322 29385). *P. L. Irish coins.*

Early World Coins
7-9 Clifford Street, York, YO1 9RA (08454 900724).

Eden Coins
PO Box 77, Brierley Hill, West Midlands DY5 2GS (01384 834648). *P. English coins, tokens and medals.*

Edinburgh Coin Shop (ANA)
11 West Crosscauseway, Edinburgh EH8 9JW (0131 668 2928 fax 0131 668 2926). Mon-Sat 10.00–17.30. *L. World coins and medals. Postal auctions.*

Christopher Eimer (ANA, BNTA)
PO Box 352 London NW11 7RF (020 8458 9933 fax 020 8455 3535, email art@christophereimer.co.uk). *P. Commemorative medals.*

Malcolm Ellis Coins
Petworth Road, Witley, Surrey, GU8 5LX (01428 685566, email: malcolm.ellis@wizardvideo.co.uk, website: www.malcolmelliscoins.co.uk) *Collectors and dealers of British and foreign coins and medals.*

Elm Hill Stamps & Coins
27 Elm Hill, Norwich, Norfolk NR3 1HN (01603 627413). Mon. 09.00–17.00, Tues-Wed. 09.00–17.00, Thur. 0900–13.00, Sat. 09.30–15.00 *Mainly stamps, occasionally coins.*

Europa Numismatics (ANA, BNTA)
PO Box 119, High Wycombe, Bucks HP11 1QL (01494 437307). *P. European coins.*

Evesham Stamp & Coin Centre
Magpie Antiques, Paris House, 61 High Street, Evesham, Worcs WR11 4DA (01386 41631). Mon-Sat 09.00–17.30. *British coins.*

Coin Yearbook 2008

Michael E. Ewins
Meyrick Heights, 20 Meyrick Park Crescent,
Bournemouth, Dorset BH3 7AQ (01202 290674). *P.
World coins.*

I. Fine & Son Ltd
Victoria House, 93 Manor Farm Road, Wembley,
Middlesex HA10 1XB (020 8997 5055). *P. British &
World coins.*

Robin Finnegan Stamp Shop
83 Skinnergate, Darlington, Co Durham DL3 7LX
(01325 489820/357674). Mon-Sat 10.00–17.30
(closed Wed). *World coins.*

Richard N. Flashman
54 Ebbsfleet Walk, Gravesend, Kent, DA11 9EW. *L.
P. British banknotes.*

David Fletcher (Mint Coins) (ANA, BNTA)
PO Box 64, Coventry, Warwickshire CV5 6SN (024
7671 5425, Fax 024 7667 7985). *P. World new issues*

Format of Birmingham Ltd (ANA, BNTA, IAPN, IBNS)
2nd Floor, Burlington Court, Lower Temple Street,
Birmingham, B2 4JD (0121 643 2058 fax 0121 643
2210). Mon-Fri 09.30-7.00. *L. Coins, tokens
and medals.*

B. Frank & Son (ANA, IBNS)
3 South Avenue, Ryton, Tyne & Wear NE40 3LD
(0191 413 8749). Website www.b–frank–and–son.
co.uk. Email *P. L. Banknotes and cheques, coins of the
world. Organiser of the North of England fair.*

Frank Milward (BNTA)
2 Ravensworth Road, Mortimer, Berks, RG7 3UU
(01734 332843). Mon-Sat 09.00-18.00. *British and
World coins.*

Galata Coins Ltd (ANA)
The Old White Lion, Market Street, Llanfylin,
Powys SY22 5BX (01691 648 765). *P. British and
world coins.*

G. Gant
Glazenwood, 37 Augustus Way, Witham, Essex
CM8 1HH. *P. British and Commonwealth coins.*

John Gaunt
21 Harvey Road, Bedford MK41 9LF (01234
217685). By appointment. *Numismatic books.*

A. & S. Gillis
59 Roykilner Way, Wombwell, Barnsley, South
Yorkshire S73 8DY. (01226 750371, website
www.gilliscoins.com, email:
catalogues@gilliscoins.com) *P. L. Ancient coins.*

G. K. Coins
36 St George Street, London W1S 2FW (020 7518
0383, fax: 020 7518 0302, george@gkcoins.com,
www.onlinecoins.co.uk/gkcoins).
Rare and common sovereignes. British and world coins.

Richard Gladdle
(01327 858511), email: gladdle@plumpudding.org.
Tokens. P. L.

Glance Back Books
17 Upper Street, Chepstow, Gwent NP6 5EX (01291
626562). 10.30–17.30. *World coins, medals, banknotes.*

Glendining's (Bonhams) (ANA, BNTA)
101 New Bond Street, London W1Y 9LG (020 7493
2445). Mon-Fri 08.30-17.00, Sat 08.30–13.00.
Auctioneers.

GM Coins
www.gmonlinecoins.co.uk/gmcoins, email:
gmcoins@blueyonder.co.uk, (01242 701144)
Hammered and milled coins

Phil Goodwin (ANA)
PO Box 69, Portsmouth, Hants PO1 5SH (02392
423267 or 02392 752006 incl. fax. Email: phil.
goodwin.coins@cwctv.net). *P or by appointment.
L. Ancient coins and antiquities.*

Ian Gradon
PO Box 359, Durham DH7 6WZ (0191 3719 700,
email: ian@worldnotes.co.uk,
www.worldnotes.co.uk). *L. World banknotes.*

Grantham Coins (BNTA)
PO Box 60, Grantham, Lincs (01476 870565). *P. L.
English coins and banknotes.*

Eric Green—Agent in UK for Ronald J. Gillio Inc,
1013 State Street, Santa Barbara, California, USA
93101 (020 8907 0015, Mobile 0468 454948). *Gold
coins, medals and paper money of the world.*

Philip Green
Suite 207, 792 Wilmslow Road, Didsbury,
Manchester M20 6UG (0161 440 0685) *World gold
coins*

R. I. Groves
8 Catherine Street, Dumfries DG1 1JA (01387
266617, website: www.worldcoins.biz, email:
richard@I-groves.demon.co.uk). *P. British & world
coins.*

Ian Haines
PO Box 45, Hereford, HR2 7YP (01432 268178). *P.
L. British and foreign coins and banknotes.*

Anthony Halse
PO Box 1856, Newport, Gwent NP6 2JN (01633
413238). *P. L.English and foreign coins and tokens.*

A. D. Hamilton & Co (ANA)
7 St Vincent Place, Glasgow G1 5JA (0141 221 5423,
fax 0141 248 6019, website www.adhamilton.co.uk,
email jeffineman@hotmail.com). Mon-Sat 10.00-
17.00. *British and World coins.*

Peter Hancock
40–41 West Street, Chichester, West Sussex PO19
1RP (01243 786173). Tues-Sat. *World coins, medals &
banknotes.*

Munthandel G. Henzen
PO Box 42, NL - 3958ZT, Amerogngen, Netherlands.
(0031 343 430564 fax 0031 343 430542,
web www.henzen.org, email henzen.coins@tiscali.
nl). *Ancients, Dutch & foreign coins. L*

History In Coins.com
www.historyincoins.com (01949 836988) *World
Coins*

Holding History
P.O Box 508, Swansea, SA1 9BN (01792 280 797
www.holdinghistory.co.uk) *English hammered and
milled specialist*

Craig Holmes
6 Marlborough Drive, Bangor, Co Down BT19
1HB. *P. L. Low cost banknotes of the world.*

R. G. Holmes
11 Cross Park, Ilfracombe, Devon EX34 8BJ (01271
864474). *P. L. Coins, world crowns and banknotes.*

John L. Homan
Oxford Grange, Marsh Lane, Barrow Haven,
Barrow-on-Humber, South Humberside DN19 7ER
(01469 32109). *P. Greek, Roman and Byzantine coins.*

Homeland Holding Ltd (IBNS)
Homeland, St John, Jersey, Channel Islands
JE3 4AB (01534 65339). Mon-Fri 09.00-2.00. *World coins.*

HTSM Coins
26 Dosk Avenue, Glasgow G13 4LQ. *P. L. British and foreign coins and banknotes.*

T. A. Hull
15 Tangmere Crescent, Hornchurch, Essex RM12
5PL. *P. L. British coins, farthings to crowns, tokens.*

J. Hume
107 Halsbury Road East, Northolt, Middlesex UB5
4PY (020 8864 1731). *P. L. Chinese coins.*

D. A. Hunter
www.dahunter.co.uk/coins, email
coins@dahunter.co.uk. *P., L. UK and world coin*

D. D. & A. Ingle
380 Carlton Hill, Nottingham (0115 9873325).
Mon-Sat 09.30–17.00. *World coins.*

R. Ingram Coins
206 Honeysuckle Road, Bassett, Southampton,
Hants SO16 3BU. (023 8032 4258; website:
www.ringramcoins.com, email: info@ringramcoins.
com. *P. L. Dealers in UK coins*

Intercol London (ANA, IBNS)
43 Templars Cresent, London N3 3QR (020 8349
2207) *P Paper money of the world*

Peter Ireland Ltd (BNTA, IBNS)
31 Clifton Street, Blackpool, Lancs FY1 1JQ (01253
621588 fax 01253 621589). Mon-Sat 09.00-
17.30. *British and world coins, medals and tokens.*

F. J. Jeffery & Son Ltd
Haines Croft, Corsham Road, Whitley,
Melksham, Wilts SN12 8QF. (01225 703143). *P.
British, Commonwealth and foreign coins.*

Richard W. Jeffery
Trebehor, Porthcurno, Penzance, Cornwall TR19
6LS (01736 871263). *P. British and world coins.*

Jersey Coin Co Ltd
26 Halkett Street, St Helier, Jersey, Channel Islands
(01534 25743). Mon-Sat 09.00–17.00. *World coins.*

J. G. Coins
PO Box 206, Southshore, Blackpool FY1 6GZ.
(01253 349138). *P. L British Coins.*

Ian Johnson
PO Box 254, Bolton, Lanc, BL1 9BZ (01204 387322).
P. L. Ancient European and Oriental coins.

I. L. Johnson
63, Sedley Close, Parkwood, Kent ME8 9QZ.
(01634 261037) *P. L. English coins 1672–1967.*

Robert Johnson Coin Co
Zeilerviertel 6, 8232, Grafendorf, Steiermark, Austria
(06644 882 301, email: rjcoinco@aol.com). *British and world coins.*

Jumbo Coins
22 Woodend Lane, Stalybridge, Cheshire SK15 2SR
(0161 338 5741). Fri-Sat 14.00-19.00. *World coins, medals and tokens.*

Kates Paper Money
Kate Gibson, PO Box 819, Camberley, Surrey, GU16
6ZU. www.katespapermoney.co.uk (01252 548026)
Banknotes

KB Coins (BNTA)
50 Lingfield Road, Martins Wood, Stevenage,
Herts SG1 5SL (01438 312661, fax 01438 311990).
09.00–18.00 by appointment only. *L. Mainly British coins.*

K&M Coins
PO Box 3662, Wolverhampton WV10 6ZW
(0771 2381880/079719 50246,
email: M_Bagguley@hotmail. com). *English milled coin*

Knightsbridge Coins (ANA, BNTA, IAPN, PNG)
43 Duke Street, St James's, London SW1Y 6DD (020
7930 8215/7597 Fax 020 7930 8214). Mon-Fri
10.00–17.30. *Quality coins of the world.*

Lancashire Coin & Medal Co
31 Adelaide Street, Fleetwood, Lancs FY7 6AD
(01253 779308). *P. British coins and medals.*

Lennox Gallery Ltd
K12/13, 4 Davies Mews, London, W1Y 1AR. (020
7629 9119 fax 020 7629 9119). *Ancient coins.*

Liberalitas
On-line dealer. (www.liberalitas.co.uk)

Lighthouse Publications (Duncannon Partnership)
4 Beaufort Road, Reigate, Surrey RH2 9DJ (01737
244222 Fax 01737 224743). *L. Manufacturers and
stockists of coin albums, cabinets and numismatic accessories.*

Lindner Publications Ltd
3a Hayle Industrial Park, Hayle, Cornwall TR27 5JR
(01736 751914 fax: 01736 751911, email
lindner@prinz.co.uk). Mon–Fri 09.00–13.00. *L.
Manufacturers of coin albums, cabinets and accessories.*

Jan Lis (BNTA)
Beaver Coin Room, 57 Philbeach Gardens, London
SW5 9ED (020 7373 4553 fax 020 7373 4555). *By
appointment only. European coins.*

Keith Lloyd
45 Bramblewood, The Beeches, Ipswich, Suffolk
IP8 3RS (01473 603067). *P. L. Greek, Roman coins.*

Lockdale Coins (BNTA)
Shops at: 37 Upper Orwell Street, Ipswich IP4
1BR.(01473 218588), 168 London Road South,
Lowestoft NR33 0BB (01502 568468) & 23
Magdalene Street, Cambridge, CB3 OAF. (01223
361163). L. (Shops open 9.30–4.30 Mon–
Sat). *World coins, medals, banknotes and accessories.*

Stephen Lockett (BNTA)
4-6 Upper Street, New Ash Green, Kent, DA3 8JJ
(01474 871464). *British and world coins.*

Lodge Antiquities (John & Margaret Cummings)
PO Box 38, Grantham, Lincs NG31 6AA (01476
593833, emails lodgeantiquities.com). *Ancient coins and artefacts.*

Mike Longfield Detectors
83 Station Road, Balsall Common, nr Coventry,
Warwickshire CV7 7FN (01676 533274). Mon-Sat
09.30-17.00. *Metal detectors.*

Richard M. Lubbock (ANA, BNTA, IAPN, IBNS)
PO Box 352, London E14 7WB (020 7790 5115 fax
020 7790 5445). *World coins and medals.*

Don MacRae Coins
PO Box 233, Uxbridge, Middlesex UB9 4HY (01895
832625). *P. British and world coins.*

David & Georgina Magnay
11 Lake Hill Drive, Cowbridge, Vale of
Glamorgan, Wales UK CF71 7HR. (01446 774335)
Toy and Model Coins, Imitation Spade Guineas.

Mannin Collections Ltd
5 Castle Street, Peel, Isle of Man, IM5 1AN (01624 843897, email: manncoll@advsys.co.uk). Mon-Sat 10.00-16.00. Closed Thu. *IOM coins, tokens, etc*

Manston Coins of Bath
Bartletts St. Antique Centre, Bath (01761 416133. *Coins, tokens, medals.*

I. Markovits
1-3 Cobbold Mews, London W12 9LB (020 8749 3000). *Enamelled coins.*

C. J. Martin Coins (BNTA)
85 The Vale, Southgate, London N14 6AT (020 8882 1509, www.ancientart.co.uk). P. L. Bi-monthly catalogue. *Greek, Roman & English hammered coins.*

M. G. Coins & Antiquities
12 Mansfield, High Wych, Herts CM21 0JT. (01279 721719). *L. Ancient and hammered coins, antiquities.*

Giuseppe Micelli
204 Bants Lane, Duston, Northampton NN5 6AH (01604 581533). *P.L. British coins and medals.*

Michael Coins
6 Hillgate Street, London W8 7SR (020 7727 1518). Mon-Fri 10.00-17.00. *World coins and banknotes.*

David Miller Coins & Antiquities (ANA, BNTA)
PO Box 711, Hemel Hempstead, HP2 4UH (tel/fax 01442 251492). *Ancient and hammered English coins.*

Timothy Millett
PO Box 20851, London SE22 0YN (tel: 020 8693 1111, fax: 020 8299 3733. Website www.historicmedals.com). *L. Historical medals.*

Frank Milward (ANA, BNTA)
2 Ravensworth Road, Mortimer, Berkshire RG7 3UU (01734 322843). *P. European coins.*

Graeme & Linda Monk (ANA, BNTA)
PO Box 201, Croydon, Surrey, CR9 7AQ (020 8656 4583 fax 020 8656 4583). *P. Fair organisers.*

Moore Antiquities
Longmace House, Mill Lane, Arundel, West Sussex BN18 9AH (01243 824 232, 07850 037 091, www.mooreantiquities.com, email moore.antiquities@virgin.net) *Coins and artefacts up to the 18th Century*

Mike Morey
19 Elmtrees, Long Crendon, Bucks HP18 9DG. P. L. *British coins, halfcrowns to farthings.*

Peter Morris (BNTA, IBNS)
1 Station Concourse, Bromley North Station, Bromley, BR1 1NN or PO Box 223, Bromley, BR1 4EQ (020 8313 3410 fax 020 8466 8502, website www.petermorris.co.uk, email info@petermorris.co.uk). Mon-Fri 10.00–18.00, Sat 0900-14.00 or by appointment. *L. British and world coins, proof sets and numismatic books.*

James Murphy
PO Box 122, Chorley, Lancashire PR7 2GE. *(01257 274 381). P. L. Ancient coins and antiquities.*

Colin Narbeth & Son Ltd (ANA, IBNS)
20 Cecil Court, Leicester Square, London WC2N 4HE (020 7379 6975 fax 01727 811 244, website http://www.colin-narbeth.com). Mon-Sat 10.30-17.00. *World banknotes.*

New Forest Leaves
Bisterne Close, Burley, Ringwood, Hants BH24 4BA (014253 3315). *Publishers of numismatic books.*

Peter Nichols
2 Norman Road, St Leonards on Sea, East Sussex TN37 6NH. (01424 436682, website www.coincabinets.com, email coincabinets@freezone.co.uk).

Wayne Nicholls
PO Box 44, Bilston, West Midlands. (01543 45476) *L. Choice English coins*

Northeast Numismatics (BNTA)
10 Concord Crossing Suite 220, Concord MA 01742, USA (001 978 369 9155, fax: 001 978 369 9619, www. northeastcoin.com). *British and world coins.*

North Wales Coins Ltd (BNTA)
1b Penrhyn Road, Colwyn Bay, Clwyd (01492 533023/532129). Mon-Sat (closed Wed) 09.30–17.30. *British coins.*

NP Collectables
9 Main Street, Gedney Dyke, Spalding, Lincs PE12 0AJ (01406 365211Ireland (010 35322 29385). P. L. *English Hammered and Milled coins.*

Glenn S. Ogden
53 Chestnut Crescent, Culver Green, Chudleigh, Devon TQ13 OPT. (01626 859350 or 07971 709427). *P. L. English milled coins.*

John Ogden Coins
Hodge Clough Cottage, Moorside, Oldham OL1 4JW (0161 678 0709) *P. L. Ancient and hammered.*

Michael O'Grady (IBNS)
PO Box 307, Pinner, Middlesex HA5 4XT (020 428 4002). *P. British and world paper money.*

Colin James O'Keefe
5 Pettits Place, Dagenham, Essex RM10 8NL. *P. British and European coins.*

Don Oliver Gold Coins
Stanford House, 23 Market Street, Stourbridge, West Midlands DY8 1AB (01384 877901). Mon-Fri 10.00–17.00. *British gold coins.*

Ongar Coins
14 Longfields, Marden Ash, Ongar, Essex IG7 6DS. *P.World coins.*

Orpington Coins and Medals
242 High Street, Orpington, Kent BR6 0LZ (01689 890045). Mon-Sat 09.45–17.30 (closed Tue). *Coins, medals, banknotes, badges, militaria, cigarette cards etc*

Roger Outing
PO Box 123, Huddersfield HD8 9WY www.banknotes4u.co.uk email: rogerouting@aol.com (01484 860419). *World banknotes*

Tim Owen Coins
63 Allerton Grange Rise, Leeds 17, West Yorkshire *P. L. Quality hammered coins.*

Oxford Coins
25, Weldon Road, New Marston, Oxford OX3 0HP (01865 726939). *British coins.*

P&D Medallions
PO Box 269, Berkhampstead, Herts HP4 3FT. (01442 865127, email P&D@medallions.freeserve.co.uk). *Historical and Commemorative medals of the world. P.*

Pavlos S. Pavlou
Stand L17, Grays Antique Market, 1-7 Davies Mews, Mayfair, London W1Y 2LP (020 7629 9449) email: pspavlou@hotmail.com. *Ancient, Medieval & Modern Coins*

Penrith Coin & Stamp Centre
37 King Street, Penrith, Cumbria CA11 7AY (01768 64185). Mon-Sat 09.00–17.30. *World coins.*

Pentland Coins (IBNS)
Pentland House, 92 High Street, Wick, Caithness KW14 L5. P. *British and world coins and world banknotes.*

Gary Phelps
PO Box 136, Benfleet, Essex SS7 4WG
(garyph@blueyonder.co.uk, www.garyphelps.co.uk)
Modern patterns and crowns.

John Phillimore
The Old Post Office, Northwood, Shropshire SY4
5NN. *L. Foreign coins 1600–1950.*

Philip. P. Phipps
PO Box 139, Tiverton, Devon EX16 0AU (tel 07850
864554, email p.p.phipps@tesco.net). *P. L. World and
German banknotes.*

David C. Pinder
20 Princess Road West, Leicester LE1 6TP (0116
2702439). *P. Greek, Roman and Byzantine coins.*

Pobjoy Mint Ltd (ANA)
Millennium House, Kingswood Park, Bonsor
Drive, Kingswood, Surrey KT20 6AY (01737 818181
fax 01737 818199). Mon-Fri 09.00–17.00. *Europe's
largest private mint. New issues.*

S. R. Porter (BNTA)
18 Trinity Road, Headington Quarry, Oxford OX3
8LQ (01865 766851). *P. L. Ancient and British coins,
some foreign, tokens, banknotes and accessories.*

David Pratchett
Trafalgar Square Collectors Centre, 7 Whitcombe
Street, London WC2H 7HA. (020 7930 1979, fax 020
7930 1152, website www.coinsonline.co.uk, email
info@coinsonline.co.uk). Mon-Fri 10.00–7.30.
Specialist in gold and silverworld coins.

Predecimal.com
Hauptstr. 33, Burkhardsdorf, 09235, Germany.
(+491741 477182) www.predecimal.com. *British coins*

George Rankin Coin Co Ltd (ANA)
325 Bethnal Green Road, London E2 6AH (020 7729
1280 fax 020 7729 5023). Mon-Sat 10.00-18.00 (half-
day Thu). *World coins.*

Mark Rasmussen (BNTA)
PO Box 42, Betchworth RH3 7YR (01737 84100,
website www.rascoins.com, email
mark.rasmussen@rascoins.com).
Hammered and milled coins. L

Mark T. Ray (Collectors World)
188 Wollaton Road, Wollaton, Nottingham, NG8
1HJ. (0115 928 0347). *P. British coins.* Mon-Sat

Rhyl Coin Shop
12 Sussex Street, Rhyl, Clwyd (01745 338112).
Mon-Sat 10.00-17.30. *World coins and banknotes.*

Chris Rigby
PO Box 181, Worcester WR1 1YE (01905 28028). *P.
L. Modern British coins.*

Roderick Richardson (BNTA)
The Old Granary Antiques Centre, King's Staithe
Lane, King's Lynn, Norfolk. (01553 670833, www.
roderickrichardson.com) *L.English, Hammered and
early milled coins.*

Charles Riley (BNTA)
P.O Box 733, Aylesbury HP22 9AX (01296 747598
charles.riley@virgin.net) *Coins, medals and medallions*

F. J. Rist
PO Box 4, Ibstock, Leics LE67 6ZJ
(01530 264278). *P. L. Ancient and medieval coins,
British coins and antiquities.*

Robin-on-Acle Coins
Parkeston House, Parkeston Quay, Harwich, Essex
CO12 4PJ (01255 554440, email: enquiries@robin-
on-acle-coins.co.uk). *Ancient to modern coins and
paper money.*

S. J. Rood & Co Ltd
52–53 Burlington Arcade, London W1V 9AE (0171
493 0739). Mon-Sat 09.30-17.00. *World gold coins.*

Royal Gold
PO Box 123, Saxonwold, 2132, South Africa,
e-mail royalg@iafrica.com (+27 11 483 0161, email:
royalg@iafrica.com) *Gold Coins*

Royal Mint Coin Club
PO Box 500, Cardiff CF1 1YY (01443 623456). *P.
New issues struck by the Royal Mint.*

Colin de Rouffignac (BNTA)
57, Wigan Lane, Wigan, Lancs WN1 2LF (01942
237927) *P. English and Scottish hammered.*

Chris A. Rudd (IAPN, BNTA)
PO Box 222, Aylsham, Norfolk, NR11 6TY (01263
735007 fax 01263 731777, website
www.celticcoins.com). *P. L. Celtic coins.*

Colin Rumney (BNTA)
26 Caer Felin, Llanrheadr, Denbigh, Clwyd LL16
4PR (074 578621). *All world including ancients.*

R & J Coins
21b Alexandra Street, Southend-on-Sea, Essex SS1
1DA (01702 345995). Mon-Sat 10.00–16.00 (closed
Wed). *World coins.*

Safe Albums (UK) Ltd
16 Falcon Business Park, 38 Ivanhoe Road,
Finchampstead, Berkshire RG40 4QQ. (0118 932
8976 fax 0118 932 8612).

Saltford Coins
Harcourt, Bath Road, Saltford, Bristol, Avon BS31
3DQ (01225 873512, www.saltfordcoins.com,
email: info@saltfordcoins.com). *P. British,
Commonwealth and world coins.*

Satin
PO Box 63, Stockport, Cheshire SK4 5BU. (07940
393583 answer machine)

David Seaman
PO Box 449, Waltham Cross EN9 3WZ. (01992
719723, email davidseamancoins@lineone.net). *P. L.
Hammered, Milled, Maundy.*

Patrick Semmens
3 Hospital Road, Half Key, Malvern, Worcs WR14
1UZ (0886 33123). *P. European and British coins.*

Mark Senior
553 Falmer Road, Woodingdean, Brighton, Sussex
(01273 309359). By appointment only. *P. L.
Saxon, Norman and English hammered coins.*

S. E. Sewell
PO Box 149, Stowmarket, IP14 4WD (01449 782185
or 07739 071822, www.sewellmedals.co.uk, email:
sewellmedals@hotmail.com). *Mainly British milled..*

Shepshed Coins & Jewellery
24 Charnwood Road, Shepshed, Leics LE12 9QF
(01509 502511). Mon, Wed-Sat 09.15-16.30. *British
coins.*

Simmons Gallery (ANA, BNTA, IBNS)
PO Box 104, Leytonstone, London E11 1ND (020
8989 8097, email info@simmonsgallery.co.uk,
www.simmonsgallery.co.uk). *Organisers of the
London Coin Fair, Holiday Inn, Bloomsbury,
London W1. L. Coins, tokens and medals.*

E. Smith (ANA, IBNS)
PO Box 348, Lincoln LN6 0TX (01522 684681 fax
01522 689528). *P. Organiser of the Morley, Leeds,
monthly coin fair. World coins and paper money.*

J. Smith (BNTA)
47 The Shambles, York YO1 2LX (01904 654769).
Mon-Sat 09.30–17.00. *World coins.*

Neil Smith
PO Box 774, Lincoln LN4 2WX (01522 522772 fax 01522 689528). *GB and World Gold coins 1816 to date, including modern proof issues.*

Jim Smythe
PO Box 6970, Birmingham B23 7WD (e-mail Jimdens@aol.com). *P. L. 19th/20th century British and world coins.*

S&B Coins
Suite 313, St Loyes House, 20 Loyes Street, Bedford MK40 1ZL (01234 270260). *P. L. British coins and medallions.*

George Sowden
Coins Galore, The Lizard, nr Helston, Cornwall TR12 7NU (01326 290300). *P. World coins.*

Spink & Son Ltd (ANA, BNTA, IAPN, IBNS)
69 Southampton Row, Bloomsbury, London. WC1B 4ET (020 7563 2820, fax 020 7563 4066, website www.spink.com, email info@spinkandson.com). *Ancient to modern world coins, orders, medals, banknotes and books*

SPM Jewellers (BNTA)
112 East Street, Southampton, Hants SO14 3HD (023 80 223255/020 80 227923, fax 023 80 335634, wwbsite www.spmgoldcoins.co.uk, email user@spm.in2home.co.uk).
Tue-Sat 09.15–17.00, Sat 09.15–16.00. *World coins and medals.*

Stamp & Collectors Centre
404 York Town Road, College Town, Camberley, Surrey GU15 4PR (01276 32587 fax 01276 32505). Mon, Tue, Thu, Sat 09.00–17.00, Wed, Fri 09.00–1900. *World coins and medals.*

St Edmunds Coins & Banknotes
PO Box 118, Bury St Edmunds IP33 2NE. (01284 761894)

Sterling Coins & Medals
2 Somerset Road, Boscombe, Bournemouth, Dorset BH7 6JH (01202 423881). Mon-Sat 09.30–16.30 (closed Wed). *World coins and medals.*

Strawbridge
Tanglewood, Ivy Tree Hill, Stokeinteignhead, Newton Abbott, Devon TQ12 4QH (01626 873783, emailjim@strawbridge.co.uk).
P. L. Coins, tokens, medals, banknotes.

Studio Coins (ANA, BNTA)
16 Kilham Lane, Winchester, Hants SO22 5PT (01962 853156 fax 01962 624246). *P. English coins.*

Time Line Originals
PO Box 193, Upminster, RM14 3WH Tel: (01708) 222384. Mobile 07775 651218, Email: sales@time-line.co.uk

Stuart J. Timmins
Smallwood Lodge Bookshop, Newport, Salop (01952 813232). Mon-Sat 09.30–17.00. *Numismatic literature.*

R. Tims
39 Villiers Road, Watford, Herts WD1 4AL. *P. L. Uncirculated world banknotes.*

Trafalgar Square Collectors' Centre (ANA, LM, OMRS)
7 Whitcomb Street, Trafalgar Square, London WC2H 7HA (020 7930 1979). Mon-Fri 10.00–17.30. *World coins and commemorative medals.* **D. A. Travis**
8 Cookridge Drive, Leeds LS16 7LT. *P. L. US coins.*

Michael Trenerry Ltd
PO Box 55, Truro, Cornwall TR1 2YQ (01872 277977 fax 01872 225565, email veryfinecoins@aol.com). By appointment only. *L. Roman, Celtic and English hammered coins, tokens.*

Vera Trinder Ltd
38 Bedford Street, Strand, London WC2E 9EU (020 7836 2365/6). Mon-Fri 08.30-17.30. *L. Coin catalogues and books, albums, envelopes, cases etc*

Robert Tye
7-9 Clifford Street, York, YO1 9RA (0845 4 900 724 e-mail: orders@earlyworlscoins.com. *P. European and Oriental hammered coins.*

Valda Coins
80 Aberfan Road, Aberfan, Mid Glamorgan CF48 4QJ. (01443 690452). *P. L.*

Vale (ADA BNTA)
21 Tranquil Vale, Blackheath, London SE3 0BU (020 8852 9817. Mon-Sat 10.00–17.30 (closed Thu). *British coins and medals.*

Valued History
27 Elm Hill, Norwich, NR3 1HN. (01603 627413. website www.historyforsale.co.uk). *Coins and antiquities.*

Tony Vaughan Collectables
PO Box 364, Wolverhampton, WV3 9PW (01902 27351). *P. L. World coins and medals.*

Victory Coins (BNTA)
184 Chichester Road, North End, Portsmouth, Hants PO2 0AX (023 92 751908/663450). Thurs-Sat 09.00–17.00. *British and world coins.*

Viking Metal Detectors
1 angela Street, Mill Hill, Blacburn, Lancashire BB2 4DJ (01254 55887 fax 01254 676901, email viking@metaldetectors.co.uk)). *Metal detectors and accessories*

Mark J. Vincenzi (BNTA)
Rylands, Earls Colne, Essex. CO6 2LE (01787 222555). *P. Greek, Roman, Hammered.*

Vista World Banknotes
5 Greenfields Way, Burley-in-Wharfedale, Ilkley, W. Yorks LS29 7RB. (Email vistabanknotes@barclays.net).

Mike Vosper
PO Box 32, Hockwold, Brandon IP26 4HX (01842 828292, website www.vosper4coins.co.uk, email mikevosper@vosper4coins.co.uk).

B. M. & S. A. Weeks
PO Box 1447, Salisbury, Wilts SP5 2YG (01725 510311). *L. British coins, world crowns and medals.*

Weighton Coin Wonders
E-shop www.weightoncoin.com (01430 879060) *Modern gold, silver proofs and sets.*

John Welsh
PO Box 150, Burton-on-Trent, Staffs DE13 7LB (01543 73073 fax 0543 473234). *P. L. British coins.*

Pam West (IBNS, BNTA)
PO Box 257, Sutton, Surrey SM3 9WW (020 8641 3224, website west-banknotes.co.uk, email pamwestbritnotes@compuserve.com). *P. L. English banknotes.*

West Essex Coin Investments (BNTA, IBNS)
Croft Cottage, Station Road, Alderholt, Fordingbridge, Hants SP6 3AZ (01425 656 459). *British and World coins and paper money.*

West Wicklow Coins
Blessington, Co Wicklow, Ireland. (00353 45 858767, email: westwicklowcoins@hotmail.com)

R & J White (IBNS)
29 Shortacre, Basildon, Essex SS14 2LR (01268
522923). *P. L. Banknotes and world ephemera.*

Whites Electronics (UK) Ltd
35 Harbour Road, Inverness IV1 1UA (01463
223456 , email sales@whelects.demon.co.uk) *Metal
detectors*

Whitmore (BNTA)
Teynham Lodge, Chase Road, Upper Colwall,
Malvern, Worcs WR13 6DT (01684 50651). *P.
World coins, tokens and medals.*

World Coins
35–36 Broad Street, Canterbury, Kent CT1 2LR
(01227 768887). Mon-Sat 09.30–17.30 (half-day
Thu). *World & British coins, tokens & banknotes.*

Worldwide Coins (IBNS)
PO Box 11, Wavertree, Liverpool L15 0FG. email:
sales@worldwidecoins.co.uk,www.worldwidecoins.
co.uk. *World coins and paper money.*

World Treasure Books
PO Box 5, Newport, Isle of Wight PO30 5QE (01983
740712). *L. Coins, books, metal detectors*

WRB Notes - Rare Currency & Banknotes
PO Box 52, Downham Market, PE38 0WX. *English
and world banknotes. P*

Barry Wright
54 Dooley Drive, Bootle, Merseyside. L3O 8RT. *P.
L. World banknotes.*

I. S. Wright (Australia Numismatic Co)
208 Sturt Street, Ballarat, Vic. Australia 3350 (0061
3 5332 3856 fax 0061 3 5331 6426, email
ausnumis@netconnect.comau. *P. Coins, banknotes,
medallions, tokens.*

B. N. Yarwood (ANA)
Yarwood Hall, Luttongate Road, Sutton St
Edmund, Spalding, Lincs PE12 0LH.
P. British and US coins.

York Coins
P.M.B #387 7211 Austin Street, Forest Street, New
York 11375 – 5354. Tel/fax: (718) 544 0120 email:
antony@yorkcoins.com

Banks, Mints and Numismatic

Bureaux

of the world

Many national banks and mints operate numismatic bureaux and sales agencies from which coins, medals and other numismatic products may be obtained direct. The conditions under which purchases may be made vary considerably. In many cases at the present time bureaux will accept orders from overseas customers quoting their credit card number and its expiry date; but in others payment can only be made by certified bank cheque, or international money order, or by girobank. Cash is seldom, if ever, acceptable. It is best to write in the first instance to enquire about methods of payment.

A

National Mint, Baghe Arg, Kabul, Afghanistan

Bank Mille Afghan, Kabul, Afghanistan

Banque d'Algerie, Sucursale d'Alger, 8 Boulevard Carnot, Alger, Algeria

Banco de Angola, Luanda, Daroal, Angola

Casa de Moneda de la Nacion, Avenida Antartica, Buenos Aires, BA, Argentina

Royal Australian Mint, Department of the Treasury, Canberra, ACT, Australia

GoldCorp Australia, Perth Mint Buildings, GPO Box M924, Perth, Western Australia 6001

Oesterreichsiches Hauptmunzamt, Am Heumarkt 1, A-1031 Wien, Postfach 225, Austria

Oesterreichische Nationalbank, A-1090 Wien, Otto Wagner-platz 3, Austria

B

Treasury Department, PO Box 557, Nassau, Bahamas (*coins*)

Ministry of Finance, PO Box 300, Nassau, Bahamas (*banknotes*)

Bank of Bahrain, PO Box 106, Manama, Bahrain

Eastern Bank, PO Box 29, Manama, Bahrain

Monnaie Royale de Belgique, Avenue de Pacheco 32, B-1000 Bruxelles, Belgium

Banque Nationale de Belgique SA, Caisse Centrale, Bruxelles, Belgium

Banque de Bruxelles SA, 2 Rue de la Regence, Bruxelles 1, Belgium

Casa de la Moneda, Potosi, Bolivia

Banco Central de Bolivia, La Paz, Bolivia

Casa da Moeda, Praca da Republica 173, Rio de Janeiro, Brazil

Hemus FTO, 7 Vasil Levski Street, Sofia C-1, Bulgaria

Banque de la Republique, Bujumbura, Burundi

C

Banque Centrale, Douala, Boite Postale 5.445, Cameroun

Royal Canadian Mint, 320 Sussex Drive, Ottawa 2, Ontario, Canada K1A 0G8

Casa de Moneda, Quinta Normal, Santiago, Chile

Casa de Moneda, Calle 11 no 4-93, Bogota, Colombia

Numismatic Section, The Treasury, Avarua, Rarotonga, Cook Islands

Banco Centrale de Costa Rica, Departamento de Contabilidad, San Jose, Costa Rica, CA

Central Bank of Cyprus, PO Box 1087, Nicosia, Cyprus

Artia, Ve Smekach 30, PO Box 790, Praha 1, Czech Republic

D

Den Kongelige Mønt, Amager Boulevard 115, København S, Denmark

Danmarks Nationalbank, Holmens Kanal 17, 1060 København K, Denmark

Banco Central de Santo Domingo, Santo Domingo, Dominican Republic

E

Banco Central, Quito, Ecuador

Mint House, Abbassia, Cairo, Egyptian Arab Republic

Exchange Control Department, National Bank of Egypt, Cairo, Egyptian Arab Republic

Banco Central de la Republica, Santa Isabel, Equatorial Guinea

Commercial Bank of Ethiopia, Foreign Branch, PO Box 255, Addis Ababa, Ethiopia

F

Currency Board, Victoria Parade, Suva, Fiji

Suomen Rahapaja, Katajanokanlaituri 3, Helsinki 16, Finland

Suomen Pankki, PO Box 10160, Helsinki 10, Finland

Hotel de Monnaie, 11 Quai de Conti, 75-Paris 6e, France

G

Banque Centrale Libreville, Boite Postale 112, Gabon

Verkaufstelle fur Sammlermunzen, D-638 Bad Homburg vdH, Bahnhofstrasse 16–18, Germany

Staatliche Munze Karlsruhe, Stephanienstrasse 28a, 75 Karlsruhe, Germany

Staatliche Munze Cannstatt, Taubenheimerstrasse 77, 7 Stuttgart-Bad, Germany

Bayerisches Hauptmunzamt, Hofgraben 4, 8 Munich, Germany

Hamburgische Munze, Norderstrasse 66, 2 Hamburg 1, Germany

Bank of Ghana, PO Box 2674, Accra, Ghana

Pobjoy Mint, Millennia House, Kingswood Park, Bonsor Drive, Kingswood, Surrey KT20 6AY

Royal Mint, Llantrisant, Mid Glamorgan, Wales, CF7 8YT

Royal Mint Coin Club, PO Box 500, Cardiff, CF1 1HA

Bank of Greece, Treasury Department, Cash, Delivery & Despatch Division, PO Box 105, Athens, Greece

Casa Nacional de Moneda, 6a Calle 4-28, Zona 1, Ciudad Guatemala, Republica de Guatemala CA

States Treasury, St Peter Port, Guernsey, Channel Islands

Bank of Guyana, PO Box 658, Georgetown, Guyana

H

Banque Nationale de la Republique d'Haiti, Rue Americaine et Rue Fereu, Port-au-Prince, Haiti

Banco Central de Honduras, Tegucigalpa DC, Honduras CA

State Mint, Ulloi utca 102, Budapest VIII, Hungary

Artex, PO Box 167, Budapest 62, Hungary

Magyar Nemzeti Bank, Board of Exchange, Budapest 54, Hungary

I

Sedlabanki Islands, Reykjavik, Iceland

Indian Government Mint, Bombay 1, India

Arthie Vasa, Keabajoran Baru, Djakarta, Indonesia

Perum Peruri, Djakarta, Indonesia

National Mint, Tehran, Iran

Bank Markazi Iran, Tehran, IranCentral Bank of Iraq, PO Box 64, Baghdad, Iraq

Central Bank of Ireland, Dublin 2, Republic of Ireland

The Treasury, Government Buildings, Prospect Hill, Douglas, Isle of Man

Israel Stamp and Coin Gallery, 4 Maze Street, Tel Aviv, Israel

Istituto Poligraphico e Zecca dello Stato, Via Principe Umberto, Roma, Italy

J

Decimal Currency Board, PO Box 8000, Kingston, Jamaica

Mint Bureau, 1 Shinkawasakicho, Kita-ku, Osaka 530, Japan

Numismatic Section, Treasury Department, St Helier, Jersey

Central Bank of Jordan, Amman, Jordan

Banque Nationale du Liban, Rue Masraf Loubnan, Beirut, Lebanon

K

Central Bank, PO Box 526, Kuwait

L

Bank of Lithuania, Cash Department, Gedimino av. 6, 2001 Vilius, Lithuania

Caisse Generale de l'Etat, 5 Rue Goethe, Luxembourg-Ville, Grande Duche de Luxembourg

M

Institut d'Emission Malgache, Boite Postale 205, Tananarive, Madagascar

Central Bank of Malta, Valletta 1, Malta

Casa de Moneda, Calle del Apartado no 13, Mexico 1, DF, Mexico

Le Tresorier General des Finances, Monte Carlo, Principaute de Monaco

Banque de l'Etat du Maroc, Rabat, Morocco

Banco Nacional Ultramarino, Maputo, Republica de Mocambique

British Bank of the Middle East, Muscat

N

Royal Mint, Dharahara, Katmandu, Nepal

Nepal Rastra Bank, Katmandu, Nepal

Rijks Munt, Leidseweg 90, Utrecht, Netherlands

Hollandsche Bank-Unie NV, Willemstad, Breedestraat 1, Curacao, Netherlands Antilles

Central Bank of Curacao, Willemstad, Curacao, Netherlands Antilles

New Zealand Post Stamps Centre, Private Bag 3001, Wanganui 4540, New Zealand

Banco de Nicaragua, Departamento de Emison, La Tresoria, Apartada 2252, Managua, Nicaragua

Nigerian Security Printing and Minting Corporation, Ahmadu Bello Road, Victoria Island, Lagos, Nigeria

Central Bank of Nigeria, Tinubu Square LB, Lagos, Nigeria

Norges Bank, Oslo, Norway

Den Kongelige Mynt, Hyttegaten, Konigsberg, Norway

P

Pakistan State Mint, Baghban Pura, Lahore 9, Pakistan

National Development Bank, Asuncion, Paraguay

Casa Nacional de Moneda, Calle Junin 791, Lima, Peru

Central Bank of the Philippines, Manila, Philippines

Bank Handlowy w Warszawie, Ul. Romuald Traugutta 7, Warsaw, Poland

Desa Foreign Trade Department, Al. Jerozolimskie 2, Warszawa, Poland

Casa da Moeda, Avenida Dr Antonio Jose de Almeida, Lisbon 1, Portugal

R

Cartimex, 14-18 Aristide Briand St, PO Box 134-135, Bucharest, Roumania

Bank of Foreign Trade, Commercial Department, Moscow K 16, Neglinnaja 12, Russian Federation

Banque Nationale du Rwanda, Boite Postale 351, Kigali, Republique Rwandaise

S

Numismatic Section, Box 194, GPO, Apia, Samoa

Azienda Autonoma di Stato Filatelica-Numismatica, Casalla Postale 1, 47031 Repubblica di San Marino

Banque Internationale pour le Commerce, 2 Avenue Roume, Dakar, Senegal

Bank of Yugoslavia, PO Box 1010, Belgrade, Serbia

The Treasury, PO Box 59, Victoria, Seychelles

Bank of Sierra Leone, PO Box 30, Freetown, Sierra Leone

The Singapore Mint, 20 Teban Gardens Crescent, Singapore 608928

South African Mint, PO Box 464, Pretoria, South Africa

Government Printing Agency, 93 Bukchang Dong, Chungku, Seoul, Republic of South Korea

Fabrica Nacional de Moneda y Timbre, Jorge Juan 106, Madrid 9, Spain

Bank of Sri Lanka, PO Box 241, Colombo, Sri Lanka

Hong Kong and Shanghai Banking Corporation, PO Box 73, Colombo 1, Sri Lanka

Sudan Mint, PO Box 43, Khartoum, Sudan

Bank of Sudan, PO Box 313, Khartoum, Sudan

Bank of Paramaribo, Paramaribo, Suriname

Kungelige Mynt och Justeringsverket, Box 22055, Stockholm 22, Sweden

Eidgenossische Staatskasse, Bundesgasse 14, CH-3003, Berne, Switzerland

Central Bank of Syria, Damascus, Syrian Arab Republic

T

Central Mint of China, 44 Chiu Chuan Street, Taipei, Taiwan, ROC

Royal Thai Mint, 4 Chao Fah Road, Bangkok, Thailand

Numismatic Section, The Treasury, Nuku'alofa, Tonga

Central Bank of Trinidad and Tobago, PO Box 1250, Port of Spain, Trinidad

Banque Centrale de Tunisie, Tunis, Tunisia

State Mint, Maliye Bakanligi Darphane Mudurlugu, Istanbul, Turkey

U

Bank of Uganda, PO Box 7120, Kampala, Uganda

Numismatic Service, US Assay Office, 350 Duboce Avenue, San Francisco, CA, 94102, USA

Office of the Director of the Mint, Treasury Department, Washington, DC, 20220, USA

Philadelphia Mint, 16th and Spring Garden Streets, Philadelphia, PA, 19130, USA

Franklin Mint, Franklin Center, Pennsylvania, 19063, USA

Banco Central del Uruguay, Cerrito 351, Montevideo, RO del Uruguay

V

Ufficio Numismatico, Governatorato dello Stato della Citta de Vaticano, Italy

Banco Central de Venezuela, Caracas, Venezuela

Y

Yemen Bank, Sana'a, Yemen.

Z

Bank of Zambia, PO Box 80, Lusaka, Zambia

Chief Cashier, Reserve Bank, PO Box 1283, Harare, Zimbabwe

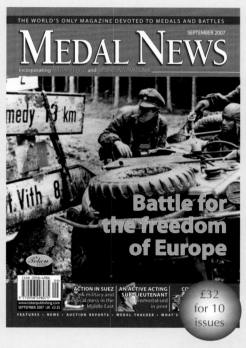

More great titles
from Token Publishing Ltd

Order any of the titles below on line
www.tokenpublishing.com
or call 01404 44166

Numismatics and
The Law

Counterfeit Currency

A counterfeit is a forgery or imitation of a coin or banknote produced with the intention of defrauding the revenue of the State or deceiving members of the public. By the Coinage Offences Act (1861) it was a felony to counterfeit gold or silver coins. Lesser offences included the gilding of farthings and sixpences to pass them off as half-sovereigns, the possession of moulds, machines or tools clandestinely removed from the Royal Mint, the impairment or diminution of gold or silver coins by filing or clipping (or even the possession of such filings and clippings).

The Coinage Act of 1870 made provision for the counterfeiting of base-metal coins, or the stamping of letters or words on coins of any kind, or the forging of colonial coinage. The most celebrated prosecution under this Act occurred in 1930 when Martin Coles Harman was convicted and fined £5 for issuing bronze coins resembling the British penny and halfpenny for the island of Lundy of which he was then the proprietor. Interestingly, no attempt was made to prosecute the Birmingham Mint which actually struck the coins (prudently omitting the H mintmark).

The making of medals or coins resembling current coin became a misdemeanour under the Counterfeit Medal Act of 1883. This Act is invoked from time to time against manufacturers or distributors of medallic pieces or coin jewellery. Such pieces, often struck in 9 carat gold, are deemed to infringe the Act if, for example, they have a figure even vaguely resembling St George and the Dragon on one side. The use of the royal effigy, however, without due authorisation, is regarded as a misdemeanour punishable by an unlimited fine and the confiscation of tools, dies and instruments. At the present time it is a serious offence to make a counterfeit of a currency note or coin with the intention of passing it off or tendering it as genuine. This offence carries a maximum penalty of ten years' imprisonment or an unlimited fine, or both. Making a counterfeit of a currency note or coin without lawful authority incurs a penalty up to two years' imprisonment or an unlimited fine, or both.

Passing or tendering as genuine anything which is known or believed to be a counterfeit of a currency note or coin renders the criminal on conviction to a term of ten years' imprisonment or an unlimited fine, or both. The mere possession of any forged note or coin is itself a criminal offence. Possessing countertfeits without authority or permission so to do, and doing so knowingly, renders the possessor liable to two years' imprisonment or an unlimited fine, or both. The Act also stipulates that the reproduction of a current banknote—of the Bank of England or of the Scottish and Northern Irish banks is a serious offence. This clause covers even such apparently innocent acts as making a photocopy (whether in black and white or full colour) of a current banknote, the photography of such a note or the illustration of such a note in any book, magazine or newspaper. Strict regulations are laid down concerning the legitimate illustration of notes, whether current or not, in books and periodicals; such illustrations must be either greatly reduced or enlarged *and* must bear a prominent defacement, such as SPECIMEN or CANCELLED. It is also a serious offence to utilise a reproduction of a current British banknote in any medium. Theoretically this includes such things as tea-towels, T-shirts, mugs, plates and other souvenirs in glass or ceramics, but in practice the law seems to turn a blind eye to such practices. Imitations and parodies of notes and coins are also regarded as infringements of the law, but in these instances prosecution of the offender seldom proceeds; a warning is generally regarded as sufficient, provided that the offending article or articles are withdrawn and suppressed.

The advent of high-definition colour photo-copying in recent years has brought the offence of reproduction into prominence once more. The regulations have been tightened considerably and there have been several cases of successful prosecution. In each case, however, the intent deliberately to deceive the public by uttering a colour photocopy as a genuine note was proved. Technically the offence takes places as soon as the photocopy is made, for whatever purpose, but as a rule only those cases in which an element of fraudulent deception subsequently arose are pursued with the full rigour of the law. The law is quite clear, however, and it is a criminal offence to make a photocopy or photograph of any current British note unless permission to do so has been obtained from the Treasury. The maximum penalty on conviction is an unlimited fine.

The note-issuing banks have, of course, taken steps in recent years to incorporate further security devices into their notes, notably the use of latent images and underprints in colours which are difficult, if not impossible to photocopy accurately. At the same time, the adoption of metal strips and more complex watermark devices has theoretically made the task of the forger much more difficult. If, by some unlucky chance, someone passes a dud note on to you, you must make no attempt to pass it in turn. To do so renders you liable to prosecution for uttering a forgery. Forged notes must be handed over to the police as soon as possible. If you receive a forged note in payment for goods or services you are entitled to claim its face value from the person who gave it to you. Even if the person giving you the note did not realise that it was counterfeit, it is assumed in law that he or she represented to you that the note was worth its face value at the time the note was passed. If the tenderer knew that the note was forged, he can be prosecuted; but at the end of the day he is still liable to you for the fraud and can be sued in the civil courts for the recovery of the sum involved. If, on the other hand, you received the money as a gift, you have no legal claim against the person who gave it to you. If you pay someone with a counterfeit note or coin unknowingly, you have committed no offence, but you must pay again. The degree of culpability is often difficult to prove or disprove, but it is unlikely that a prosecution would be initiated on the basis of a single note or coin.

It is also a serious offence to manufacture blanks, discs or washers which are intended to defraud the proprietors of vending machines, or to possess tools and equipment for the dishonest manufacture or alteration of such blanks for this purpose. Under the Gold and Silver Export Control Act (1920) melting down gold or silver coins to extract their precious metal content is an offence punishable by a fine of £100 or two years' imprisonment, or both.

Legal Tender

The dictionary defines this as currency which a creditor is bound by law to accept as payment of a money debt. Debts and purchases must be paid for in cash of legal tender unless the creditor or seller is willing to accept payment in another form, such as a postal order, money order, cheque

or, nowadays, credit card. Bank of England notes of any denomination are legal tender in England and Wales. Formerly Bank of England pound notes (but no other) were legal tender in Scotland. Technically, since the demise of the pound note, no Bank of England notes are legal tender in Scotland, although in practice they circulate freely north of the Border. Even more surprisingly, Scottish banknotes are not legal tender anywhere, not even in Scotland! The subtle difference is reflected in the actual wording of the promise on English and Scottish banknotes. Thus English notes are inscribed "*I promise to pay the bearer on demand the sum of . . .*" without stipulating any specific place, the promise being made by the Chief Cashier. Scottish notes, on the other hand, have the promise in the third person. It is the bank itself which makes the promise "*to pay the bearer on demand . . . pounds sterling at their head office here in Edinburgh, by order of the Board*". In practice, however, Scottish banknotes are accepted without question, not only throughout Scotland but also in parts of England, and are generally accepted in London, although there is no obligation on the part of a creditor so to do.

Apart from gold coins, the base-metal pound coin is legal tender for payment of any amounts. So, too, presumably, are the various two-pound and five-pound base-metal coins of recent years, even though they have been struck as commemoratives and not intended for general circulation in the ordinary sense. Smaller denominations are only legal tender up to a maximum value in each case. In the case of 50p coins, 25p crowns and 20p coins, they may be used alone, or in combination with each other, in payment of amounts up to £10. 10p and 5p coins, alone or in combination, may be used for sums up to £5. Bronze 1p and 2p coins, however, can only be used for payment of amounts up to 20p. In practice, of course, you can probably get away with making payment in larger quantities (within reason!) although strictly speaking there is no obligation on the part of your creditor to accept them.

An Offence to Possess Legal Tender Coins

From the foregoing it will be seen that gold coins are, and always have been, legal tender. Since 1817 the legal tender gold coin of the United Kingdom has been the sovereign (with its sub-division and multiples). Yet there have been times when actual possession of these legal tender coins has been, *per se*, an illegal act. The first attempt to regulate the movement and possession of gold coins arose in 1947 with the passage of the Exchange Control Act which made it illegal to buy, borrow, lend or sell any gold or foreign currency, unless authorised to deal in gold. Moreover it was stipulated that "*any person possessing gold should offer it for sale to an authorised dealer at a price not exceeding the authorised price, unless the Treasury consented to this retention of the gold*".

The serious implications of this Act were mitigated in the case of numismatists by the Exchange Control (Collectors' Pieces Exemption) Order 1947, which allowed collectors to hold on to "*any gold coin which was minted in 1816 or earlier, and any gold coin which was minted after 1816 and which has a numismatic value greater than the value of the gold content which would have been received if the coin had been sold to an authorised (bullion) dealer*". In effect this meant that numismatists and coin dealers were not hindered from buying and selling gold coins as long as the coins were in collectable condition and possessed numismatic interest. This loophole was brazenly breached in the 1960s and led to the Exchange Control (Gold Coins Exemption) Order of 1966 which aimed to prevent the loss of currency reserves caused by the import of gold coins from abroad, and to eliminate the hoarding of gold by speculators. By the terms of this Order no one was permitted to hold more than four gold coins minted after 1837 unless they had received express permission from the Treasury. The maximum was set at four coins so that people who had one or two sovereigns as mementoes could keep them without breaking the law. Numismatists who possessed more than four post-1837 gold coins on April 27, 1966 had to apply to the Treasury for permission to retain them. To do so they had to prove that they were *bona fide* collectors by completing form GC 1, providing a detailed list of the coins in their possession—not only in gold, but also in silver (pre-1816, 1816–1919 and post-1919) and base metals (before and after 1860). Several individuals were successfully prosecuted under this draconian legislation and their holdings of gold sovereigns confiscated, although no one was imprisoned or heavily fined as the legislation provided. The 1966 order was rescinded in 1970, re-imposed in a modified form in 1975, and finally revoked in 1979. Since that date numismatists and speculators alike have been free to collect (or hoard) gold to their hearts' content.

Value Added Tax

This is a matter which primarily concerns dealers, but it also applies to those who dabble in coins on a part-time basis, and has implications for collectors at all levels. Briefly, anyone conducting a business, or in self-employment, who has a turnover in excess of £43,000 per annum, must register with HM Customs and Excise for the collection

and payment of Value Added Tax. Anyone whose turnover is less than £43,000 is exempt from the obligation to register, but is at liberty to register if he or she feels that this would be advantageous. It is nice to think that there is an element of choice in this, although one would be hard pressed to think why anyone would voluntarily register for VAT unless they absolutely had to! Incidentally, the government raised the VAT registration level by 40 per cent to £35,000 in March 1991 with the avowed intention of relieving a large number of businesses from this burden, at a time when the rate of tax was increased from 15 per cent to 17.5 per cent. Assuming that you are a dealer with a turnover above the magic limit, then you are committing a serious offence if you fail to register. Registration then lays you open to the full machinery of the system. You have to charge VAT on all goods and services, issuing VAT invoices and receipts and keeping detailed accounts which are liable to snap inspection at any time. You have to make quarterly returns to Customs and Excise of the amount of tax you have collected. From this you are allowed to deduct the VAT which you yourself have paid out in the course of your business, and you then have to remit the difference to the VAT collector. Of course, should the amount you have paid exceed the tax you have collected, you receive a repayment in due course. This arises in businesses which handle zero-rated goods and services, but coins and medals do not come within that category.

For dealers in gold bullion, coins or medals, there is a special VAT leaflet which covers regulations specific to such matters. Since January 2000 investment gold has been exempt from VAT. A coin is classified as investment gold if it satisfies the following conditions: 1. Minted after 1800; 2. At least .900 fine; 3. Is or has been legal tender of its country of origin; 4. Is of a description of coin that is normally sold at a price that does not exceed 180% of the open market value of the gold contained in the coin. This is a complicated issue and further advice can be obtained from Customs & Excise Public Notice 701/21/99. A list of coins qualifying as investment gold is published in Public Notice 701/21A/99. When VAT is applicable of course it needs to be accounted for on the profit margin. It is vital therefore to maintain accurate records of all buying and selling, and which coins and medals are subject to VAT and which are exempt. Furthermore, the onus is on you to ensure that the source of the gold you bring into the country is impeccable. There are extremely heavy penalties for smuggling gold, and ignorance of the law, or apparently innocent handling of smuggled gold subsequently, are no defence.

From January 1, 1995 the special margin scheme

of accounting for VAT currently available for certain second-hand goods, such as cars, was extended to almost all second-hand goods. The scheme allows businesses buying and selling eligible goods to account for VAT only on the difference between the buying and selling prices of these items.

A special system of accounting exists which enables some dealers to account for VAT without the need to keep a detailed record of every transaction. Certain works of art, antiques and collector's items, including "secondhand" coins, defined in Notice 712 *Second-hand goods*, were exempt from VAT at import. From January 1, 1996 these items became subject to VAT at import at an effective rate of 2.5 per cent.

Export and Import

Some coins do require an export licence before they can be taken out of the country and unfortunately these controls have been extended during the past year. Following the lifting of the export regulations relating to gold coins in 1979, then prior to April 1, 1993 the only coins which required any export licence were those with a value in excess of £35,000. However the agreement by the UK to implement an EC directive on the removal of cultural goods has resulted in a fresh interpretation of previous UK legislation on these coins which are on the market as a result of an archaeological find. Therefore as from April 1, 1993, any coin *whatever its value* which has come from an archaeological source within the UK will require an export licence even to take it to another EC country. Certain other coins of EC provenance other than the UK will now require an EC export licence. The value limit for non-archaeological source coins has been increased to £39,600 (Ecu 50,000). Both types of licence are issued by the Department of National Heritage, 2–4 Cockspur Street, Trafalgar Square, London SW1Y 5DH who can also supply a handy flow-chart to enable you to tell at a glance whether a licence is needed and what type.

These new regulations are imposing an enormous additional burden on the trade and the British Numismatic Trade Association has held numerous meetings with the authorities in an attempt to reduce to a minimum the number of licence applications needed. Hopefully, by next year's edition there will be better news.

The restrictions applied to the importation of gold coins were removed in 1979, as previously mentioned. Coins of any kind are now permitted under Open General Import licence from any country and a specific or individual licence is no longer required. Details of any duties which may be payable on imported coins can be obtained from HM Customs and Excise, King's Beam House, Southwark, London SE1 or any local Customs and Excise office. Until recently, the only gold coins under embargo were Krugerrands. This was a political decision, aimed at tightening sanctions against South Africa, and applied to the importation of new gold coins from that country, but not to Krugerrands which had been brought into the United Kingdom, or any of the countries of the European Community, prior to the imposition of sanctions. In practice, it was very difficult to regulate the movement, let alone the importation, of Krugerrands, and with the relaxation of Apartheid this regulation has been lifted.

Importing Coins by Mail

Elsewhere in this volume will be found the names and addresses of mints, banks and numismatic bureaux around the world from whom it may be possible to obtain currency direct. It is a wise precaution to write to these bodies in the first instance for details of their sales and distribution. In some cases they appoint a dealer in Britain as an agent and this is a method of purchase that removes a great deal of the hassle and red tape. Nowadays, however, many mints and banks are quite happy to use the credit card system to make it easy to part you from your money. The problem arises, however, when the coins are despatched. As a rule, banks and mints stipulate quite clearly that they will not accept orders prepaid in cash, and it is an offence to send coins or banknotes out of the country as payment, except through banks authorised for this purpose. Cheques drawn on British banks should not be used. Indeed, this may be actively discouraged by the imposition of heavy clearance and handling charges at the other end. The converse is also true, although Americans seem to think that dollar cheques drawn on some obscure mid-West bank will be eagerly accepted here, and are consequently aggrieved when it is tactfully pointed out to them that this creates enormous problems—to say nothing of the swingeing bank charges incurred in converting such cheques to sterling. Other than credit cards, the Girobank system is probably the best method of remitting currency from one country to another; full details may be obtained from any post office. Details on the preferred method of sending remittances, or transferring cash to another country, as well as the transmission of coins by post to different countries, will be found in the *Royal Mail International Service Guide*. This also lists, among the prohibitions pertaining to each country, which countries accept gold or silver, and which ban the transmission of precious metals by post.

The receipt of postal packets containing coins from abroad makes you liable for Value Added Tax on their importation. As a rule, the despatching mint or bank will have affixed a Customs declaration to the packet, listing the contents, their weight and value, and it is on that basis that VAT will be calculated. The position regarding the import and export of coins by post is more complicated, and applies also to goods sent on approval. In such cases you must consult your Customs and Excise office who will advise you on the correct procedure and what your liabilities will be to tax in either case. This also applies to dealers taking stock out of the country to a coin show and then re-importing the unsold stock afterwards, or importing material purchased at the show.

Buying and Selling

When goods are sold, the seller and the buyer enter into a contract which confers rights and imposes obligations on both parties. The contract need not be in writing. There is no law governing the quality of goods sold by a private individual. If you purchase a coin from a fellow-collector as a result of an informal meeting at the local numismatic society it is incumbent on you to ensure that what you buy is what you think you are buying. If you purchase something from a dealer or shopkeeper, however, you are entitled under the Sale of Goods Act to goods of "merchantable quality" which means that they must be reasonably fit for their purpose. Items sold under a specific description, on the other hand, must correspond exactly with that description. If they do not, the seller *even a private individual* can be sued under the Sale of Goods Act. This is an important distinction because there is an erroneous notion that the Act does not apply to transactions between private individuals.

If A sells a coin to B, purporting it to be a rare date, and B subsequently discovers that the date has been deliberately altered, then B can sue A. Even if A claims that he made the sale in good faith, believing the coin to be a genuine rare date, he will still be liable for restitution (giving B his money back) and may also face a claim for damages. The Sale of Goods Act thus overturns the traditional adage *caveat emptor* which, in its full formula, translates as "let the buyer beware for he ought not to be ignorant of the nature of the property which he is buying from another party". Traditionally this was the maxim applicable at auctions. Once the auctioneer's gavel had dropped, the successful bidder had, in effect, made a contract with the vendor and was bound to pay for the lot, even if he subsequently discovered that what he had purchased was not what he had imagined. The view was that it was up to the purchaser to ensure beforehand that what he purchased was genuine and answered the description in the sale catalogue.

Because of vexatious disputes arising from questions of authenticity, and with the Sale of Goods Act breathing down their necks, many auctioneers now have a safety net, in the form of extensions. These enable successful bidders to delay payment for two or three weeks while they seek expertisation of doubtful material. In other words, the law allows a cooling-off period, but only for he legitimate purpose of verifying the authenticity of items over which there may be some doubt. This is only operative in cases where a coin or medal is sold as genuine, and described and estimated in value accordingly. In many doubtful cases, however, an auctioneer will cover himself by adding the crucial words "as is" to the description of a lot. Then, indeed, it is a case of *caveat emptor*. The auctioneer has done everything humanly possible to draw attention to the controversial nature of the item, and it must then rest on the judgment of the purchaser.

On the subject of auctions there are legal aspects which are not always apparent, as well as subtle differences in law and practice between England and Scotland. These tend to arise in cases where coins and medals come up for sale at provincial general mixed auctions, rather than in the sales conducted by numismatic auctioneers. Goods up for auction may be subject to an upset price which is made public as the price at which the bidding will start. A reserve price, on the other hand, is known only to the auctioneer, and if it is not reached, the goods will not be sold. Upset prices are common in Scotland, reserve prices in England. If no upset price is specified and the goods are not subject to a reserve price then the highest bid secures them, even though it may not be as high as the vendor hoped for. If a seller notifies other bidders that he is bidding for his own goods, or that he has employed an agent to bid for him, the bidding is legal. If he does not give notice and bids himself, or gets someone to bid for him, thus forcing up the price, the sale is fraudulent, and the buyer can purchase the goods for the amount of the last bid he made before fraudulent bidding started.

One frequently hears dark, but usually apocryphal, tales of "the ring" in action to depress the bidding and secure items below the price commensurate with their actual value. This is a fraudulent practice and in law is regarded as a criminal conspiracy. In practice, however, it would be very difficult for a group of dealers or other individuals to keep the bidding down merely by sitting on their hands. This practice could only operate successfully in sales which were largely, if not entirely, frequented by dealers. But coin sales, like other specialist collector-orientated auctions, are characterised by a high proportion of private bidders in attendance. Any conspiracy by a ring would merely allow some private bidder to step in and secure the lot at a bargain price. Rings are illegal, but in practice prosecutions are very rare as it is extremely difficult to obtain proof of their operations. What is more likely to happen is that dealers have been known to act in concert to force up the bidding to frighten off some unwelcome interloper. Here again, such tales are legion, but astonishingly lacking in specific details. The golden rule in attending auctions is to know what you are going after, and to have a pretty precise idea of how much you are prepared to pay. Do not be stampeded in the heat of the moment into going way beyond your limit.

Taxation of Profits on Disposal

The Inland Revenue define an asset as "any form of property (other than sterling) wherever situated". A disposal includes a sale, exchange or gift of an asset, or the receipt of a capital sum in respect of them. In layman's terms you dispose of an asset when you sell it, give it away, exchange it or lose it. A transfer of assets between husband and wife doesn't count (unless they are legally separated), nor does the transfer of an asset you leave when you die. If a disposal results in a profit you could be liable to tax. Any profit made on the sale of certain assets, including coins, medals and other collectables, constitutes a capital gain and is subject to Capital Gains Tax (CGT) which is now charged at the same 25% and 40% rates as income tax. However the government allows you to make a total capital gain in the current tax year of £5,500 before tax becomes chargeable. If this is the case, and the total proceeds from disposal do not exceed £10,000, then a simple declaration to this effect is all you need to make in the relevant section of your annual tax return.

In any one year you are allowed to dispose of items with a total value of no more than £6,000 without needing to declare the fact to the Inland revenue. Above that, Capital Gains Tax (CGT) is payable on the actual gain, although the Annual Exempt Amount (AEA) set for 2005-6 is £8,500. In practice, you would have to dispose of quite a valuable coin or collection before tax becomes liable. Computing the actual capital gain is a complicated matter. Suppose you purchased

a coin in 1960 for £5,000 and sold it in 1993 for £12,000. On the face of it, you've made a capital gain of £7,000 and you might think that you were liable to CGT because the gain was over £5,500. However, the *length of time* you've held the asset also has to be taken into consideration. From April 6, 1988 the law was altered so that only gains made after March 31, 1982 are now taxable. In effect, you are taxed as if you acquired the coin on March 31, 1982. The initial value of the coin is deemed to be its market value at that date. If the gain from March 1982 to the time of disposal is greater than the overall gain from acquisition in 1960 to disposal in 1993, you take the lesser of the two figures. If this produces a gain, whereas the old method of working it out would have produced a loss, you will be regarded, for tax purposes, as having made neither a gain nor a loss on disposal. You have a choice of opting for computing from the time of actual acquisition or from March 1982, whichever seems the more advantageous; but once you've made your choice you cannot subsequently change your mind.

How do you establish what the coin was worth in March 1982? The Inland Revenue tend to regard Seaby, Krause or other relevant catalogues as their yardstick. The difference between the nominal or catalogue value in 1982 and what you eventually got for the coin *assuming that the latter was greater,* might be regarded as the capital gain, but even then the position is complicated by inflation in the intervening years eroding the real value of the coin.

At this stage things get really complicated as you have to work out the indexation allowance. This is determined by the Retail Prices Index (RPI), and you need to know the RPI for (a) the month of disposal, and (b) the month in which you acquired the asset, or March 1982, if later. The RPI is announced each month by the Departmenrt of Employment and is published in its *Employment Gazette* which ought to be available in your local public library. Take the RPI for the month of the disposal and subtract the RPI for the month when indexation commenced. Then divide the result by the RPI for the month when indexation began, and work out this figure to the nearest third decimal place. This is known as the indexation factor, which you then multiply by the initial value of your coin. Simple isn't it? In most cases, however, I expect you will have made a capital loss in real terms, so these sums, though necessary to satisfy the Inland Revenue, are largely academic.

Treasure
and the Law

Until the introduction of the new Treasure Act, the legal position regarding articles of value, found long after they were hidden or abandoned, was not as simple and straightforward as it might be supposed. Furthermore, this was a case where the law in England and Wales differed fundamentally from that in Scotland.

Treasure Trove was one of the most ancient rights of the Crown, deriving from the age-old right of the monarch to grave treasure. In England and Wales, the law applied only to objects made of, or containing, gold or silver, whether in the form of coin, jewellery, plate or bullion. Moreover, the object had to be shown to have been deliberately hidden and the owner could not be readily found. The English law therefore excluded precious stones and jewels set in base metals or alloys such as bronze or pewter. It also took no account of artifacts in pottery, stone, bone, wood or glass which might be of immense antiquarian value.

In recent years, as a result of the rise in metal-detecting as a hobby, the archaeological lobby brought pressure to bear on Parliament to change the law and bring it into line with Scotland where the rules on Treasure Trove were far more rigorously interpreted. In Scotland the Crown is entitled to *all* abandoned property, even if it has not been hidden and is of little value. This applies even to objects dumped in skips on the pavement. Strictly speaking you would be committing a criminal offence if you removed an old chair from a skip without the owner's permission, although in practice such helping oneself rarely proceeds to a prosecution. In 1958 an archaeological expedition from Aberdeen University found several valuable artifacts on St Ninian's Isle, Shetland. These included silver vessels and ornaments, as well as

Metal detecting can be fun—but be sure you know the rules!

a porpoise bone which had incised decoration on it. The archaeologists challenged the rights of the Crown to this treasure, arguing that the Crown would have to prove that the articles had been deliberately hidden, and that a porpoise bone was in any case not valuable enough to count as treasure. The High Court, however, decided that as long as the property had been abandoned, it belonged automatically to the Crown. Its value, intrinsic or otherwise, or whether or not it was hidden, did not make any difference. Since then, as a result of this decision in case law, the criteria for Treasure Trove have been very strictly applied in Scotland. It would have only required a similar test case in England or Wales to result in a similar tightening of the rules. This has been resisted, mainly by the detectorist lobby, but inevitably the government considered legislation to control the use of metal detectors, if not to ban them altogether.

In England and Wales a find of gold or silver coins, artifacts or ornaments, or objects which contain some of these metals, which appears to have been concealed by the original owner, was deemed to be Treasure Trove. It was not even necessary for the articles to be buried in the ground; objects concealed in thatched roofs or under the floorboards of buildings have been judged to be Treasure Trove. Such finds had to be notified immediately to the police who then informed the district coroner. He then convened an inquest which decided whether all or part of the find was Treasure Trove. Establishing the gold or silver content was straightforward, but the coroner's inquest had to decide whether the material was hidden deliberately and not just lost or abandoned, and that the owner could not be located. A gold coin found on or near a country footpath might reasonably have been dropped by the original possessor through a hole in pocket or purse and in such cases it was very unlikely that it would be deemed Treasure Trove, even if the coin turned out to be very rare. In this instance the coroner would then have had to determine who was the lawful owner of the find: the actual finder, the owner of the land where it was found or even the tenant of the land. As a rule, however, it was left to the finder and landowner to decide between them who the owner of the coin should be, and in some cases the matter could only be re-solved by referring to a civil court. For this reason it was vital that metal detectorists should secure permission *in writing* from landowners before going on to their land, defining rights and obligations on both sides, in order to determine the disposal or share-out of any finds or proceeds from the sale of finds, *beforehand*.

If the coroner decided that the articles were delib-erately concealed, and declared them to be Treasure

The unique Coenwulf gold penny was found by an amateur metal detectorist next to a public footpath in Bedfordshire

Trove, the find automatically reverted to the Crown. In practice the find was considered by the Treasure Trove Reviewing Committee of the Treasury. They might decide that although the articles *invariably coins* were gold or silver, they were so common that they were not required by the British Museum or one of the other great national collections, and would return them to the finder to dispose of at his discretion. If some or all of the coins were deemed vital for inclusion in a national collection the finder was recompensed with the full market value of the material. On the other hand, if someone found gold or silver which might be Treasure Trove and failed to declare it at the time, that person was liable to prosecution under the Theft Act should the find subsequently come to light. Not only could he face a heavy fine but the articles would be forfeit to the Crown, and of course no reward or recompense was then payable either.

The anomalies and inconsistencies of existing law on Treasure Trove were eliminated and the position considerably tightened up by the passage, on July 5, 1996, of the Treasure Act.

Announcing that the Treasure Act had received the Royal Assent, Lord Inglewood, National Heritage Minister, said, "This represents the first legislation on treasure trove to be passed in England and Wales and will replace common law precedents and practices dating back to the Middle Ages. The Act, which offers a clearer definition of treasure and simplified procedures for dealing with finds, will come into force after a code of practice has been drawn up and agreed by both Houses of Parliament". The Act came into force in England, Wales and Northern Ireland on September 24, 1997, replacing the common law of treasure trove.

The act was introduced as a Private Member's Bill by Sir Anthony Grant, after the failure of an earlier attempt by Lord Perth. For the first time, it would be a criminal offence to fail to report within 14 days the discovery of an item which would be declared Treasure Trove. Finders will continue to be rewarded for reporting their discoveries promptly, while landowners and occupiers will also be eligible for rewards for the first time.

The Treasure Act covers man-made objects and defines treasure as objects other than coins which are at least 300 years old and contain at least 10 per cent by weight of gold or silver; coins more than 300 years old which are found in hoards (a minimum of two coins if the precious metal content is more than 10 per cent, and a minimum of 10 coins if the precious metal content is below 10 per cent).

The act also embraces all objects found in clear archaeological association with items which are treasure under the above definitions. It also covers any object which would have been Treasure Trove under the previous definitions (e.g. hoards of 19th century gold or silver coins).

The maximum penalty for failing to report the discovery of treasure within 14 days will be a fine of £50,000 or three months imprisonment, or both.

In Scotland the police pass the goods on to the procurator fiscal who acts as the local representative of the Queen's and Lord Treasurer's Remembrancer. If the articles are of little value, historically or intrinsically, the finder will usually be allowed to keep them. If they are retained for the appropriate national collection then a reward equal to the market value is payable.

A favourite haunt of metal-detectorists these days is the beach, and many hobbyists make quite a lucrative living by sweeping the beaches especially just after a Bank Holiday. It's surprising how much loose change gets lost from pockets and handbags over a holiday weekend. Technically the coins recovered from the beach are lost property, in which case they ought to be surrendered to the police, otherwise the finder may be guilty of theft. In practice, however, the law turns a blind

The Langtoft hoards were discovered by three keen metal detectors — the larger of the hoards being found in its original pot.

eye to coins, on the sensible grounds that it would be impossible to prove ownership. On the other hand, banknotes are treated as lost property since someone could in theory at least identify a note as his by citing the serial number.

In the case of other objects, such as watches and jewellery, of course the law governing lost property is enforced, and the old adage of "finders keepers" does not apply. Any object of value, identifiable as belonging to someone, that is washed up on the foreshore or found in territorial waters is known technically as "wreck". This includes not just a wrecked ship, but any cargo that was being carried by a ship.

If wreck is not claimed by its owner, it falls to the Crown. In this case it is not necessary to prove deliberate concealment, as in the case of Treasure Trove. This law has a specific numismatic application in the case of the gold and silver coins washed up after storms around our shores, from Shetland to the Scillies. Such coins, emanating from wrecks of Spanish treasure ships and Dutch East Indiamen in particular, are well documented, and any such finds ought to be reported immediately to the police.

Stray finds of coins, as well as other objects of value, on public places, such as the street, a public park or a sports ground, are also subject to law. In this case the finder must take all reasonable steps to locate the owner. Anyone who keeps a coin without making reasonable effort to find the owner could be prosecuted for theft. As with the beach, however, such "reasonable effort" would clearly be impractical. Finding coins on private premises is another matter. In this case large bodies, such as the Post Office, British Rail, the British Airports Authority, bus companies, municipal authorities, hospitals, the owners of department stores, theatre and cinema proprietors and the like, may have bye-laws, rules and regulations for dealing with lost property found within their precincts, or in their vehicles. If you found a purse or wallet on a bus or train, or in a telephone kiosk or a shop, common sense (and your conscience) would tell you to hand it over to the driver, conductor, shopkeeper or official in charge. As a rule, unclaimed lost property reverts eventually to the finder, but not always; British Rail and some other organisations have a rule that in such cases the property reverts to the organisation. In any event, failure to disclose the find immediately might render you liable to prosecution for stealing by finding.

Treasure Act
Code of
Practice
—a summary

For easy reference a summary of the main points of the new law is reproduced here*. Further information will be found in the *Code of Practice on the Treasure Act*, which can be obtained free of charge from the Department for Culture, Media and Sport (telephone: 020 7211 6200, email enquiries@culture.gov.uk). Metal detectorists are strongly advised to obtain a copy of the Code of Practice which, among other things, contains guidance for detectorists, sets out guidelines on rewards, gives advice on the care of finds and has lists of useful addresses.

What is the definition of treasure?

The following finds are treasure under the Act (*more detailed guidance is given in the Code of Practice*):

1. *Objects other than coins:* any object other than a coin provided that it contains at least 10 per cent of gold or silver and is a least 300 years old when found (objects with gold or silver plating normally have less than 10 per cent of precious metal).

2. *Coins:* all coins from the same find provided they are at least 300 years old when found (but if the coins contain less than 10 per cent of gold or silver there must be at least 10 of them; there is a list of these coins in the Code of Practice).

An object or coin is part of the same find as another object or coin if it is found in the same place as, or had previously been left together with, the other object. Finds may have become scattered since they were originally deposited in the ground.

Only the following groups of coins will normally be regarded as coming from the "same find":

(a) hoards that have been deliberately hidden;

(b) smaller groups of coins, such as the contents of purses, that may have been dropped or lost and

(c) votive or ritual deposits.

Single coins found on their own are not treasure and groups of coins lost one by one over a period of time (for example those found on settlement sites or on fair sites) will not normally be treasure.

3. *Associated objects:* any object, whether it is made of, that is found in the same place as, or that had previously been together with, another object that is treasure.

4. *Objects that would have been treasure trove:* any object that would previously have been treasure trove, but does not fall within the specific categories given above. These objects have to be made substantially of gold or silver; they have to have been buried with the intention of recovery and their owner or his/her heirs cannot be traced.

The following types of find are not treasure:

(a) objects whose owners can be traced;

(b) unworked natural objects, including human and animal remains, even if they are found in association with treasure;

(c) objects from the foreshore, which are wreck.

If you are in any doubt, it will probably be safest to report your find.

What about objects found before the Act came into force?

You should report objects that come into any of the four categories just described (if found after September 23, 1997). There is no need to report any objects found before that date unless they may be treasure trove (see 4 above).

What should I do if I find something that may be treasure?

You must report all finds of treasure to the coroner for the district in which they are found *either* within 14 days after the date on which you made the find *or* within 14 days after the day on which you realised that the find might be treasure (for example, as a result of having it identified). The obligation to report finds applies to everyone, including archaeologists.

How do I report a find of treasure?

Very simply. You may report your find to the coroner in person, by letter, telephone or fax. The coroner or his officer will send you an acknowledgement and tell you where you should deliver your find. The Code of Practice has a list of all coroners' addresses, telephone and fax numbers.

There are special procedure for objects from a few areas for which treasure franchises exist, but they should be reported to the coroner in the usual way. The main franchise-holders (the Duchies of Lancaster and Cornwall, the Corporation of

London and the City of Bristol) have confirmed that they will pay rewards for finds of treasure from their franchises in the normal way.

Where will I have to take my find?

You will normally be asked to take your find to a local museum or archaeological body. Local agreements have been drawn up for each coroner's district in England and Wales to provide the coroner with a list of such museums and archaeological organisations. The Department is publishing a series of leaflets, roughly one for each country of England and one for Wales, listing the relevant coroners, museums and archaeological services in each area.

The body which receives the find on behalf of the coroner will give you a receipt. Although they will need to know where you made the find, they will keep this information confidential if you or the landowner wish—and you should do so too.

The body receiving the find will notify the Sites and Monuments Record as soon as possible (if that has not already happened), so that the site where the find was made can be investigated by archaeologists if necessary. A list of Sites and Monuments Records is in Appendix 3 of the Code of Practice.

What if I do not report a find of treasure?

If you fail to report a find that you believe or have reasonable grounds for believing to be treasure without a reasonable excuse you may be imprisoned for up to three months or receive a fine of up to level 5 on the standard scale (currently £5,000) or both. You will not be breaking the law if you do not report a find because you do not initially recognise that it may be treasure, but you should report it once you do.

What happens if the find is not treasure?

If the object is clearly not treasure, the museum or archeological body will inform the coroner, who may then decide to give directions that the find should be returned without holding an inquest.

What happens if the find is treasure?

If the museum curator or archaeologist believes the find may be treasure, they will inform the British Museum or the National Museums & Galleries of Wales. The museums will then decide whether they or any other museum may wish to acquire it.

If no museum wishes to acquire the find, the Secretary of State will be able to disclaim it. When this happens, the coroner will notify the occupier and landowner that he intends to return the object to the finder after 28 days unless he receives an objection. If the coroner receives an objection, the find will be retained until the dispute is settled.

What if a museum wants to acquire my find?

If a museum wants to acquire part or all of a find, then the coroner will hold an inquest to decide whether it is treasure. The coroner will inform the finder, occupier and landowner and they will be able to question witnesses at the inquest. Treasure inquest will not normally be held with a jury.

If the find is declared to be treasure, then it will be taken to the British Museum or the National Museums & Galleries of Wales, so that it can be valued by the Treasure Valuation Committee.

How do I know I will receive a fair price for my find?

Any find of treasure that a museum wishes to acquire must be valued by the Treasure Valuation Committee, which consists of independent experts. The Committee will commission a valuation from one or more experts drawn from the trade. You, together with the museum that wishes to acquire the find and any other interested party, will have an opportunity to comment on the valuation and to send in a separate valuation of your own, before the Committee makes its recommendation. If you are dissatisfied you can appeal to the Secretary of State.

What if the coroner or museum loses or damages my find?

They are required to take reasonable steps to ensure that this does not happen; but, if it does, you should nonetheless be compensated.

Who will receive the reward?

This is set out in detail in the Code of Practice.

To summarise:

— where the finder has permission to be on the land, rewards should continue to be paid in full to him or her (the burden of proof as to whether he or she has permission will rest with the finder). If the finder makes an agreement with the occupier/landowner to share a reward, the Secretary of State will normally follow it;

— if the finder does not remove the whole of a find from the ground but allows archaeologists to excavate the remainder of the find, the original finder will normally be eligible for a reward for the whole find;

— rewards will not normally be payable when the find is made by an archaeologist;

— where the finder has committed an offence in relation to a find, or has trespassed, or has not followed best practice as set out in the Code of Practice, he or she may expect no reward at all or a reduced reward. Landowners and occupiers will be eligible for rewards in such cases.

How long will it take before I receive my reward?

The Code of Practice states that you should receive a reward within one year of you having delivered your find, although this may take longer in the case of very large finds or those that present special difficulties. If no museum wants to acquire the find it should be disclaimed within six months or within three months if it is a single object.

> *Reproduced from "The Treasure Act, Information for Finders of Treasure (England and Wales)" leaflet DCMSJ0229NJ, published by the Department for Culture, Media and Sport.*

Another Great Title
From Token Publishing Ltd.

Ensure you never miss an issue of Britain's best-selling coin magazine: take out a subscription to COIN NEWS today! From just £34 for 12 issues, you are guaranteed to have the magazine delivered to your door before it goes on sale in the newsagents and you make a saving of over £7 per year's subscription. Order your subscription today, call 01404 44166, or log on to

BRITAIN'S BIGGEST-SELLING COIN

COIN NEWS
Incorporating BANKNOTE NEWS

SEPTEMBER 2007

COINEX
Free ticket—
see inside for details

A petition to the King

PRICE GUIDE
2 AND 5 GUINEAS, PLUS COMMERCIAL BANK OF SCOTLAND BANKNOTES

www.tokenpublishing.com
SEPTEMBER 2007 UK £3.35

THE CHARIOT ON ANCIENT COINAGE
Emblems of a military must-have

A PASSION FOR COINS
An interview with Richard Beale

INHUMAN TRAFFIC
Exhibition on the Slave Trade

NEWS · FEATURES · NEW ISSUES · MARKET REPORT · VALUATIONS

www.tokenpublishing.com

Get your free sample copy from:
Token Publishing Ltd, Orchard House, Duchy Road, Heathpark, Honiton, Devon EX14 1YD
Call: 01404 44166 www.tokenpublishing.com

Token PUBLISHING

Index

to COIN NEWS

This index of persons, places, events, articles and reviews, as well as new issues detailed in the monthly magazine COIN NEWS, covers the period from September 2006 to August 2007. Entries are indicated by numbers signifying the month of issue (e.g. 9-12 relate to September to December 2006 and 1-8 refer to January to August 2007) followed by the page number.

CONTRIBUTORS

Alexander, Michael 9/52-3, 2/35-6, 5/32-4
Andrew, John 9/22-4, 9/67, 10/10, 10/20-5, 10/46, 11/22-5, 11/67, 12/23-5, 12/47, 1/22-4, 1/27-8, 1/60, 2/25-7, 2/50, 2/72, 3/49, 4/12, 4/22-4, 4/28-9, 4/47, 5/52, 6/23-4, 6/67
Baker, Paul 9/43
Baldwin, Edward 6/60
Bennett, Graham 11/51-3, 4/ 32-4
Beresiner, Yasha 9/60, 10/60, 11/60, 12/60, 1/67, 2/63, 5/70
Bird, N Du Quesne 10/33-5, 12/27-8, 1/33-4, 2/60-2, 3/60-1
Blair, Dennis G 11/43-4
Cashin, Barry 3/42-3
Caversham, Andrew 2/45-7, 3/38-40, 4/43-4, 5/47-8, 6/36-7
Colgan, Edward 9/33-5, 10/36-8
Cope, Geoffrey 9/50-1
Donnelly, Clifford 9/73, 10/73, 11/72-3, 12/73-4, 1/73-4, 2/80-1, 3/73-4, 4/73, 5/81
Goulborn, Bruce 6/57-8
Grant, Jim 12/41-2, 1/36-7, 4/39-40
Horrocks, Carl 9/26
Mackay, James 9/56-8, 10/57-8, 11/57-9, 12/ 57-9, 1/57-9, 2/39, 2/57-9, 3/19, 3/56, 4/57-8, 5/18, 5/57-8, 5/66-8, 5/77, 6/52-4
Mackay, Ken 9/39
Matthews, David 11/30-1
McGroarty, Derek 11/37-8
Meadowcroft, Alan 6/30-1
Morgans, Geraint 10/40-1
Noone, Michael 12/37-9
Palermo, Raymond 11/26-9, 12/30-1, 1/29-30, 2/41-3, 3/30-2, 4/29-30
Plant, Richard 9/46, 9/71, 10/69, 10/71, 11/69-/70, 12/69-70, 1/46, 1/71, 2/77, 3/69, 3/71, 4/70, 5/71, 5/79, 6/71, 6/75
Pottinger, David 3/45-6, 6/47-9
Pyne, R.S. 10/51-2
Rudd, Chris 5/36-8

Rogers, Dr Kerry 9/16, 9/36-7, 10/16, 10/22-5, 10/29-30, 10/44, 11/16, 11/34, 11/61, 12/10, 12/16, 1/16, 1/43, 1/55, 2/31-2, 3/52, 4/10, 4/16, 4/60, 5/22, 5/59-61
Selby, Peter 9/29, 5/43-5
Tameanko, Marvin 10/26-8, 12/33-4, 3/33-4, 6/26-8
Thompson, Peter R 5/56-7
Tielens, Frederik 3/50-1, 4/35-6, 5/40-1, 6/33-4
Webb, Denzil12/51-2, 1/50-2, 2/48-9, 4/49-50
Wilkin, Trevor 9/19-20, 10/18-9, 11/18-9, 12/18-9, 1.18-9, 2/20-21, 3/22, 4.18
Williamson, Roy 6/40
Young, David 6/43-4

New Publications
The Abbey and Mint of Bury St Edmunds to 1279 2/72
The Bronze Coinage of Great Britain 2/72
Coins in India 11/46
Double Eagle 11/46
English Paper Money 4/68
The Galata Guide to the Pennies of Edward I & II 4/68
The Gold Half Sovereign 10/14
The Gold Sovereign Jubilee Edition 10/14
A Handbook of Islamic Coins 2/72
The Mining and Related Tokens of West Cumberland 5/77
The Pistrucci History 1783-1855 10/14
The Pub Checks of Wales 11/46
The Short-Cross Coinage 1180-1247 2/72
The Voided Long Cross Coinage 1247-1279 2/72

NEW ISSUES
Australia 9/18, 10/18, 11/18, 12/18, 2/20, 3/22, 4/18, 6/18
Austria 1/18, 2/20, 4/18, 5/24
Bahamas 2/21

British Virgin Islands 9/18, 12/18, 1/18, 5/24
Brunei 4/19
Canada 6/18
Cape Verde Islands 1/18, 2/20
Cayman Islands 2/21
Congo 12/18
Cook Islands 4/18
Falkland Islands 9/18, 12/19, 5/24
Haiti 3/23
Isle of Man 2/20, 3/22, 6/18
Israel 11/18
Kazakhstan 6/19
Korea 5/25
Latvia 9/18, 12/18, 1/18
Lebanon 11/19
Lithuania 11/18, 3/22, 6/18
Malawi 11/18
Mexico 3/23
Mozambique 10/19
New Zealand 4/18
Pakistan 9/19
Palau 9/18, 12/18, 1/18
Pitcairn Islands 3/22
Poland 3/23
Romania 4/19
Russia 9/18. 10/18, 11/18, 3/22
Sierra Leone 10/18, 11/18, 5/24
Singapore 1/18. 2/20, 6/18
Slovakia 2/20, 4/18
Solomon Islands 5/25
Somalia 12/18
South Georgia & South Sandwich Islands 10/18, 5/24
South Korea 9/19
Switzerland 10/18, 4/18, 5/24
Turkmenistan 1/19
USA 10/18
Vietnam 12/19

OBITUARIES
Allen, Leslie 2/14
Bryant, Ken 2/14
Davies, Nigel 2/14
Marsh, Michael 10/14
Pottinger, David 5/18
Schwer, Siegfried 2/14